Some reviews of the hardcover editio

'*The Suspended Revolution* is a *tour de force* in the form of a sustained argument about the nature of mental illness, its assessment and treatment. Drawing on anthropological, historical, philosophical, scientific, social and medical sources, David Healy has produced a book of considerable popular appeal that is likely to encourage and stimulate discussion among all groups with an interest in mental health.' *Times Higher Educational Supplement*

'A thoughtful, provocative, never dull book. It will not be the last book on psychiatry, but there won't be many as challenging.' Anthony Clare, *Sunday Times*

'The most challenging attempt I've seen in a long time to offer us a new lexicon and map for mental disorders and their treatment . . . It is a very fine book.' Roy Porter, Wellcome Institute for the History of Medicine

'The fluent style and evident enthusiasm should hold the attention of the lay reader and of the specialist.' Michael Shepherd, *Evening Standard*

'This is a most rewarding work, written in an engaging way, rich with analogy, restatement and metaphor. It is a highly commendable achievement, having evaluated such a complex topic so clearly and objectively from many perspectives within a single cover.' *British Journal of Medical Psychology*

'Enormously stimulating and should be read by all practitioners.' *British Journal of Psychiatry*

THE SUSPENDED REVOLUTION

David Healy was born in Dublin and studied Medicine, and later Psychiatry, at University College Dublin. At the time of writing this book he was a consultant psychiatrist and clinical research associate at the University of Cambridge School of Medicine. He is now Senior Lecturer in the Department of Psychological Medicine at the University of Wales. He has undertaken research focused mainly on the biology of depression. He has written extensively on depression and schizophrenia. *The Suspended Revolution*, which was widely praised on publication in hardback, is his first book.

The Suspended Revolution

Psychiatry and Psychotherapy Re-examined

DAVID HEALY

faber and faber

LONDON · BOSTON

First published in 1990
by Faber and Faber Limited
3 Queen Square London WC1N 3AU
This paperback edition first published in 1991

Phototypeset by Input Typesetting Ltd, London
Printed in England by Clays Ltd, St Ives plc

A CIP record for this book is available from the British Library

ISBN 0–571–16222–3

For Sara

Contents

Acknowledgements   viii
Introduction   ix

1   Mind, Psyche and Brain   1
2   The Suspended Revolution   39
3   The Successors of Paracelsus   73
4   The Romantic Science   102
5   The Dynamics of a Psychosis   133
6   Insights and Oversights   170
7   The Science of Psychotherapy   199

References   222
Index   229

Acknowledgements

Most of the ideas in this book have been stolen from elsewhere, have had their number plates removed and been repainted prior to being put on the road again. A minimal number of clues to the robberies have been left in the references. This is particularly so in the case of robbery from friends and colleagues, especially Donal Harrington, Mauvis Gore, Brian Leonard, German Berrios, Fraser Watts and Mark Williams. Prior to my putting this second-hand vehicle on sale, a number of essential repairs were undertaken by Roger Osborne of Faber and Justin Brophy, without which several serious flaws would have prevented it from starting at all. Neither, however, should be held responsible if the vehicle falls apart on the purchaser a little bit down the road.

A number of people who have one way or the other ended up being 'treated' by me may also recognize some of the ideas. Possibly from the perspective of feeling as though they had been run over by them. Some others may recognize themselves in these pages. It is these two groups whom I most need to acknowledge. The principal stimulus to writing has come from finding out that many of those who have come to me for help have been people whom in many cases I have deeply admired and liked. This has caused a crisis as many of the professional influences on me would suggest that the qualities of others that induce such reactions in me and such reactions from me are part of the problem rather than part of the solution. This I cannot accept as I hope the rest of this book will make clear.

Introduction

Several years ago some fishermen off Madagascar caught a fish they had never seen before. Fortunately, perhaps influenced by the fish's extreme ugliness, they did not throw it back into the water but set about finding out what it was. To the astonishment of the scientific world it turned out to be a coelocanth, a fish that had been thought to be extinct. Not only had no coelocanth ever been caught before, but also the most recent fossil had been lain down over a 100 million years ago. When it became clear what had happened, the interest that was aroused led to the discovery being reported in the popular press as well as in scientific journals. Inevitably with some variation on the title of 'Discovery of Living Fossil'.

Something similar happened in 1988, but it is unlikely ever to be reported in the newspapers. Ballière Tindall published a book by Professor Andrew Sims entitled *Symptoms in the Mind*. This is a book on psychopathology. Its price and attractive presentation suggest a book that its publishers think might appeal to a wider market than the hard-core group of trainee psychiatrists who seem certain to read it. Presumably they feel that the time is ripe for the resurrection of what if not a fossil has certainly been seen as a corpse. Whether what has been exhumed is dead or turns out to be alive, there is a story here for the alert news-hound. If dead, there is the oddity of the disappearance of an entire branch of science. If alive, psychopathology shares with the coelocanth an arresting awkwardness of shape and the stigmata of an older evolutionary molding.

In the nineteenth century psychopathology was a flourishing science. It reached what retrospectively has looked like its acme in the early years of the twentieth century with the 'revolutions' of Emil Kraepelin and Karl Jaspers, which transformed our ideas of insanity. Since then all revolutionary development in psychopathology has been suspended and there has been no further progress in the destigmatization of madness. It is as if nothing had happened in physics after Einstein and

Bohr, or in biology after Darwin. The very word psychopathology has disappeared from use. Even medical or psychological readers, if asked to specify what it meant, might be stumped. Neither Jaspers nor psychopathology rate an entry in the recently published *Oxford Companion to the Mind*.

Psychiatric textbooks abound, but psychiatry is not the same thing as psychopathology. Psychiatry refers to the practice of treating a mental illness whereas psychopathology is the science of what mental illnesses are. One can treat a mental illness without necessarily having a clear idea of what it is one is treating. Psychiatric texts list the incidences of the various mental illnesses and who is most likely to get them. They state what the common course of these illnesses is. And where pills are available for treatment which pills should be used, in what doses and combinations, and the likely side-effects that may be encountered. On the issue of what a mental illness is they remain silent or give potted outlines of the principal competing theories. Trainees in psychiatry learn these facts. They are not at present encouraged to venture behind the facts. Even researchers are not encouraged to put it all together. Rather, they are advised to concentrate on producing more facts. Books on psychopathology are scarce even in medical libraries. Many will not carry copies of Jaspers' *General Psychopathology* and few will have Schneider's *Clinical Psychopathology*. Both have been out of print for years.

Can a flourishing science, whose participants fifty years ago felt themselves to be on the verge of major discoveries, just vanish? The prospect seems alarming – if one science can disappear presumably so could others. Perhaps evolutionary theory might fragment, leaving only a set of biological techniques behind that are necessary for practitioners of the biological arts but are not something capable of catching the imagination. Or perhaps theoretical physics might also begin to wither and fade away, leaving behind the technologies for nuclear power or advanced informational capacities but not the Holy Grail currently provided by the attempt to produce a grand unified field theory.

As these examples might suggest, the issue is not just an interesting academic question concerning the disappearance of a science. The demise of psychopathology has stripped psychiatric practice of much of its resonance. The situation is similar to the fate of Christianity after the Reformation. With the collapse of an agreed order has come increasing fragmentation, a progressive loss of comprehensiveness, and bitter internal wars. In the case of psychopathology, the competing churches have stemmed from Freud on the one side and Kraepelin and Jaspers on the other. They have fought each other to a standstill. These religious wars are outlined in Chapter 2.

An internecine war in psychopathology was made almost inevitable by events that occurred two hundred years earlier, before psychopathology existed at all. When Descartes formulated the mind-brain relation in a way that made it the mind-brain problem that it has been ever since, he helped to set Renaissance science free to advance in the way it did. But in so doing, he booby-trapped the path of those sciences that would later arise to deal with the mind and the psyche, and in particular any science that would attempt to handle mental illness. As the issue of whether a 'mind' can meaningfully be 'ill' is the background, in the foreground of which the psychopathological wars have been fought, an attempt is made in Chapter 1 to establish what minds, brains, and psyches are, what the relations of each to the other are, and what malfunctions of each should look like.

Another background difficulty left by Descartes, which is raised in acute form by the mental illnesses, is the issue of whether there can be a science of the mind. To see why this has been a problem needs some account of the development of both science and ideas about what science is, and in particular of the rise of the human sciences and their significance for psychopathology and psychiatry. This is undertaken in Chapter 3.

If the mind–brain problem, the mental illness problem, and the science of mental life problem have formed the needle on which the science of psychopathology has pricked its finger, there is some indication that this sleeping science is slowly wakening. In the past decade, psychology has developed a new confidence and has begun to talk about its cognitive revolution. One of the new branches of psychology has begun to flourish and bear fruit – this is the science of neuropsychology. Another older branch, dynamic psychology, after a vigorous pruning, has also begun to show signs of new life. These developments and their significance for psychopathology are detailed in Chapters 4 and 5.

While developments in neuropsychology and dynamic psychology lay the basis for a new understanding of what a 'mental illness' is, the final answers to this question are not going to be established by simply discovering a few more scientific facts. Both the latest facts in this area and the facts yet to be discovered come already encrusted in fundamental human concerns. The apparently abstract debates about mind and brains, science and non-science, and whether the proper treatment of a mental illness should be with pills or psychotherapy have not, in the case of psychopathology, happened in some scientific vacuum. They have, rather, intimately interacted with public prejudices and concerns.

Unlike the origins of the universe or of life, which are questions which awe us into silence, the origins of our own distress and the proper treatment thereof are issues many of us feel qualified to talk about and certainly to worry about. The citizens of California were worried enough to recently pass a law banning the use of ECT. Here in Britain we worry as the seemingly humane cause of returning the care of mental illness to a community setting appears to be going inhumanely wrong. Others of us have taken up arms and are suing doctors who have prescribed minor tranquillizers in amounts that have made them the most prescribed drugs in the land. Has there not been an inappropriate medicalization of misery in such cases? Should medicine be involved with misery at all – is mental illness only a myth? Chapter 6 attempts to handle some of these issues. But not by weighing facts on some scientific balance. The emphasis is on showing how the same facts can look quite different from different perspectives.

This issue links up with the question of the readership this book is addressed to. Should the arguments not be directed at a professional readership? I would suggest not. This is where psychopathology is quite unlike theoretical physics or theoretical biology. Whatever the issues are regarding the existence of mental illness, what brings individuals into mental hospitals is not the illness but the way it is handled – by the affected subject and by their kith, kin and general practitioners or social workers. This handling is pre-psychiatric. In most respects it is determined by popular culture. Developments in psychopathology will only yield fruit in so far as they penetrate into this culture. In great part many of the difficulties surrounding current psychiatric practice stem from the fact that this culture has been dominated by one psychopathological view – the Freudian view – whereas psychiatric thinking is dominated by another, the Jasperian.

This book is concerned with perspectives rather than with facts. Accordingly, the facts have been selected to illustrate points rather than to establish them. Many readers may be aware of other facts that might appear inconvenient to my argument and may wonder whether selection or exclusion has been my principal concern. All that I can say is that the present view has not been formed in ignorance of inconvenient facts. This is particularly the case where the argument touches on matters of psychopharmacology – the discipline in which I have been explicitly

trained. On these details I have been most sweeping in my generalizations, claiming a number of things that are not at present orthodox.

To those who think that such a cavalier treatment of facts cannot be
scientific, I would offer the example of Einstein and the special relativity
theory. When Einstein sent the article in which his ideas were first
outlined to *Annalen der Physik* in 1905, it was supported by few facts
and contrary to many established views. In 1906 it was experimentally
discredited by Walter Kaufmann. Yet even at this time a number of
physicists were rallying around it. Because as Max Planck put it, it was
more appealing, more beautiful than competing views. This beauty lay
not in the novelty of relativity theory as such, but in its ability to apply
across a variety of physical problems rather than to simply solve one of
them.

Something similar is aimed at here. But there is a difference in that
the originality of an Einstein is not one of the issues that is likely to
cause problems of acceptance. There is precious little or nothing at all
in these pages that is original. More comprehensive treatment of the
various issues raised is available elsewhere and similar models of mental
illness have been advanced before; the first by Birnbaum as early as
1929. Throughout the text I have attempted to reference these sources
and the data that I have drawn on, even if in many cases the interpretation put on the data differs to the original. Far from resistance to ideas
of the sort being put forward arising from the almost inevitable distrust
of the new, the fact that similar views have run into trouble before this
would suggest an old difficulty. Resistance, it will be argued, has been
as intimately shaped by the mind–brain and mental sciences controversies as the notion of mental illness itself.

Given this resistance, I have taken the advice offered by David Hume,
in the introduction to his *Treatise on Human Nature*, that one does not
conquer a territory by capturing an outpost here or a village there, but
by marching directly on the capital. Whether this is the correct strategy
for a territory so heavily defended as the one I have chosen to invade is
not clear. But this is what I have done. The lay reader should be alerted
to the fact that there are vast areas that lie on either side of the swathe
through mental illness that I have attempted to cut. There are the various
different neuroses, their genesis and clinical features, which have been
ignored in this book. As have the different types of personality disorder
and the interaction of personality and temperament with the affective
illnesses and schizophrenia. Leaving out these details I have oversim-
plified the problems faced by practising psychiatrists or therapists.

Presenting the material, as I have done, risks creating the impression that there is little but political connivance that stands in the way of the revolution I am arguing for and the benefits that it would bring. This is not the case. (One of the readers of earlier drafts of this book suggested that a warning to this effect needed to be posted – preferably on the front cover.)

Looking back over the past, as this book attempts to do, suggests that a certain height has been climbed from which the patterns that have made up the past can be discerned. Psychopathology is in the business of providing patterns (frameworks) into which the data of other sciences – biology, psychology, sociology, anthropology, ethology and others – can be fitted. If for the past fifty years there has been a certain paralysis of the ability or will to provide new frameworks, there has certainly been no lack of data produced which some framework will eventually have to be able to accommodate. It is from a vantage point situated somewhere on this data mountain that the present book has been written.

Looking back from a mountainside is normally only of momentary interest if the bulk of mountain looming overhead suggests that the summit is a long way off. The really interesting vantage point would be somewhere close to the summit, as then not only would certain local patterns be clear, but also the lie of the surrounding countryside. From the present point of view it seems as though much of what is now thought of as mental illness is a mist that will soon be cleared by winds sweeping round the mountain. It also looks as if the major psychiatric illnesses, depression, mania, and schizophrenia could soon be treated with psychotherapy rather than solely with drugs. But a psychotherapy very different to that popularized in Hollywood screenplays and in dramas and novels. One that will not depend on the charisma or esoteric knowledge of heroic therapists,* but which it should be possible to make accessible to many for the purposes of self-therapy. Some pointers toward what such a psychotherapy might be are offered in Chapter 7.

Whether the glimpses of what lies ahead stem from being somewhere close to the summit or are the sometimes cruel deceptions one can have on the shoulder of a mountain will be for the reader to decide.

---

* The term therapist throughout this book will refer to anyone who 'treats' individuals with 'mental illnesses'. This includes nurses and social workers as well as psychiatrists, psychologists, or formally trained psychotherapists.

ONE Mind, Psyche and Brain

In 1637, in his *Discourse on Method*, René Descartes distilled what it was that was intellectually novel in Renaissance thought. In so doing he created a paradigm, or launching pad, for the development of modern science and philosophy. However, his achievement had entirely different consequences for the development of the mental sciences. Far from being a launching pad, the proposal that minds and brains are entirely separate but interacting entities has been more of a stumbling block. This dualist view of how minds and brains relate has been widely dismissed as creating a ghost in the machine. Like all good ghosts, however, this one seems to survive the rapier thrusts of its enlightened opponents.

Nowhere is its presence more likely to be found hovering than in psychiatry. Mental disorders, such as the neuroses, look very different to brain illnesses such as Parkinson's disease or cerebral tumours. Conversely, patients with these latter disorders are not thought of as being mad. Observations such as these make most, if not all, psychiatrists dualists in practice if not in principle.

However, accepting Descartes' view sets up major difficulties. By definition, a brain illness involves biological disruption. As the neuroses differ so much from brain illnesses and do not appear to involve brain disruption, it might seem reasonable to suggest that part of the difference must lie in the neuroses being 'illnesses' that occur in the absence of brain disruption. But if this is the case, what is there to stop immorality being classified as an illness? And if immorality is not to be classified as a mental illness, why not? What exactly is a *mental* illness?

THE HISTORY OF THE MIND

Part of the difficulty with the mind–brain problem stems from treating it as though Descartes conjured it up out of nothing. He didn't. Rather the dualism he proposed, that minds and brains are essentially separate

1

but interacting entities, was forced on him by developments in the science of his day. To understand this requires an appreciation of the origins of our concept of minds. It might seem surprising to suggest that the mind, in the sense that this word is now used, is a relatively recent discovery, but in a very real sense we have not always had minds. The mind that caused Descartes' problems was a discovery of the classical Greeks.[1]

All cultures invented languages and thereby developed the capacity to enshrine the story of their origins in poetry and myth and to pass on social knowledge and teaching. All thought about the universe and developed sophisticated cosmogonies. But Greek philosophers, reflecting on this knowledge, came to grips with 'man the knower' (with the mind that knows the universe that is known) in a way that no other contemporary thinkers had done. Their progress in the discovery of the mind can be traced from the epics of Homer, in which the gods inspired men and dictated their actions, to the histories of Herodotus and Xenophon, where the central events are shaped by human actors, unsupported by divine intervention.

Along with this increasing emphasis on man as the shaper of his destiny, was an increased awareness that communal truths and everyday statements were open to critical review. This culminated in Socrates' insistent demands for definitions. It led to Plato's characterization of man as the seeker after truth who heeding the call of reason attempts to turn toward the light of truth and see things as they actually are. And it found its fullest expression in Aristotle's canons of syllogistic logic by which not only could one be critical of one's own or others' conclusions, but one also could demonstrate reliably that certain conclusions were false.

Given these advances, man was no longer at the mercy of the gods and muses but became the author of his own destiny. The critical faculty of the soul that permitted self-reflection and self-direction was named reason. Reason could be overpowered on occasion by passions and could be confused by competing pressures. But these failures only served to differentiate it further from the other spiritual capacities of man. These capacities could have, indeed given their competing influences almost must have, different seats. The life force itself might lie in the blood, the passions reside in the heart, various humours in the other organs and a rational faculty elsewhere.

'Elsewhere' was ill-defined. While the head in some sense appeared to be the favoured site, given the role of the face in expression and the mouth in language, this should not be taken to mean that rationality was thought to reside in the brain. As late as the sixteenth century many authorities still saw the function of the brain more in terms of a filter to cleanse the blood rather than as a thinking machine. While 'elsewhere' is an important question for us, it was not for the Greeks. The reason being that the mind was for them an *experience* to be fathomed rather than a thing to be located.[2]

Neither Aristotle nor Plato were concerned with the issue of what exactly a mind was. Rather they were captured by a growing awareness that there lies within each of us a drive for coherence in the light of which we can resist personal and social disorder. For them what had been discovered brought a new drama to human living best caught by the condemned Socrates, who addresses his accusers with the words 'and now it is time for us to go, I to die and you to live, but it is not clear who of us takes the better way'. The love of wisdom for Plato and Aristotle was not a matter of word games or logical argument. But so successfully did they articulate a new questioning orientation to the mystery of existence that the symbols they used, such as the mind (nous), developed a life of their own. This has both obscured the original experiences that gave rise to the symbols and has given the impression that the mind was a definite something, that must have a location.

The scientific revolution of the Renaissance saw two developments of pertinence to this issue. The first was the early discoveries of Copernicus, Galileo and others which were synthesized by Descartes into a vision of a mechanical universe. Prior to this the universe was the cosmos, which had variously been the playground of the gods or the theatre of operations of the God. Descartes proposed that it was a machine, similar in some respects to a clock. A machine which might originally have been wound up and set going by a god but which now appeared largely capable of continuing to operate without further divine intervention. The universe was in the process of being desacralized. It was becoming profane.

The second set of developments concerned the emerging biological sciences. Along with increased interest in the scientific dissection of the world to see how it worked, came interest in dissecting man and studying him. This study led to the demonstration by Harvey that the heart, far from being the seat of the passions, was a pump to propel blood around the body – a mechanical device. Other anatomical developments saw the discovery of nerves, with the implication that they transmitted some fluid responsible for vitality. And the dissection of the eye with the discovery of its lens, which given developments in optical mechanics,

3

suggested that it also was a machine. Was man then also a machine? Yes and no came the answer from Descartes. He was happy to localize mechanical functions such as perception and reflex movement in the brain. But he stopped at positing the brain as a thinking machine. The mind he argued was in the machine but was not itself mechanical. It acted on the cerebral machine at some interface, perhaps at the pineal gland. It hovered ghostily somewhere in the machine.

There were two reasons for taking this step. The first but less important lay in the difficulties of grasping the idea of a thinking machine. The more important reason, however, lay in the fact that making man totally mechanical would suggest that he, like the universe, could get by without constant communion with the divine. This was a step that neither Descartes nor his contemporaries were prepared to take – and one that was not required by the needs of Renaissance science. Hence the necessity of dualism.

The majority of philosophers prior to Descartes were not dualists (for example, Aristotle and Aquinas), so dualism cannot be seen simply as a primitive philosophical position that more enlightened times would do away with. None of the earlier philosophers, however, had had the job of defending the spiritual against the encroaches of mechanism in quite the way that Descartes had. Previously the body, while encasing the spirit, was also an extension of the spirit or its material manifestation. Older texts talk of an entrapment of the spirit in the body, but by this was meant the potential overpowering of reason by the clamour of the passions and the limitations of bodily existence rather than any profound dualism of spiritual and material beings. Even the early atomic philosophers in Greece who believed that atoms were the essential constituents of reality were not talking about material atoms in quite the way we do nowadays. For the atomists the spirit was also something composed of atoms.

Body and mind therefore become radically different things, for the first time, with the advent of a partly mechanical man. One hundred years after Descartes, Julian Offray de La Mettrie propounded the first wholly mechanical view of man in a book entitled *Man a Machine*. In it, he commented on the debt we all owe to Descartes for his part in conceiving the possibility of a desacralized universe and almost desacralized man. But he also condemned Descartes for his failure to follow his ideas to their logical conclusion, commenting that Descartes was 'a genius made to blaze new trails and to go astray in them'. But *Man a*

Machine was a *succès de scandale*. De La Mettrie's ideas did not supplant those of Descartes.

The notion of the mind as a thinking machine only became orthodox with the development of the computer. While minds may not function in the same way as computers, computers are obviously able to deduce, infer and compute without the need for ghosts floating around inside their works. One might expect therefore that all the dilemmas raised by Descartes' dualism would now be solvable. As computer operations involve both software and hardware, the sense or non-sense of a computer output can be determined by both the adequacy of its hardware (brain cells) and by the logic and ingenuity of the programs in its memory banks. If brains are thinking machines similar in some ways to a computer, could one not have hardware disorders – Parkinson's disease and brain tumours – and software disorders such as the neuroses. One might expect such disorders to look quite different.

However this simple analogy does not lay to rest the ghost raised by Descartes. If mental illnesses involve faulty software how can they be distinguished from immorality and illogicality which also presumably involve software errors? Raising this question reveals something more of the pressures on Descartes. While man might have a profane body, it seemed obvious that there was also something spiritual about him. This reflects the yearning for order and personal coherence discovered by the Greeks. Accordingly, as this yearning was central to the Greek notion of the mind, it seemed that the mind in some way at least could not be entirely reduced to a mechanical operation. Conceiving of a calculating machine might be possible but do we even now expect that there will ever be a machine that strives for authenticity?

In order to tackle this issue we need to look afresh at possible relations of mind to brain, in the light of the findings of modern science. One profitable way to do this might be to attempt to return to the *experience* of Plato and Aristotle rather than to try to locate the mind somewhere in the brain.

EMERGENCE AND EVOLUTION

Hydrogen and helium, followed in decreasing frequency by the more complex elements, obeying electromagnetic, weak, strong and gravitational forces are the basic building blocks of the universe. Within these initial constraints, the vast variety of life as we know it has come into being. How can so much diversity arise from such simple initial conditions? Given the initial physical conditions, the elements form a set of building blocks with varying properties that may variously fit together. For example, by virtue of its structure carbon has a valency of four. This means that its atomic arrangement is such that there are effectively four sticky bits on it for other elements to adhere to. While carbon is always and only ever carbon, an enormous variety of different chemical compounds may be built up, depending on what bonds to it. These combinations are possible by virtue of the atomic structures of the various elements. But they are not *necessary* or *predicted* by physical laws. While there are over a hundred elements, many are extremely rare and many others are unreactive or have no capacity to fuse with other elements to form compounds and molecules.

In practice, the variety of chemical compounds we have around us results from interactions among a limited number of physical elements. What appears to have happened is that, given a large set of elements and possible combinations, there was always the possibility that some of these could be organized into a more complex or higher system.

There are a number of interesting aspects to the relations between higher organizing and lower organized systems. First, once a higher system, such as the chemical system, emerges, it will tend to persist provided the underlying physical conditions are not extreme. It has stability. Simply by virtue of the covalent or other bonds between them, chemicals resist disintegration into their physical components provided the pressures pulling them apart do not exceed those that hold them together. All things being equal hydrogen and oxygen remain combined as water, ice or vapour and do not dissociate into their component physical parts. Carbon compounds may be both complex and yet remain stable in that a number of carbon atoms may react with each other to form a ring structure. Or crystals, such as diamonds. Dissipative chemical structures have also been identified. These are complex collections of chemicals which are not chemically bonded to each other but resist dispersal by virtue of sets of ongoing interactions. These structures, furthermore, show tendencies to evolve.[3]

Second, what emerges has some autonomy. While chemical compounds are built from physical elements and their construction does not violate any physical laws, the interactions that take place and the compounds that result are new and subject to a new non-physical set of laws. These laws are neither deducible from the properties of the physical elements nor reducible simply to those elements or to the laws which govern them. For example, there is no physical law or principle that would predict the properties of water from a prior consideration of the physical nature of hydrogen and oxygen, or that would predict the unpleasant smell produced when hydrogen and sulphur combine. Thus while the new chemical compounds are crucially dependent on physical elements and there is nothing in a chemical that is not reducible to a physical element, and while all chemical elements obey physical laws, something new has emerged with the evolution of chemical compounds.

Laws such as the law of mass action are not physical laws. They are additional to the laws of physics. Physical laws indicate what is not possible on a chemical level but are quite neutral to what is possible. Therefore it follows that the proper study of chemicals is chemistry rather than physics. Indeed the laws and properties of a higher system can potentially be worked out without reference to the laws and properties of the underlying system. In the case of chemistry, they were largely worked out before atomic physics shed further light on the issues involved.

Having made this point it must be added that a full understanding of the higher level of organization is only likely when the lower level has been worked out. Chemicals are made of physical elements in much the same way that automobiles are made of chemical compounds. While one can know all about automobiles and how they work without knowing about the materials of which they are made, a full appreciation of why they are designed the way they are and the circumstances in which they are liable to break down will only be possible if one knows a good deal about their constituent materials.

Third, while the higher level of organization is dependent on the lower level, it also has aspects to it that are independent. For example, water can be made out of the combination of two or three hydrogen atoms with one or two oxygen atoms. Thus while water is only hydrogen and oxygen it also seems not to be totally determined or reducible to fixed constituents.

Fourth, the higher level exploits the potentialities of the underlying system. For example, the combination of hydrogen and oxygen forms a compound that can assume many different physical properties, depending on the surrounding temperature and pressure. While physical elements such as hydrogen or helium can exist as either liquids, solids or gases they typically can only do so given much greater variations in critical physical parameters. Thus chemical compounds, while being potentially disrupted by environmental extremes, are also more respon-

7

sive to environmental variations. They can avail of or respond to the presence of more subtle aspects of the physical environment such as whether the surface on which they lie is smooth or rough; a number of chemical reactions will only take place when the chemicals in question occur adjacently on a smooth surface.

Fifth, a consequence for higher organizations of composition from lower elements is vulnerability from beneath. Typically higher organizations will only hold good over a certain range of lower conditions and beyond that range the higher level of organization will disintegrate. Thus if physical conditions become extreme the chemical organization of things breaks down and the constituent physical elements of chemicals dissociate.

Sixth, a further consequence of the emergence of a higher level of organization is that the higher level itself provides elements that are capable of being further organized. This possibility of successive levels of organization we can call a principle of emergence. While it may be intuitively implausible that chemicals should ever evolve into anything so complex as life, local accumulations of various chemicals (for example, through their dissolution in pools of rainwater or in primal oceans) and the catalysis of possible but improbable reactions through contact with appropriate physical agents does make possible the evolution of complex chemical systems.[4] This process indicates how life may have evolved, in apparent defiance of the second law of thermodynamics. Once a higher organization emerges it maintains itself and while initial odds may be against its formation, subsequently the odds are that it will not be disorganized.

THE EMERGENCE OF LIFE

As the relationship of higher to lower levels will be important for our consideration of minds, brains and psyches, it seems worthwhile to make clearer what is involved by further concrete examples in the context of the correspondence between chemical and biological systems. The emergence of chemical compounds provides a set of elements that can be and have been further organized into higher stable biological systems. Living structures involve an organization of underlying chemical compounds. Just as chemical compounds, by virtue of chemical bonds, resist disintegration into their constituent physical elements, so living systems resist disintegration into their constituent chemicals. They are stable.

Just as chemical properties are not predicted by physical theories or laws and are not reducible to physical elements, so biological systems, while only composed of chemicals and containing no extra 'vitality ingredient', have properties which are not predicted by any chemical law or theory. The obvious property in question is the property of life. This is not a chemical property. No amount of consideration of chemical laws can account for its quality. It is a matter of professional indifference to a chemist that certain chemicals hang together in chemically improbable combinations for lengthy periods of time, that they incorporate other chemicals into their midst, that they move around purposively and that some of the chemicals in question appear to have dedicated tasks. Accordingly, as chemical laws and theories have little to say about these matters, the proper study of living systems will involve a biology. And biologists will develop their own laws to account for statistical regularities that cannot be explained in chemical terms.

However, while the proper study of living systems is a biology and while most if not all biological laws could be established without any consideration of chemistry, it remains that biological systems are composed entirely of and only of chemicals. A complete understanding of the actual details of biological operations will only be had by adding to biology and its sub-disciplines of genetics, anatomy, physiology and others, a study of biochemistry. This study is not just a matter of adding the fine print to the biological story but one that is essential to a proper understanding of that story. While biological laws can be erected on the statistical regularities demonstrated by biological systems and while these statistical regularities will involve chemicals doing things that are not predictable from chemical laws, a full understanding of why biological regularities are the way they are requires an understanding of the constraints within which biological systems operate. These constraints are in large part determined by the characteristics of the biochemicals that constitute biological systems. Thus while the laws of genetics were worked out in substantial detail long before the discovery of DNA, many anomalies in the data could only be fully understood when the precise molecular nature of genes was elucidated.[5]

Furthermore, while biological laws differ from chemical laws and the proper study of life involves the discovery of those regularities found only in living systems, at no point are chemical or physical laws suspended in the operation of biological systems. In other words biological laws are additional to chemical and physical laws. And biochemicals are chemical compounds elaborated in a manner that permits a specialization of function. They are not some other mysterious compounds.

While absolutely dependent on their chemical constituents, being composed of these and nothing else, biological systems show a relative independence from their underlying chemical constituents. Most living things can tolerate a range of concentrations in most if not all of their constituent parts. The same organism can tolerate considerable food deprivation and lose much weight, yet remain demonstrably the same entity. Even in strategically important specialized molecules such as haemoglobin, a wide variety of slightly different types of haemoglobin will do the necessary oxygen carrying task. And in any one organism, a wide range of haemoglobin concentrations will permit normal functioning. Owing to this, no precise optimum level can be set for haemoglobin values.[6]

Nevertheless biological organizations remain vulnerable to disruption from below. While a certain range of chemical compositions may be tolerated, too great a degree of variation will lead to breakdown of the biological system in question. At some stages of development, biological systems are more than usually sensitive to the disruptive effects of minor degrees of variation in chemical composition. And at all stages they may be sensitive to the introduction of even minute amounts of alien chemical compounds.

In addition to vulnerability from below, lower systems are vulnerable from above. Thus the incorporation of minor amounts of a toxin by poisoning a biological system may lead to its disintegration. In this case not only will the biological system disintegrate, but so also will the chemical compounds of which it is composed. Alexander and earthworms become dust rather than sugars and proteins when they die.

Just as chemical compounds exploit the potential of physical systems to produce a much more varied and complex set of entities from physical building blocks, so, chemicals are exploited when they are further organized by biological systems. This can be seen most clearly in a comparison of the complexity of chemical compounds found outside of biological systems with that of biochemicals. While non-biological chemicals can involve structures comprised of several different physical elements in repeating sequences or ring structures, biochemicals such as nucleic acids, proteins, sugars and lipids are vastly more complex molecules often running to sequences of millions of physical elements and thousands of chemical compounds. These sequences involve more than just large numbers. Typically elements and compounds are arranged such that reactive sites for enzymatic reactions are strategically presented to the physiological milieu and capable of being removed from that milieu in response to subtle changes in its composition.

META-BIOLOGICAL EMERGENCE

Following the example of chemical systems whose emergence both organized underlying physical elements and laid the basis for the emergence of further levels of organization, we can postulate that the emergence of biological systems also provides elements that can be further organized. In this context we must distinguish between non-emergent evolution and emergent evolution. In non-emergent evolution there is development without the emergence of anything radically new. For example, the physical elements appear to have all evolved essentially from hydrogen or from hydrogen and helium. There is an increase in atomic weight with each of the new elements that appeared and some difference in properties. But essentially they are all the same kind of thing. Similarly, chemical compounds have evolved in complexity. But although new compounds differ from those already in existence, none differ as radically as the first chemical compounds did from the physical elements. Accordingly, we can expect biological systems both to develop in complexity and to provide the basis for the emergence of something radically new.

In terms of development in complexity, there has been a non-emergent evolution from single to multicellular organisms. At a certain level of complexity some of the cells of multicellular organisms specialize. Whereas a single-celled organism respires without lungs, moves about in its environment without legs, senses the presence of obstacles without specialized senses, digests food without a gut, is able to circulate digested nutrients around the entire cell without a blood system and is able to reproduce itself without reproductive organs, in a multicellular organism these different functions are taken over by groups of specialized cells. Stomachs digest, hearts and blood vessels circulate, livers detoxify, kidneys excrete and muscles provide propulsive force. Given the increased complexity of having possibly millions of cells in one organism dedicated to various tasks, the need for communication between cells and co-ordination of function becomes increasingly important. In plants, communication appears to be essentially by an endocrine system; a system of chemical messengers. In animals, unlike plants, the differentiation of function that has taken place has permitted the development of an additional and a more efficient co-ordination system, the nervous system.

There is nothing radically new with the development of a nervous system. Basically it is simply some cells specializing for the task of communication and co-ordination. Hence this would seem to be a case of non-emergent evolution rather than emergent evolution. But just as in the case of the emergence of chemical compounds from physical elements (it was certain well-suited physical elements and chemical compounds, which laid the basis for subsequent emergent evolution) so the development of nervous cells has provided the launch pad for something radically new.

Radically new does not simply mean something of increased complexity. While evolutionary processes foster an increasing complexity under the pressure of environmental circumstances and the necessity to survive, evolution also fosters development from objects that constitute the environment to organisms increasingly able to act on it. Accordingly, it can be expected that the next emergent step in evolution will involve some dramatic enhancement of the capacity to solve environmental problems.

EMERGENCE OF THE PSYCHE

The most dramatic development of this kind has come with the evolution of the psyche. This is a new emergent level of organization, a psychological system, that arises from possibilities inherent in nervous systems. By a psychological system, I mean a system with capacities for intelligent behaviour, perception, memory and learning, imagination and emotion. The point at stake is that these are qualities that would not be predicted from a simple consideration of nervous functioning.

Most animals have relatively simple nervous systems which can sense, learn and respond reflexly, as well as co-ordinate motor and vegetative activities such as sleep and appetite and drive regulation and instinctive activity. These functions are carried out in what are now termed old brain structures (the brain stem and mid-brain). In higher animals such as mammals, however, there has been a huge evolution in brain capacity with the addition of a cortex to the brain. This is not found in earthworms, for example, or only found in rudimentary form in other lower order animals. Obviously not all this capacity is needed for sensory, motor or learning purposes as earthworms sleep, eat, move about purposively and learn. Yet equally obviously so much brain tissue is not likely to be simply there for adornment.

It used to be thought quite simply that as higher animals have cortices and are more intelligent than lower animals then the cortex must be simply about intelligent behaviour. But some interesting experiments conducted by David Oakley and colleagues at University College, London make this issue seem anything but simple.[7] Rats were taught a visual discrimination task, success at which led to a reward or to escape from a shock. Rats, as is well known, are relatively intelligent creatures and learn this task quite readily. Most surprisingly, however, when the same or similar rats have the cortex of their brains removed they perform the task as well if not more efficiently. This was very unexpected as not only was the area of the brain that was supposedly responsible for intelligent behaviour removed, but so also were those parts of the cortex responsible for visual discrimination.

It has recently become clear that such findings are not confined to rats. Something similar can be demonstrated in humans and has been termed blindsight. It appears that patients who have suffered the loss of their occipital cortex (the part of the brain responsible for the registration of visual information) experience themselves as blind but seem able to make visual discriminations. When put in front of objects and asked to locate them or asked to walk an obstacle course, they do so in a manner that would not be expected from someone who could see nothing. When asked to explain their success they insist that they cannot see but often report some vague awareness.

Perception and imagination

It can be postulated that what is happening is that in the absence of a cortex, rats and people are able to resort to a more primitive or 'old brain' form of vision. Arguably the term sensation rather than vision is more appropriate as old brain sensation is relatively undifferentiated. The evolution of a psyche, however, is not simply a question of differentiation of this synaesthesia into separate sensory systems, but involves the emergence of perceptual systems. What the sensory cortices appear to do is to process sensory information in a manner that permits the construction of internal representations of outer events or features (percepts). Perceptions permit the development of distant sensation. While this provides unparalleled opportunities, it also points to an ambiguity that will follow us through this book. As the apostle Thomas put it, when you put your hand into a wound you know what you have, but seen from a distance can one be sure? Perception involves a bet on what is out there in a way that sensation does not. What is apparently seen and heard is not identical with what is sensed. Rather it is a construction by the psyche of a working hypothesis.

This can be shown clearly in experiments where subjects are shown a set of dots or lines that are suggestive of certain shapes. Typically subjects *see* the shape in question. If they cannot, one can presume brain damage of some sort. Demonstrations such as these only entered psychology this century with the development of gestalt psychology. But for centuries painters have known that their art resides in choosing what to leave out of the representation of reality rather than what to put in. The same point is illustrated in cases where one gets the construction wrong. For example, in conversations we sometimes not only put a different sense on a message to that intended, but we also can 'hear' a different set of words. Or, for example, when witnesses to a crime describe the scene in ways that may be quite inconsistent.

It seems that all perception is imagination and that we hang onto some imagined sensations because they are consistent with the further evidence we look for, as opposed to others we dismiss as just imagination because no confirming evidence can be found. Such experiences point to the fact that all seeing is in the 'mind's eye' (i.e. while what one sees depends on sensory input the image is constructed in the mind and projected out). Normally what is 'out there' and our images of it correspond so closely that we deceive ourselves that what we are seeing really is what is out there. It is only when we start to scrutinize what is out there for the purpose of drawing it that we come to appreciate that our prior vision was a good and workable approximation rather than a photocopy. Such images can also be constructed and seen without being projected out into the world; as our dreams and fantasies prove.

These internal representations are radically different and novel emergent properties of neural operations. No consideration of the laws of nervous functioning would ever lead to the notion that nervous operations would yield images or other percepts. That there are such representations has only recently been conceded and then not by all. The value of such representations is that they permit more skilful performance. For example, it now seems that rats trained to run in a maze do not learn their skills by simply accumulating a complex set of stimulus–response reflexes, but form a map of the maze and can adjust their performance by reference to the map. On simple tasks a decorticate rat may appear as intelligent as one with a cortex. But once the task becomes complex, as in running within a sophisticated maze, the limitations of a learning by building up chains of stimuli and responses becomes more apparent.

The operation of constructive abilities on such mental models not only develops sensation into perception, but also provides the capacity for imagination. If perception involves the construction of a model to match the likely features of external stimuli, there would seem to be no a priori reason why animals able to perceive should be unable to construct models freely. This appears to be the case with humans and there seems to be no good reason to suspect that it is not true for other animals also.

Such a prospect has alarmed many philosophers, for whom seeing inner visions smacks too much of ghosts in the machine of the type for which Descartes has been criticized. For many years scruples about the reality of such an inner life and inner visions led to behaviourist psychologists proscribing the study of introspection. Such images are literally the stuff of fantasy for most of us and we can appreciate a scientist's or philosopher's concern about the difficulties in speaking scientifically or philosophically about them. Ignoring imagination or acting as though we only imagine our imaginations may thus have seemed necessary for the purposes of philosophic or scientific discussion. But these local difficulties and an agreement on the means to circumvent them should never have been taken as indicating that we really agree that we are not imagining things (Chapter 4). Given our daily recourse to imagery and the intense vividness of our fantasies, one can only suppose that those of us who go along with or have gone along with scientific and philosophic proscriptions of imagination have done so in deference to the high esteem in which scientists and philosophers are generally held. Happily the fear of images and imagination appears to be receding and the study of images has once again become psychologically respectable.[8]

The facts appear to have caught up with those who deny reality to imagery. It has recently been shown that strokes or other brain disturbances can modify the images we generate or the screen on which they are displayed. For example, after certain kinds of stroke it is common to find that subjects will claim to be unable to see things in one half of their field of vision even though their eyesight may be absolutely normal. What was not appreciated until more recently was that such subjects asked to imagine and describe well-known scenes also only appear to be able to see one half of the scene in their mind's eye.

A current rearguard philosophic and scientific response to these kind of facts is to suggest that the mind is like a computer that can provide for images as optional extras in the program. The brute facts, however, argue against this attempt to make imagery an inessential second-grade phenomenon. Mentally handicapped subjects totally incapable of abstract thought have rich imaginal lives – sometimes too rich.[9,10] This should not be happening if imagery is some extra, since if the software were faulty one might expect the extras to be the least likely function to be still working. Far from being an optional extra to abstract propositions, current work on imagining suggests that this form of thinking antedates abstract- or reality-oriented thinking. What Freud would have called primary process thinking.

Vast areas of cortex in the brain appear to be dedicated to supplying features and details to the construction of images. Thus some areas colour percepts, others shape them, others rotate them, size them and put them in perspective. Still others identify, name them and code for the use of the percept in question. Thus after strokes causing limited damage to some areas of the brain patients may be able to correctly identify or name objects but be unable to make use of them. Others may be unable to name them but are able to put them to the correct use and still others may see them and be able to name them but find them a different colour to what they were before. One patient of mine saw bananas as blue.

Emotion, memory, motivation

Other novel properties emerge on the psychological level. Thus animals without cortices appear to be essentially stimulus bound. Their behaviour is to a large extent predetermined in instincts, drives and reflexes. Corticate animals appear to be less stimulus bound and to spend more time exploring their environment with apparent curiosity, coincidentally building up maps of it.

This motor behaviour requires planning in a way that reflex movement or drive-dominated activity does not. And, in contrast to the inflexibility of reflex movements, the large motor areas of the cortex appear dedicated to the carrying out of planned or voluntary movement that can be modified based on feedback from the environment. This clear difference between the two forms of activity is most manifest in playful activity which is confined to corticate animals and involves action for the sheer enjoyment of it rather than for strictly utilitarian purposes.

Just as perception has a constructive or modelled component, so has planned activity. And just as such percepts can be constructed in isolation from sensory inputs to yield images, so motor plans or constructs can be isolated from actions. Ulric Neisser has proposed that these inner aspects of actions are experienced as emotions.[11] That is emotions are to actions what imagination is to sensation. That emotions are closely related to actions is indicated by how often it is easy to read off what someone else's emotional state is by looking at their face or posture. These betray the *action* on their mind. For example, angry people commonly look like people about to strike someone and others can read their emotions even if the subjects themselves may be unaware of them. This constructive component to action, just like imagination, should be potentially detachable from actual actions leaving us able to be privately emotional – another possibility that has alarmed philosphers but which common sense tells us must be the case.

Along with the development of perception, imagination, planned movement and emotions there is memory. In corticate animals the constructive activities involved in perception and activity are also found in memory. In old brain animals learning takes place on a stimulus–response basis, building up habit strengths so that even if something does not happen for some period of time the propensity to act in certain ways is still found. In corticate animals, however, where memory is a constructive activity and environmental situations can be modelled, in addition to the recall of things by habit, there is the possibility of reviewing models of the relations in question. Some such remembering seems necessary to account for the complexity of social relations, such as the complex relations of dominance and subordination found among primates, for example. These would seem to require some form of modelling, as with development the same animal may occupy many different rungs on the ladder and may have a variety of different relations to varying members of the social group to remember and put into practice consecutively. A habitual response to others would be much too limited to subserve social relations of any but the most primitive kind.

This distinction between habit and memory is even more recent than the discovery of blindsight, but arguably reflects the same distinction between psychological and neurological types of operation. That there is a need for such a distinction is obvious clinically. Many brain-damaged patients, who are amnesic such that they cannot remember an interviewer's name two minutes later and who may have no idea of the day of the week, may nevertheless be able to find their way around a hospital ward after some time, even though they were never in it before they

17

became amnesic. In other words they seem able to learn. What they cannot do is to consciously call to mind what they have learnt. In general, being unable to call things to mind seems to be no bar to building up habits, which appear to be the memory's equivalent of blindsight. In contrast, remembering is something that we normally experience as a re-seeing. A re-imagining.

The question of motivation also emerges on the psychological level. Lower order animals are commonly instinct- and drive-dominated. Internal physiological dictates as well as environmental stimuli shape their behaviour. With the emergence of the psyche comes a relative detachment from environmental and physiological exigencies. Along with basic needs other requirements consequent on living in a more complex world emerge. These can all be modelled and strategies devised to optimize the meeting of needs. Thus it becomes pertinent to talk of the motives of animals rather than simply to see their behaviour as dominated by drives. A takeover as pack leader may lead to a more secure meeting of needs. But how to do it or when? These issues cannot be settled on the basis of drives.

Individuality and selective attention

As perception, emotion, motivation and memory are constructive activities rather than simply a registering of incoming stimuli and a reflex response to such stimuli, it follows that prior experiences and the constructions put on those experiences will influence present or future constructions. As experiences differ among individuals, individuality in perceptual differentiations, emotional responses and motivational strategies will become increasingly apparent. Thus it becomes increasingly appropriate to review an animal's response at any one point in time in terms of a history of prior responses that may have been significantly shaped by social factors and by accidental or traumatic events.

In other words it makes sense to talk of an individual animal's affective development or personality as many owners of dogs will testify. Higher animals can be reared in a way that gives them a crestfallen or submissive personality. They can be made neurotic (or maladaptive) by frequent exposure to the experience of failure at problem solving. Again depending on prior history, individual animals can be shown to switch attention creatively between competing aspects of a situation or problem, or can be shown to attend exclusively to certain aspects of a situation apparently almost unable to see other features of the situation that may be relevant to their purposes.

Another development that occurs on the psychological level is that of selective attention. The point behind constructive activity or model building would appear to be one of allowing a review of possible solutions to problems rather than tying the animal to a predetermined set of instinctive responses. If behavioural responding is not tied reflexly to imperative stimuli but is freed to experiment with responses, it follows that from the range of ongoing stimuli an animal must select out those that are pertinent to the problem in hand. That is, it will attend to certain factors that may provide a solution to a problem, paying no heed to others until it becomes apparent that the solution must be found elsewhere.

Attention to certain aspects of a problem does not mean a complete ignoring of other things that may be going on. Rather it appears to mean that the most sophisticated constructive capacities are brought to bear on certain aspects of a problem. One may still be aware subliminally of other aspects going on in the background. For example, we are not normally aware of searching for words, of organizing our thoughts before speaking or even of getting our vocal equipment in readiness to produce requisite vocalizations, unless we are doing crosswords, preparing important speeches or having articulation difficulties. That is unless there is a problem to be solved. In other words, routine operations are unconscious but may be highly complex and skilled. In general we process more information and organize many more activities than we are aware of. For example, all readers who drive a car have probably been aware of spells when they have driven for several miles apparently paying little or no heed to the road. In such cases we have to presume that vast amounts of information are being processed by our brains unbeknown to us. Therefore it should come as no surprise that much of ourselves is hidden from ourselves or not immediately given to awareness. That is a conscious and subconscious emerge and the contents of each will be shaped by prior constructive activities, prior solutions and what is routine or novel for each individual.

A consequence of a flexible response system to problems and a need for an animal to find its own solution to a problem rather than simply to execute a predetermined response, is that in situations of difficulty and inability to find an answer, attention will be kept at a high pitch. This state of constant arousal and vigilance can, if sustained, become itself a source of generalized vigilance or anxiety. That is being constantly aroused will in itself become a problem and therefore something to be anxious about. The propensity to anxiety will, like the partition between conscious and subconscious found in each individual, be partly determined by prior experiences and the success or otherwise of prior responses to related difficulties.

Another consequence is the possibility of going wrong or of inappropriate responses. As a consequence of prior constructive activities, one animal may persist in a particular set of responses long after another has switched set. Prior constructive sets may militate against the acquisition of what may be further necessary adaptive skills. In other words the psyche becomes structured in response to earlier problems and opportunities in a manner that may be less than helpful later. Therefore distinctively psychological problems can emerge that do not involve neurological disturbances.

Psyche – brain correspondence

The purpose of this lengthy exposition was to give the reader the flavour of the different quality of events that emerge on the psychological level. These events are not simply more complex neural events. Laws derived from an investigation of neural functioning would not predict imaginative and emotional consequences. More complex habits perhaps, increasingly efficient strategies to meet the needs of various drives, but not behaviours that are playful or primarily social rather than utilitarian. Do the other principles of correspondence between higher and lower levels outlined earlier also apply to relations between the psyche and its brain?

In all cases, psychological functioning involves neural activity and only neural activity. There are no ghostly screens or ghostly movie watchers floating around between the interstices of neural connections. But equally the study of perception is something that can be conducted readily by psychologists with little or no knowledge of neural structures or nervous functioning. The laws of memory and perception and of skilled performance can be worked out without any consideration of neural laws. However, in no case will psychological functioning violate neural laws. Thus, although psychological functioning involves more complex patterning of neural activity than is normally found in animals with primitive nervous systems, at no point will the neural impulses correlating with psychological events be found to travel quicker than impulses in experiments on isolated nerve cells would suggest they should.

Equally, however, while the laws of perception may be worked out by someone who has no knowledge of what lies inside the skull, as a matter of fact perception results from nerve cell activity. Hence a full understanding of why certain things happen the way they do is only likely to be found when there is an adequate account of nervous functioning. Such an account can be expected to clarify why there are certain constraints imposed on perceptual capacities, such as why there is a noticeable lag of defined duration between stimuli and responses to those stimuli or why we can only see so far or see best in certain lighting conditions. It will need an understanding of neural pathways and of which brain regions are liable to be damaged in cases of brain haemorrhage to explain the structure of certain perceptual abnormalities after a stroke.

Just as biological systems show a relative independence from their constituent chemicals, so also psychological functioning appears to have a certain independence from the underlying neural correlates it organizes. Thus the term bighead is only a figurative one for someone who knows it all.[12] Or as we age, we lose brain cells but may well know more than when we were younger, remember more or be more skilful. Crucially, we appear to be able to remember the same things if called upon even though we may have much fewer nerve cells than before. Similarly experiments on neurotransmitters indicate that there is a huge redundancy in the level of different neurotransmitters in the brain, both in the amounts of any one neurotransmitter and also in the number of neurotransmitters necessary for the functioning of mammalian neural systems. It takes a loss of 85 per cent of brain dopamine to produce Parkinson's disease.

While independent to some extent of its underlying neural components, psychological functioning always involves the actions of neurones and neurotransmitters. In the limit, therefore, disorders of nerve cell functioning or of neurotransmitter production can be expected to inhibit psychological functioning such as happens in Parkinson's disease, after strokes or as a consequence of inborn errors of metabolism.

While psychological functioning is vulnerable from below, both neural and overall biological activity are vulnerable to breakdowns occasioned by the activities of the psyche. Thus while psychological as opposed to neural functioning in the main, frees animals from exclusively dedicated activity that may be harmful, such as the attraction of moths to a flame, nevertheless playful activity or the defence of hierarchical positions, carry their own risks to life and limb. Similarly, while fear may occur in many animals if instinctive goals are frustrated or predators are nearby, it may also occur in higher animals in situations where social roles rather than bodily integrity are under threat. Such anxiety feeding into the general co-ordination of vegetative behaviours may lead to their disco-ordination with consequent physiological breakdowns such as duodenal ulceration.

The development of psychological capacities can also be expected to lead to an enrichment of underlying systems. In the first place as evidence of such enrichment we can point to the vastly greater number of nerve cells and complexity of nervous systems that are found in animals with psyches. As one goes up the evolutionary ladder in higher animals it becomes increasingly appropriate not just to talk about the presence of a cortex but about the degree of complexity of cortical architecture. It also appears very much the action of the psyche that produces this complexity rather than this complexity that produces the psyche. Animals kept restrained and unstimulated show an impoverishment of cortical development compared to their active con-specifics. Similarly it appears that there is a vast explosion in the number of neurotransmitters and modes of neurotransmission found in the nervous systems of higher animals. More importantly, however, behaviour is also enriched becoming increasingly dexterous, perceptually sensitive, socially complex and in general both more structured and yet more flexible in its tailoring to environmental contingencies.

META-PSYCHOLOGICAL EMERGENCE

As the psyche has been described, many will have taken it for the mind. We have mentioned individuality and the ghostly images on internal screens that are castigated by some philosphers as 'mental' fictions, as well as those other private experiences not popular with the philosophers, the emotions. These psychological constructions are the aspects of 'mental' operations that are currently being modelled by computer programers.

However, there are several problems with leaving things simply at a psyche and brain stage and postulating that man is simply the most psychologically sophisticated animal. While undoubtedly psychologically sophisticated compared to other animals, this could arise in three different ways. First, it may be that animals effectively have no psyche. But owners of dogs or keepers of chimpanzees or research workers with rats would dispute this. Alternatively, increased psychological complexity could be part of the non-emergent evolutionary process of increasing complexity that one sees in the animal kingdom as one moves, for example, from mice to chimpanzees. But while animals, and particularly primates, can be emotional, skilful problem solvers, and live in complex social arrangements appearing almost human in many ways, humans appear to be much more sophisticated than animals. And there also seems to be some difference of kind as well as of degree.

Another option is that man differs from animals not simply by virtue of the complexity of his psyche, but because of the emergence of a further organizational level. A consequence of such an emergence would be that psychological capacities would flower under the influence of a higher organization. Their flowering would mean that many psychological faculties would be so transformed by this enrichment as to appear almost distinctly different in much the same way that many biochemical molecules are vastly more complex than any inorganic molecules. Biochemical molecules, however, no matter how complex, remain chemicals.

In a very similar way if there is a meta-psychological level of organization, one can expect a much richer emotional life in humans compared to animals, a much more complex personality structure and imaginative capacities and immeasurably more sophisticated skills and complex social arrangements. In all these cases while such features may be distinctively human, they would not be what radically defines the human.

For example, defining man as the animal with language, just because no other animals speak, or thinking that language has been a driving force behind human evolution would be a mistake. The technical skill of producing movements of the degree of complexity found in vocalizing (or piano-playing) is not beyond some animals, particularly primates. Furthermore, it can be noted that communication between individuals of a species is not something that arises with man but can be found in quite unsophisticated animals. There is also the precedent of vocalization as a means of communication, most notably among birds. In all these cases, however, the difference between animal and human seems better characterized by the kinds of concepts communicated (their abstract and symbolic quality) rather than by any technical dexterity. Sustained technical dexterity put to the service of higher ends, seems a better account of why man differs from animals regarding language, than an account which postulates that the possession of language defines the human.

If this is the case, then the psyche must differ from something else which can be called the mind. Before going on to characterize the mind, we need to consider why this might seem a novel proposal even though the idea that there are distinctions between psyche and mind is not a novel idea. Both Plato and Aristotle distinguished between the lowest capacities of the soul, involving the appetites and drives found in all organisms, from intermediate levels which co-ordinate the sensory, emotional and activity capacities found in higher animals. The former we have located in the brain, the latter in the psyche. They also distinguished both these sets of capacities from the highest levels of the soul which were found only in man and which consisted of man's rational capacity. This tripartite division of mental capacities was the norm until Descartes (Table 1). The rise of mechanism as we have noted necessitated a new radical distinction. A distinction between organic machinery and man's spiritual essence of which rationality was the hallmark. Hence the emphasis on a mind–brain distinction rather than on a set of mind, psyche and brain distinctions.

The seeming immateriality of images, emotions and consciousness meant that they, as well as rationality, were taken into this essentially new concept of the mind. Indeed, paradoxically, these psychological capacities have come to be seen as the ghost in the machine. That is, there seems less problem now with the idea of a thinking machine but there are still difficulties with the idea of an emotional, imaginative or individual machine. This is rather interesting as there can be little doubt but that animals have personalities and are emotional. Thus we claim to be able to model much of what is distinctively human but cannot manage what is distinctively animal.

While distinctions between mind, brain and psyche go back to 300 BC and modern conceptions of mind, psyche and brain refer to roughly the same entities as these terms have always referred to, modern concepts can be expected to be radically different from Greek notions. Just as the modern atom is both the same and radically different to the Greek atom. This definition and redefinition of terms was occasioned by the Greek differentiation of philosophy from common sense, which broke individuals down into minds, brains and psyches in the first place, and the subsequent differentiation of science from philosophy, which is responsible for the modern redifferentiation of these terms.

While the sciences began to develop out of philosophy in the Renaissance, not all the sciences emerged at the same time. The last of the major sciences to emerge was psychology. The first proper psychologists who were not also philosophers – Wundt and coworkers – appeared only at the end of the nineteenth century. It seemed obvious to them that the proper study of psychology as opposed to philosophy involved the inves-

TABLE 1. Changing definitions of key concepts

	MIND	PSYCHE	BRAIN
Aristotle	Spiritual – voice of reason and virtue	Spiritual – perception, emotion, imagination, memory, consciousness	Spiritual – appetites, drives and instincts
Descartes	Spiritual – voice of reason, memory, emotion, imagination, consciousness, intelligence, soul		Material – appetites, drives and instincts, ? brain
Cognitive Revolution	Material – organization of psyche and nervous system aimed at authenticity	Material – brain's software, perception, emotion, intelligence	Material – brain's hardware, appetites, drives and instincts, and basic learning prewired
Needed?		Material – organization of nervous system supporting perception, imagination, emotion, individuality, memory, intelligence	Material – nerve cells with appetites, drives and instincts, and basic learning prewired

tigation of memory, perception and other mental processes such as the study of imagery.[13] Given that all newly developing sciences have started shakily, it is not surprising that both other scientists and philosophers attacked the early psychologists as being non-scientific.[14] The focus of attacks was the unscientific nature of an enterprise that attempted to investigate ghosts in the machine. The psychological response to this was to switch course and focus only on issues that, retrospectively, we can term neural rather than psychological. Primitive forms of learning and memory based on stimulus–response considerations and the formation of habit strengths became the focus of attention rather than the more complex psychological operations which involved mental representations.

With the increasing development of psychology and with its renewed focus on mental representations and imagery, it is now the mind and philosophers who need defending rather than psyches and psychologists. Just as Descartes only saw the need to radically distinguish between brains and minds, the development of computers and their use in psychology, with a corresponding increase in appreciation of the brain as a thinking machine, also leads to a bipartite distinction. That between software and hardware. And psychologists rather than philosophers, historians or sociologists are now the scientists who study the software of the brain. It is common these days to refer to psychology's new found confidence and interest in 'mental' processes as its cognitive revolution and a recent comprehensive account of this revolution by Howard Gardner is revealingly called *The Mind's New Science*.[15]

Regarding the software/hardware dichotomy, an important point can be noted. Software does not evolve from hardware. Neither is it an emergent property of hardware. The informational potentialities of hardware systems emerge because they are organized by man. Therefore, while in some respects computers may allow us to model psychological processes and provide an analogy for mind–brain relations, in important respects they differ radically from the human situation and the mind or psyche cannot be simply an organic computer. This point is conceded by many psychologists, even among those at the forefront of the cognitive revolution.[16] It is also a point now being made by a number of philosophers.[17,18]

Another assault on the distinction between minds and psyches came from Freud. Along with Wundt he was responsible for the modern discovery of the psyche (Chapter 2). Before Freud, mental disorders were either some derangement of man's spiritual capacities or else brain disorders. With Freud there emerges for the first time the notion of a disorder that is neither a brain disorder nor a spiritual disorder. Having discovered this new domain dynamic psychologists exploring the dynamics of the psyche have increasingly given the impression that the only important motives and issues of personal concern are psychological ones rather than mental ones. The mind often seems to have become a ghost in the dynamics of the psyche.

THE EMERGENCE OF THE MIND

In one sense it seems superfluous to argue for the emergence of the mind in that no one appears to doubt that there is such a thing. But what is being argued for here is that there is something called the mind that differs distinctly from the psyche and the brain, but has emerged from them. Something that has always been recognized in some sense, but whose modern sense has not yet been fully defined. The psychological capacities of perception, emotion, memory, the ability to grasp relations between things, capacities for skilled performances, selective attention and personality lay the basis for the mind. What is it that emerges given that complex emotions, social arrangements and individuality of personality all seem to have a basis in the psyche?

One possible answer is a capacity for abstraction and symbolism that takes the human being beyond the world of immediate experience. Unlike animals, humans are not tied to a world of immediacy. The process of human growth involves moving into a world that is not immediately present but is mediated by meaning. This difference between humans and animals is caught by references to man the symbolic animal who lives not by bread alone. From the endeavour and agility of the mountaineer striving to conquer a peak and plant a national flag on its summit to the dexterity of the virtuoso musician straining to reproduce the musical nuances that bring audiences to their feet in tumultuous applause, muscles, nerves and heart respond precisely to the undertones and overtones of symbols. Not only muscles, nerves and hearts, but also memories, the capacity to grasp relations and the ability to imagine possibilities are harnessed to the tasks of discovering the dimensions of the universe and ways to shape natural events to suit man's purposes. Even in the matter of appetites and biological impulses, humans are not wont to behave like animals but make of their passions and needs dramatic enterprises whose symbolic resonances are caught by the efforts of actors, poets and novelists. While animals have psyches, they do not go on hunger strike out of political conviction, or become martyrs for religious reasons or leave posthumous instructions of the type left by Crazy Horse who requested that his heart be buried at Wounded Knee, the site of the Indians' most serious defeat.

While this world of meaning is radically human in a way that emotions and personality are not, the internal representations that animals form in perceptions or motor activities might also be accounted abstractions or symbols. The difference is that these abstractions or symbols are effectively tied to the animal's immediate experiences. While man is the animal that has solved the problem of solving problems, through the use of internal representations animals also solve problems. Whether this difference is one of degree or of kind is hard to say. Whereas the various developments found in animal species are responses to environmental demands and increasingly sophisticated ways of handling such demands, man is the animal who remakes his environment. He alone is capable of planning, establishing reliably the conditions necessary for the survival of his schemes and of taking the steps necessary to realize those conditions. His freedom from the determination of outer condition is dramatically shown in his leaving earth altogether. Man is not only the apex of evolution but, as the ultimate solution to the need for solutions, has also become self-evolving.

There is some difficulty therefore in specifying the distinctive features of the mental. One might either argue for a characterization that stresses the abstract and symbolic abilities of man, or argue that even these differences do not radically distinguish man from animals. This is the kind of difficulty one would expect if a higher mental level of organization leads to the flowering of psychic capacities. This raises the question of whether there is some quality that appears exclusive to humans. One such possibility is the use to which such abstracting and symbolizing is put. Man is the creature who is concerned about truth and conduct. Whereas psychological integration of neural capabilities made animals freer from environmental constraints, this further mental organization not only makes man freer again, but also makes him responsible. Truth and responsibility have no meaning in the animal kingdom. Animal projects can be successful or unsuccessful but not true or false. Animal interactions can be fortunate or unfortunate but cannot be good or bad.

This characterization of the mind finds support from earlier Greek conceptions of the mind. Reading Socrates, Plato and Aristotle, one is struck by the fact that for the Greeks philosophy was not the accumulation of facts or opinions.[19,20] Rationality was that faculty that enabled man to decide between truth and falsity so that he could then pursue the good course of action. Truth was something one did rather than what one knew and recorded on parchments. Equally in less philosophical and more religiously-oriented cultures, such as Israel, revelation or divinely-inspired knowledge was not knowledge about the structure and detail of the world but knowledge about correct courses of action. In both traditions, the issue of the spiritual or immortal soul of man (the ghost in the machine) was linked closely with the question of the quality of the life that had been led. Thus the rational animal was the virtuous or moral animal. So much so that Socrates could argue that men could only be immoral through ignorance.

Given that the meaning of the terms mind, psyche and brain have changed since they were first established by the Greek philosophers, talking in terms of virtues or of being moral is not really likely to convey just what was involved for them. In modern parlance the Greek concern was with authenticity. This kind of authenticity was not some state of grace or serene freedom from material limitations, but something acquired by an individual subject only after a struggle to heed the call of reason. Reference to authenticity today, however, is liable to suggest to readers that something psychological is being talked about, as psycho-analysts and other psychodynamic psychologists seem to have acquired theatre and screen rights on the dramas of individuals' struggles to know and be true to themselves.

Mind – psyche – brain correspondence

In the case of a mental organization of psychological capacities, the principles of correspondence between higher and lower elements worked out for other organizational levels can again be expected to apply. In the first place what emerges is a stable organization that has the distinc-tive features hinted at above. The mind is only a set of physical elements, but these have been organized into chemical compounds, cellular sys-tems, psychological operations and mental abilities. Only physical elements ever exist in minds. There is no other mental ingredient, no immaterial ghost, just as there is no other vital ingredient added to living systems to give life. It is the organized movements of such elements that constitutes the mind. But although these movements are highly non-random, they are not something that a physicist can shed much light on, except to say that they do not violate physical laws.

This conception of the mind desacralizes it. What is being proposed is that from material psychological possibilities, a material mind would always have been liable to emerge. Many may baulk at the characteriz-ation of a mind being offered here. It may appear to suggest qualities often associated with 'spirituality', but this should not be taken to mean that ghosts are somehow being readmitted to the machine. Any mental level of organization that could emerge from psychological possibilities must have qualities that differ radically from any other qualities pre-viously in existence. This radical difference should lead to the need for radical conceptual contrasts such as that between mechanical and spiri-tual man. But in the final analysis, the mind only consists of the psycho-logical capacities of perception, imagination, skilled activity, emotion, memory, motivation and intelligence pressed into the service of a search for meaning. A meaning that is not just another skill to be mastered by linguistic dexterity or symbolic manipulation, but which is a requirement of authentic human living without which human subjects are liable to self-destruct.

Whether there is any further transcendent reality or further transcen-dent levels of organization to man is a question that is not pertinent to this analysis, other than to note that if there is a *transcendent* reality, by any usual definition of that word, it is not liable to be localized within the cerebral machinery. Equally, however, this analysis suggests that computers are a poor model for the mind – despite their capacity to model psychological processes. Qualities, such as a need for authen-ticity or for a passionate search after meaning, are not qualities a com-puter can be expected to realize. As John Searle has suggested, you probably cannot produce a non-living mind. Indeed you probably cannot produce a mind at all without first starting off at some very early evolutionary stage such that as an end result the need to be authentic is something felt in the marrow and its achievement is a matter of having guts as much as it is a matter of having a mind.[21]

As outlined here, the mind is an autonomous level of organization. Its operations will conform with all physical, chemical, biological and psychological laws, but it will have its own laws that are not deducible from those other laws. As a consequence neither biologists, psychol-ogists, physicists or chemists will have much to say about economics, history, logic or philosophy, at least from their respective professional points of view.

Nevertheless, in order to understand why human beings behave the way they do, one must appreciate that they are both animals and psycho-logical animals, as well as psychological animals that have minds. That is their behaviour will be influenced by biological imperatives such as the need to feed, protect themselves and reproduce. While the desire for authenticity may dictate a course of action that would involve self-deprivation or even self-sacrifice, such a course of action will have to compete against deep rooted self-interest and instincts for self-preservation, leading perhaps to the compromise of wishing to be authentic but not yet. Human capacities to solve problems will also be shaped by factors such as the limits of memory or dexterity and thus certain problems may be better handled by programmed computers or robots than by human beings.

Just as with other levels, the mind can be expected to show a certain amount of independence from both psyche and brain. Thus both mental and psychological operations continue as one ages even though a great number of brain cells may be lost. Similarly, humans are no less symbolic or moral animals even though they lose perceptive capacities (e.g., become blind) or their memories begin to fail. Great works of art may be accomplished even though dexterity is radically limited, as when handicapped painters paint with their feet. The amount of information one may have stored as a result of education, or the amount of skills one may have learnt to master, do not necessarily make one any better a person. Many a person with little exposure to cultural matters will produce art of great cultural significance. Many others from stunted emotional backgrounds live lives of great moral quality.

Nevertheless, the mind is vulnerable from below and can only tolerate a certain range of psychological make-ups. Too distorted an affective development leads to a loss of effective moral freedom. Thus there are criminals and psychopaths. Everyday morality involves building up responsible habits and such sets are what we commonly call character as opposed to personality. But in some cases habits laid down early in life or established later during periods of stress such as the propensity to depend on alcohol may resist the efforts of otherwise estimable characters to uproot them. There are people who lack the moral courage necessary to be seen protesting in public against some injustice, but there are also those who are unable to be seen in public for any reason whether good or bad because of overwhelming anxiety. A concern that things be done properly is an otherwise estimable quality, but undue anxiety about how well things are being done can paralyse all action. A vocation to a life of service to others may indicate all that is best in human life. Or it may indicate psychological stunting from over-restrictive parenting or indoctrination in childhood.

Just as the higher level of organization is vulnerable to disruption by lower levels the higher level can affect lower levels deleteriously. More than any other animal man is likely to poison himself causing chemical disturbances or biological breakdown, whether intentionally or through habitual alcohol consumption or by virtue of a poorly balanced diet. Furthermore, in the course of human living the occasions of anxiety are greatly increased as not only does human life contain problems of the sort that face animals but it is in itself a problematic project. Unlike an animal which can simply get on with life if particular problems remain unsolved, for humans the programme of action crucially revolves around the act of self-creation. As the correct answer to this problem is shrouded in mystery, human life, although free from many natural dangers, will nevertheless be fraught with moral concern. It follows that human living may be an anxious enterprise, that may lead to psychosomatic illnesses.

One can also expect mental stresses to cause psychological disturbances that need not affect underlying biological systems deleteriously. For example, under stress humans display hysterical phenomena. In these cases there may be no apparent neurological deficit and no psychosomatic illness, but there may be an apparent inability to walk or talk. There may be paralysis of the capacity for selective attention under the stress of an interview or after the shock of a bomb blast, leading to an inability to remember critical details such as one's own name. Macbeth, stressed at the contemplation of murder, shows how one may be unable to distinguish between imaginings and actuality and take hallucinated daggers for the real thing. It also follows that the perils of human living may stunt and warp our personalities and shrink our capacities to imagine.

One can expect a mental level of organization also to enrich underlying neural and psychological elements. The presence of a mind seems associated with further cortical development, in particular of the frontal lobes. The precise function of these areas of the brain is still a matter of some dispute, but there appears to be some degree of agreement that frontal lobe functioning is essential to our being able to stand back from our experiences, allowing us to respond flexibly to problems in a way that has some involvement with our being able to exercise freedom of will.

On the psychological level the emergence of the mind not only leads to the technical dexterities noted earlier but it charges imaginative and affective development and the development of personality with the call to authenticity. The ability to imagine possibilities is not simply important for solving the environmental demands to find shelter and food but is also central to how one tackles the issue of responsibility for self-creation. The link between emotion and action becomes even more apparent on the human level. Emotionless activity is associated with robots rather than with humans. Persuading others to act is very much a question of making them emotional about the course of action proposed. Given that human living is not tied to the immediacy of time or place and that imaginative and affective development are enormously complex, personal histories become dramatic. This drama of character is celebrated in novels. It is, however, not something simply confined to novels but is the central concern of all of us.

Equally important to stress is the enrichment of social living that takes place and the social drama that occurs only on the human level. Increasingly the environmental problems to be solved as we ascend up the evolutionary tree are social. Simply by a process of enrichment of social capacities by virtue of their coming under the influence of a higher mental integration, one can expect vastly more complex social arrangements among humans than among any other animals. The development of economies to provide material goods and infrastructures, politics to resolve the competing needs of different groups, technologies to permit increasingly unnatural living arrangements and the dissemination of information, as well as the recording of the history of various social organizations has permitted the development of ever more complex societies and institutional arrangements.

The issue, however, is not simply one of social complexity but one of how we are to behave toward others. Who is my neighbour? For many this issue and the problem of the origin of the evil we do to each other outweighs the mystery of the origin of the universe and why we are here at all in the first place. This issue is not solely one of the physical violence we inflict on each other, but also involves the degree to which we participate in each other's self-creation. Through the medium of language and art we can communicate imaginative possibilities to each other thereby expanding each other's horizons. Through the use of appropriate symbols we can also encourage others to action – actions which give further cause for self-reflection to all of us. However, through the institutions we create we may also stunt the possibilities for growth in each other. Either by a failure to provide the necessary support to others to lead lives not dominated by the need to struggle for the bare necessities of life or else by overweening paternalism which so inhibits the exercise of individual liberty that possibilities for authentic growth are restricted.

MORALITY, PSYCHOLOGY AND ILLNESS

That such 'mental' issues are not irrelevant to the question of mental illness is attested to by current 'psychological' concerns with authenticity; by the common suspicion that psychotherapy involves an attempt to make people better or morally fitter rather than just in the sense of being free from illness; by repeated calls to treat mental illnesses as moral disorders (Szasz and others) or as disorders of morale; and by the recurrent appearances of some form of moral treatment regularly in psychiatric history, as well as by the common reluctance of patients to take psychotropic medication on moral or ethical grounds.

Given the analysis outlined here, one would expect that as man was once seen as a wholly spiritual being all illnesses should have once been seen as spiritual problems and as such should have carried a stigma. Space does not permit a detailed analysis of this issue, but that this was the case can be seen clearly in examples such as the well-known bible story of the cripple at the pool of Bethesda. It appears from this narrative that observers of this man's condition took it as a matter of course that his physical disability resulted from some failing or sin on the part of the subject or his parents and was evidence of some moral inferiority. It was only with the advance of the medical sciences in the Renaissance that such attitudes began to be overthrown. Despite these advances, however, many diseases such as leprosy retained a stigma for a long time afterwards. Even today, in the face of disturbing new diseases such as AIDS, it seems that such attitudes quickly re-emerge, suggesting that they have never been totally relinquished.

As man has been progressively desacralized, it follows that there should be evidence that some illnesses lost the taint of moral disorder earlier than others. Not surprisingly, brain illnesses have been among the last to be destigmatized, and those brain illnesses involving subtle disturbances of function seem still to be a source of confusion. A consideration of the history of speech disorders illustrates this.[22] Loss of speech was, until the eighteenth century, a theological problem rather than a medical one. In the eighteenth century it was first appreciated that destruction of the cerebral machinery by strokes could lead to a variety of speech problems. In the late nineteenth century precise locations in the brain responsible for various different speech functions were established. Despite this, more subtle speech disturbances have, until well into this century, been far more likely to be viewed in moral rather than medical terms. For example, stammering has been and often still is seen as an effort to gain attention or as evidence of some deep-seated psychological problem. This is despite longstanding knowledge that purely physical measures, such as blocking out the sound of the speaker's voice by standing behind a waterfall, can relieve it.

We can expect therefore that this dynamic might apply even more clearly to the mental illnesses. Cicero, in the *Tusculan Disputations*, giving the standard classical view of mental illness appears to bear this out. 'As there are diseases of the body, so there are diseases of the mind which are generally caused through a confusion of the mind by twisted opinions..; the diseases of this type only arise through a rejection of reason, hence as distinguished from diseases of the body mental diseases can never occur without guilt'.[23] Many of the classic accounts of spiritual desertion, from those found in the psalms to the dark night of the soul narratives of the seventeenth and eighteenth centuries and perhaps even the twentieth century poetry of Gerard Manley Hopkins, can be read today as accounts of depression. Conversely, what today would almost certainly be diagnosed as depression was often seen as a spiritual problem in the past. One of the seven deadly sins, accedie, was even created to account for such states.[24] While there has been some advance and a diagnosis of depression today would not suggest a spiritual problem, people still feel stigmatized by such diagnoses.

If the mental illnesses were essentially spiritual or passionate involving an abnegation or overpowering of reason, it then became difficult to distinguish them from immorality and illogicality which also involved such overpowerings and abnegations. Significantly no philosopher has ever succeeded in satisfactorily distinguishing the two from the Cartesian perspective. Even the best, such as Kant, have only made feeble attempts at settling these issues. In general the subject has been remarkably ignored by the philosophical community.

An alternative to resolving the issue in terms of spiritual crisis was to deny rationality or spirituality to the mentally ill. In line with this, admission to asylums until the middle of the nineteenth century was based on some derivative of the 'wild beast test'. This stemmed from the popular view that the insane person was no better than a wild animal. Some expression of this can be found in seventeenth and eighteenth century drawings and paintings of madmen and in accounts of how the populace would go to Bedlam to view the mad in much the way we might go to the zoo. As animals were not thought to have a spirit, in practice this solved the conceptual difficulty in distinguishing between immorality and mental illness.

35

Madness came to be seen as an irreversible dehumanization, as an emigration to a land of no return. Even lucid spells of apparent rationality were not taken as evidence that the illness had gone. A somewhat more hopeful approach took root during the nineteenth century with the development of a 'moral' approach to the treatment of mental illness. The shackles were struck off the limbs of the mentally ill and they were encouraged to involve themselves in useful activities around the asylum. Their status changed from that of wild beasts to that of children who could be helped to mature with the proper mix of discipline and encouragement. While some advance, this enlightened approach was steeped in paternalism and perhaps to many sufferers was as oppressive as the old regimes.

The identification of illness with biological disordering (mechanical breakdown) was a possible way to destigmatize it. But the ambiguities consequent on Cartesianism, noted above, also coloured early attempts to make of mental illness a biological disorder. From the biological point of view, the mental illnesses were typically seen throughout the nineteenth century and well into the twentieth century as hereditary degenerative disorders. Given that alcoholism, criminality and all anti-social tendencies were also seen as manifestations of this degenerative tendency in the germ plasm, it can be appreciated that there was still something very spiritual, something oppressive, about the biology being talked about.[25] There still is (Chapter 6).

Far from solving the difficulties in distinguishing between morality and illness, the re-emergence of the psyche at the end of the nineteenth century further compounded the problem. As there had always been difficulties in distinguishing immorality from illness, there was little ground in between these two concepts for the insertion of a third class of problems. Therefore, in practice, the depth psychologies had recourse both to mental and to medical languages. Their patients were patients by virtue of their inauthenticity, failure to know themselves, and the illness they suffered from was a disorder of self-knowledge or of communication. It was a short step to diagnosing all malaise as stemming from intra-psychic sources and, in so doing, to relocate the 'spiritual' dilemmas of man from the sphere of an external struggle to humanize the world to an internal stage on which blind instinct and internal societal dictates clashed.

In many ways psychoanalysis and its derivatives have had more the character of religious movements rather than that of sober sciences. Since man first consigned his musings to permanent record, it seems that humans have recognized the need to scrutinize their motives, to be suspicious of their virtues and to maintain consistency between what is thought and what is done. It did not need psychoanalysis to tell us that unhappiness stemmed from lying to ourselves. But while the depth psychologies originated in attempts to tackle specifically psychological problems (neurotic maladaptations) they have gone on in various guises to pronounce on questions of human authenticity. In so doing the notion of there being three sets of distinguishable states (brain illnesses, psychological problems and issues of authenticity) has been further confused.

These difficulties and interminglings of biological, psychological and mental issues could be predicted given the original meanings of mind, brain and psyche and shifts in these meanings since Descartes. Typically it can be seen in the confusion about the morality of using ECT or drugs in the treatment of 'mental' illness, or in the confusion about distinctions between what is psychological and what is more properly seen as mental. And, in particular, in the confusion that can be seen in the conjunction of the two terms mental and illness.

The criterion by which illness has been differentiated from sin has been one of biological disorder. The advance of science and the detailing of ever further sets of biological disorders have rescued from the darkness of sin ever more illnesses. But there must be a natural limit to how far these frontiers can be pushed back. Biological disordering is something that quite obviously may affect the brain and alter behaviour. But given the relative independence of psyche from brain and mind from psyche or brain outlined earlier, such brain disordering is not likely to have mental or psychological implications unless it is so extensive as to completely suspend the operations of the mind or psyche. Conversely mental or psychological disorder does not have to entail cerebral disorder. Rather both optimal and disordered mental or psychological functioning in the sense of being authentic or inauthentic, rational or irrational, imaginative or unimaginative or emotional or unemotional requires grossly normal cerebral functioning.

Given meanings to the terms mind, psyche and brain such as those outlined earlier, we can suggest that disorders of all three should be potentially distinguishable. One should be able to drift inauthentically through life without being neurotic or ill. Similarly it should be possible to be neurotic without being ill or without it raising questions of authenticity. Finally it should be possible to have brain illnesses that neither make one neurotic nor compromise the ability to be authentic.

It may not be easy to disentangle issues of authenticity from neuroses

37

or brain disorders as, for example, a brain illness is a stress that in its own right may cause neurotic maladaptation which may effectively suspend an individual's ability to be meaningfully authentic. Or individuals who are neurotic may also have coincidental brain illnesses or may be drifting inauthentically through life. But, in principle, it should be possible to distinguish these three sets of disorders.

This being so can a mind be ill? If illness or disease involves biological disruption, then as the terms have been defined here it would seem that neither the mind nor the psyche can be ill. However, over 150 years of psychiatric and psychological smoke about mental illnesses will doubtless strongly suggest to many readers that there must be a fire somewhere. If the general thrust of this chapter is correct what we should find behind the smoke is a repeated changing of the meaning of key terms in the debate and a progressive despiritualization of the 'mental illnesses'.

TWO   The Suspended Revolution

In 1962 a book, later to become very influential, entitled *The Structure of Scientific Revolutions* was published.[1] In it, Thomas Kuhn argued that science does not proceed by the type of uniform and systematic process of conjecture or refutation, beloved of philosophers of science. Rather scientific advance seems to involve visions and revisions. Initial visions establish a paradigm for their field of scientific enterprise. Paradigms are neither a comprehensive nor a final statement of what *is* known about particular issues, but a heuristic orientation toward what *will be* known. They either explicitly make claims about the shape of ultimate answers or latently hint at that shape by providing the crucial breakthrough on which subsequent insights are predicted. Using the paradigm, subsequent workers in the field take for granted certain central aspects of what they are looking for. However, the future course of events may force others to the conclusion that these central truths are a block rather than an aid to progress. The acceptance of paradigms means that rather than forever critically assessing everything, as the myths of science would have it, scientists assume much on trust – on the authority of others.

A consequence of Kuhn's view is that the development of scientific knowledge, which is usually seen as being comparable to the evolution of a coral reef with the labours of each scientist depositing new items onto the already accumulated pile, has a revolutionary rather than an evolutionary character. He suggested that new visions (paradigms) can make redundant what has gone before, as, for example, in the way that Copernicus' revolution made redundant a lot of the work of previous astronomers. This necessarily creates a model of scientific progress in which many factors other than the detached and disinterested desire to discover the truth will be at play. In many cases it becomes appropriate to talk of political establishments. As the beneficiaries of particular visions are likely to have risen to positions of power and influence in the new establishment, they have vested interests in not seeing their work discredited. Being the persons who decide on the distribution of prestigious posts and research funds, they have the means effectively to silence dissenting opinion. In practice therefore, many worthwhile advances in time become blocks to further progress and the process of development may be suspended until such time as the holders of academic chairs retire or the force of circumstance outflanks the blocking forces. All this is well known to practising scientists but is at odds with the myths of how science operates.

A more benign interpretation of what happens in science is to compare the visionary process to an invasion of enemy territory. Following a successful invasion, the normal task of the supporters of a new regime is to mop up the remaining resistances and to strengthen the defences of the realm against further attack. They do not immediately head further afield or plot the subversion of the new regime. The invasion usually only establishes the broad outlines of the new territory. There remains a lot of work to be done in consolidating the gains. Similarly in science, after the initial acceptance of the new vision it takes time to convert all the supporters of the old regime. Many may never convert. For example, Einstein never accepted some developments in quantum mechanics.

It is only with time that the need to move on or the need for a new revolution is felt. And then it is usually the young who feel it. Those who had supported the existing regime see how much better the conditions are under it than under the former dispensation. It is those who never knew the older state of affairs, who are more struck by how much could be improved in the current state of affairs.

When the battle lines are finally drawn it is by no means certain that the new will triumph. In many cases the assault has been repulsed. Such a defeat led Ludwig Boltzman, the founder of modern thermodynamics, to suicide. Gregor Mendels' revolution in genetics was simply ignored. In other cases the combatants may reach a stalemate, where neither view prevails and an uneasy coexistence prevails until some novel development swings the advantage to one side or the other. For example in 1915, Alfred Wegener published his theory of continental drift.[2] The 1920s and 1930s saw intense debate on the issues raised by this theory with most authorities rejecting it. Those concerned on both sides of the debate were well aware that the orthodox textbooks of geology would have to be rewritten if Wegener was right. It was not until the late 1950s, with studies on the earth's magnetism and evidence of the sea floor spreading, that the balance began to swing in Wegener's favour. The theory of continental drift finally won the day in 1963, with publication in the journal *Nature* of plate tectonic theory. This indicated exactly how continents might drift. Even so many of the old guard remained unconvinced through the 1960s and 1970s.[3]

History used to be seen as simply a chronology of the dates of battles or the accession of kings to thrones. Long after this way of seeing things went out of date in general history, the history of science was still seen in terms of the dates of important discoveries and the chronological order in which various great scientists appeared. Since Kuhn, the history of science has come to be seen in terms of turmoil. The task of the historian is seen as one of sorting out all the different forces that produced the final outcome rather than just simply noting what that outcome was. The chronology of psychiatric developments has been particularly boring and makes a poor story. But the argument of this book is that this boring chronology conceals a story rich in revolutionary turmoil. Within psychiatry there is a state of suspended revolution with a very uneven battleline drawn between the combatants, many of whom have a foot in both camps. Between the smoke of battle and political manoeuverings behind the scenes, newcomers to the field, and indeed most of the combatants, cannot be expected to see clearly what is happening or what the likely outcome will be.

THE FIRST REVOLUTIONS[4-9]

In the case of psychiatric illnesses, the first revolution, or first establishment of a psychiatric paradigm, happened in the late eighteenth century. During this century, physiology established the importance of the nerves in mobility, vitality and irritability. Nerves had been recognized prior to this, but their function had not been understood. Following these developments in physiology, pathological anatomy began to record inflammations and lesions of the nerves in a number of diseases. In the case of strokes and their resultant loss of mobility, a correlation with the obvious destruction of brain cells was found. Inflammation of nerve cells (neur-itis) was also found to correlate with behavioural changes. The suspicion grew that in many cases of fearfulness, lethargy, melancholia and convulsions there must be something wrong with the way nerve cells were working. However, no lesion or inflammation of the nerves could be demonstrated.

Despite this absence of demonstrable pathology, these suspicions were crystallized in 1785 by William Cullen, a Scots physician, who coined the term neurosis. This term conveyed the notion that nervous functioning could be disordered in ways that were not at that time detectable – that is the underlying disorder was not a neuritis. Nervous disorder, he thought, could be presumed to be present given that the signs and symptoms of certain clinical disorders were consistent with such a disordering. Such a vague or heuristic notion, was not only found in early psychiatry. In a very similar way, disorders of kidney functioning without obvious kidney lesions or inflammation (nephritis) were, and in some cases still are, termed nephroses. In many renal conditions, these vague notions have turned out to be correct and subsequent developments have served to specify the details of the initial broad outline. However, in psychiatry only the epilepsies are now neuroses in the sense of a nervous malfunctioning that does not involve the destruction or inflammation of nerve cells. Most of the conditions Cullen specified as being neurotic – hysteria, phobic and obsessive disorders and neaurasthenia – are not though of as being neurotic in a way that he would recognize. Conversely, calling epilepsy neurotic goes against the grain of what we now understand by this word.

This reversal of the meaning of words illustrates a point that Kuhn made about scientific revolutions. If science were simply a record of steady progress, one would expect to be able to understand earlier writings on a subject without too much difficulty. However, it is commonplace in historical research on scientific developments to find that the meaning of words shifts radically. One commonly has to suspend one's intuitive understanding of what a word now means in order to think one's way into the mind of pioneers in a field. When revolutions are in full progress, he argued, both sides may be using the same words in completely different ways and communication may become impossible. So much is this the case that any evidence for a radical change in the meaning of words can be taken as prima-facie evidence for the occurrence of a scientific revolution rather than a process of scientific evolution.

Cullen's coining of the term neurosis helped to crystallize something other than just medical knowledge at the time. It also set up a prototype for seeing some behavioural problems in terms of a physical illness rather than a spiritual problem. Where lassitude and fearfulness had been seen as spiritual disorders, by the end of the eighteenth century it became possible for the first time to conceive of them otherwise. This initial beach head was further extended in the next century when, for example, post-stroke brain destruction was shown to correlate with loss of speech – which up till then had been an intensely spiritual issue (Chapter 1).

Psychosis

Another heuristic notion developed shortly after this, that of a psychosis. It too has changed meaning radically. This term was coined in 1845 by an Austrian physician, Ernst von Feuchtersleben. It referred to those disorders of the mind involving disturbances of passions or judgement and characterized by hallucinations and delusions. These did not seem easily explained *solely* in terms of a disorder of the nerves. The term psychosis has, ever since, implied a defect of judgement. It has always had a flavour of the 'mental' about it that the term neurosis initially had not. Its clinical hallmarks have been delusions and hallucinations or bizarre behaviour; the stigmata of true madness. While von Feuchtersleben did not dismiss a disorder of the nerves or cerebrum being found in the psychoses, the term, at least initially, was taken up and used by mentalist (or spiritualist) thinkers. Some operation of the soul on the nerves was presumed to be necessary for a psychosis to develop. Accordingly there has been a marked tension in this term from the start, initially derived from the uncertain differentiation of brain from psyche from mind outlined in the last chapter. This is caught in a quotation from Dr Amariah Brigham, superintendent of the New York State lunatic asylum, who noted that 'if the mind could be deranged independently of any bodily disease, such a possibility would tend to destroy the hope of immortality'.

It can be suggested that the success of the concepts of neurosis and psychosis lay in their critical combination of ambiguity and usability. Having the correct amount of ambiguity, they had great scope for uniting investigators in research and giving them a common language, even though these investigators might have quite different expectations of what the ultimate shape of the neuroses and psychoses was going to be. Such creative ambiguity is found at the start of many scientific enterprises. Thus the notions of atoms and germs took hold even though there was little or no evidence to support them initially. The other significant advantage that the terms psychosis and neurosis possessed lay in their usability. Both terms are succinct and are readily converted to adjectives. This may sound a trivial advantage but it has probably counted for more than would be suspected. For example in the case of schizophrenia, this term coined by Bleuler, supplanted Kraepelin's earlier widely accepted term, dementia praecox (early onset dementia), most probably because its succinct ambiguity was heuristic, whereas dementia praecox is more plainly descriptive, but also because schizophrenia is readily made into an adjective whereas dementia praecox is not.

The functional psychoses

Along with the establishment of the concepts of neurosis and psychosis, one further concept emerged. This was the notion of a functional psychosis. The work of Auguste Bayle was seminal in the development of this concept. He demonstrated through the means of post-mortem studies in the 1820s that general paralysis of the insane (GPI) was caused by syphilis. The significance of this was that for the first time a particular mental illness was correlated with brain changes. As the brain changes found in GPI were unique to this disorder, they made it an illness distinct from other psychiatric illnesses. Therefore all psychiatric illnesses could no longer be seen as different manifestations of the one thing.

This finding provoked an intense research interest in post-mortem cerebral pathology in an attempt to find the underlying causes of other mental illnesses. This activity met with limited success, except for the later identification of characteristic brain changes in the dementias, for which Alzheimer is remembered. Apart from associations between brain tumours and brain calcification with the insanities very little else was found at post mortem. The only other significant finding was that various drugs or poisons could be shown to alter mental states, presumably by poisoning some aspect of cerebral functioning.

The psychoses that are associated with structural brain changes, or that result from toxic or metabolic factors, are now called the organic psychoses. Any brain illness can cause an organic psychosis. Clinically these disorders differ strikingly from another set of psychoses, which is comprised of depression, mania or schizophrenia. So much do they differ that one can usually make a diagnosis of organic psychosis even without recourse to X-rays, EEGs and blood tests, and without having to wait for post mortems. In contrast, despite intensive research, in 1900 manic depression and schizophrenia clearly lacked either the clinical stigmata of the organic psychoses or any demonstrable cerebral disturbance. This is still the case.

As this became clear, another implication was drawn from Bayle's discovery. In the case of general paralysis it was realized that the same set of brain changes gave rise to a number of different clinical presentations, both among individuals and within the one individual at different times. Accordingly, it came to be appreciated that one organic lesion might stabilize a clinical picture rather than give rise to all of it.

An analogy can be had with lumbar disc problems. In these cases identical lesions may lead to quite different clinical presentations depending on how stoical the individual is, on whether there are issues of compensation or secondary gain involved or on whether they have had previous back trouble and the success or otherwise of treatment for that trouble. What can be said in these cases is that the underlying disc trouble stabilizes the clinical picture, but does not necessarily directly give rise to all of it. Therefore, as opposed to the gross disturbances found in the organic psychoses, one possibility was that in some cases an underlying brain disturbance might contribute to the clinical picture but that mental factors or reactions might so shape the clinical picture as to swamp the contribution of cerebral pathology.

Furthermore, in the absence of clearcut lesions at post mortems, it was argued, as it had been earlier for the neuroses, that the disturbances underlying a psychosis might not be gross destruction or inflammation but a physiological disturbance. That is a disturbance of function rather than of structure, in much the way that heart failures are a disorder of cardiac function that leaves the heart looking normal, whereas heart attacks lead to gross loss of cardiac muscle. Or as irritable bowel syndrome appears to be as real a disorder of bowel functioning as ulcerative colitis but it has no obvious lesion or inflammation. Just like cardiac failure and irritable bowel syndrome, functional mental disturbances could be expected to be reversible, to give variable levels of disturbance at different times and in contrast to the organic psychoses would not be apparent at post mortem.

For all these reasons, the term functional psychosis came into use. If there were such things as functional psychoses, one might expect that close clinical observation should detect syndromes that remained relatively stable over time, but which showed no correlation with postmortem findings. (Syndrome = things that run together.) This would happen because, although not giving rise to all or even to a constant set of clinical features, a functional lesion should at least give enough shape to a clinical presentation to define it as an illness distinct from other mental illnesses, either at first clinical presentation or by virtue of its course over time. Just as general paralysis, although not remaining constant all the time or entirely predictable at any one time, ran a fairly characteristic course in much the same way that other illnesses did. Once established, this course could be used to make a diagnosis of the illness before post mortem just as the clinical features of tuberculosis are often used to make a diagnosis even if the tubercle bacillus cannot be isolated from a particular individual.

The flowering of psychopathology

The pursuit of syndromes between 1860 and 1920 saw the heyday of psychopathology. In France, Falret and Baillarger distinguished folie circulaire, a subset of what we now know as manic depressive psychosis. Morel described another syndrome in which young people in their prime (early twenties) appeared to lose direction and nerve. He termed the disorder démence précoce. Lasegue described anorexia hystérique (later to be anorexia nervosa), exhibitionism, folie à deux and paranoid psychosis. De Clerambault described erotomania. Capgras described an unusual syndrome which bears his name where patients insist that their closest relatives or friends are actually imposters who look like the person they claim to be but who are not. Cotard described a syndrome in which the patient is overwhelmed by nihilistic delusions. Charcot legitimized the syndrome of hysteria.

Not all these syndromes were later to survive as distinct illnesses and French dominance in the new science was also soon challenged. Following the French lead, Hecker and Kahlbaum in Germany respectively delineated the syndromes of hebephrenia and catatonia during the 1870s. Emil Kraepelin later took over these clinical syndromes and that of paranoid psychoses, and subsumed them into dementia praecox. He established the notion that there were three functional psychoses: manic depression; dementia praecox; and paranoia. Manic depression could present as depression only or as a bipolar illness with swings between mania and depression, but in either form this was typically a remitting disorder. Dementia praecox, like GPI, could present in a variety of ways (catatonia, paranoid disorders and hebephrenia), but in all these cases it followed a characteristic course which was uniformly bleak regardless of the type of initial presentation. Paranoia presented with prominent and fixed delusions about secret lovers, missions to save others or beliefs that one had been wrongly victimized.

Of central importance to the distinction drawn in the last chapter between illnesses on the one hand and psychological or mental disorders on the other are Kraepelin's views on paranoia. He regarded manic depression and dementia praecox as illnesses, but did not regard paranoia as an illness. He saw it as the natural development of certain types of personality formation. This issue has been taken up subsequently by many others, most notably by Kretschmer. It has proved a source of serious difficulties that have usually been handled by attempting to ignore the existence of paranoia (Chapter 5).

Following Kraepelin's efforts at classification, which broadly speaking stand to this day, a second generation of psychopathologists took the delineation of mental illnesses as roughly settled and set about attempting to explain why these illnesses took the forms they did. This group included Jaspers, Birnbaum, Schneider, Kretschmer and Bleuler. Between 1910 and 1920 there was a feeling in psychopathology that a final understanding of mental illnesses, and in particular of the two great illnesses manic depression and schizophrenia, was imminent.

Ever since Kraepelin these two disorders have been termed the functional psychoses. There still has been no structural defect found in either. Disturbances of function are still being sought to account for them. The clinical picture of these two disorders still differs from that of all known organic disorders. This difference indicates an ambiguity and tension in the concept of the functional psychoses. If they differ so strikingly from the organic disorders, while they may involve some disorder of organic function surely they cannot just be organic disorders. Accordingly, if not just organic disturbances do they have psychological origins and might they even respond to psychotherapy? All of these possibilities were contained in von Feuchtersleben's use of the term psychosis. The term functional psychosis therefore, has been a term containing a tension of opposites.

Maintenance of this creative ambiguity has always been under threat, with the medical establishment tending to see these disorders as soon-to-be-seen-as organic psychoses. Accordingly, just as one would not think of treating the behavioural problems one might get with a brain tumour by psychotherapy, so also there is a prejudice against treating the functional psychoses by psychotherapy. In contrast the anti-medical lobby has, ever since 1860, seen the notion of the functional psychoses as a political move by the medical establishment to gain control over what should more appropriately be seen as a set of behavioural or social problems. After all these are behavioural disorders for which no demonstrable cerebral disturbance has been found despite intensive investigation.

A second set of revolutions have compounded rather than alleviated these tensions.

THE FREUDIAN PARADIGMS

That psychological rather than nervous factors could be operative in the neuroses began to be appreciated during the second half of the nineteenth century. The most dramatic illustrations of this point were made by the neurologist Charcot. During his ward rounds, patients had fits or were paralyzed under hypnotic suggestion, or were cured of shock-induced paralysis by hypnosis. These hysterical paralyses and fits differed from those of non-hypnotic epilepsies and paralyses which suggests to us today that they may have been 'put on'. This was not Charcot's belief. He argued that these 'dynamic' disorders were real in the sense of involving real disorders in nervous functioning which were unmasked by psychological stress. This interpretation was opposed by Bernheim who argued that hysterical disorders were put on under the influence of suggestion and could be removed by persuasion. In other words hysteria was a feigned illness. These two interpretations were the first hint of a psychological, as distinct from a spiritual interpretation, of a behavioural disorder.

The psychological paradigm
One of Charcot's pupils was Sigmund Freud. In his work as a clinician specializing in neurology Freud was faced with many cases of hysteria. Following in Charcot's footsteps he accepted that hysteria was brought on by shock. But in contrast to Charcot, he argued that rather than a nervous malfunctioning what had happened was that shock had caused an emotional blockage, which needed releasing. It was a short step from this idea to notions of defence mechanisms, which acted to remove the traumatic image from consciousness. And to an unconscious where the image would still be registered and which might be probed by hypnosis. Initially Freud's clinical investigations led him to suspect that the emotional shock that hysterical subjects had sustained followed on the occurrence of incest or sexual assault. He came to doubt the veracity of this idea, despite good evidence of incest in a number of the cases he saw. In some cases it seemed to him that he might be planting the idea in patients' minds by suggestion.

Looking around for a way to exclude this possibility he hit upon the method of free association. His insight was that a detached observer scrutinizing the behaviours and communication of any one might be able to detect latent content to the communication or unconscious motivations at work in the behaviour. In other words, a different interpretation might be put on what was happening to that held by the undetached subject. Thus in the case of a young man (Oedipus) who intemperately kills an old man at a crossroads (Laius, his father), one can suspect his protestations that he did not mean to handle the old man roughly, particularly if he goes on to marry the old man's wife. If this is the case, then, the problem behaviour might have to do with a disjunction between the patient and reality rather than with a nervous malfunction within the patient.

Such a hypothesis implied that the clinical neurosis, hysteria, was not actually a neurosis in the sense of being the result of a nervous malfunction, as Cullen's definition of neurosis would suggest. Rather it was a psychological or mental disorder that was most appropriately treated by psychological means. The signs and symptoms told a story, if only one knew how to read the text, rather than indicated an illness. Cures were to be effected by enabling the patient also to read the script. Freud went on to claim generalized anxiety, phobias and obsessive–compulsive disorders as psychological rather than nervous problems. He also took over the non-melancholic depressions; that is those depressions that do not show gross sleep and appetite disturbances and that look much more like problems or states of demoralization rather than cases of chemical or hormonal imbalance (melancholia). These so-called milder depressions have often been termed neurotic depressions as a consequence.

Effectively, most of the neuroses became psychological disorders. So much so that the original sense of the word neurosis was inverted and rather than being conditions in which there was a disturbance of nervous functioning, the neuroses became disorders in which nervous functioning was assumed to be normal. For a while Cullen's neuroses were distinguished from Freud's psychoneuroses to emphasize the change in meaning. But the revolution gained acceptance so quickly, that the new word never caught on and the old word, neurosis, took on a meaning diametrically opposite to its former meaning. Echoes of these events can still be found in popular usage of the words 'nerves' and 'nervous breakdown' to mean an emotional rather than a nervous problem.

A scientific revolution had happened. Freud had established a new territory to be explored, the dynamic unconscious, a new science to explore it, depth psychology, and a set of new methods for the new science. His breakthrough opened up a perspective in which dreams, creativity and anxiety and much else that seemed irrational in human living had a meaning. This was the first comprehensive distinction of a psyche from a soul and first outlining of a set of psychological problems that were not spiritual problems. This can be illustrated by comparing Freud's view of hysteria with those of Charcot and Bernheim. Charcot's view of hysteria teetered on the psychological brink but remained, in essence, a neurological view. Bernheim's also teetered on the brink but was much more rational and moral than Freud's conception.

Freud was not initially concerned with the psychoses and he never involved himself with psychotic patients, but there seemed no reason to most other analysts why the psychoses in turn should not yield up their meaning. They were simply a more complicated problem to solve, one to which Jung devoted much of his efforts. During the 1950s, in particular, the issue of the psychotherapy of schizophrenia was the foremost issue on the agenda of the depth psychologies.

The psychoanalytic paradigm

Early in the development of the new science problems arose. If clinical disorders come about because of a disjunction between the patient and reality, how could one know what was reality and what degree of disjunction from reality was likely to give rise to distress of clinical intensity? Having established the notion of the unconscious, Freud went on to answer these issues by attempting to define the structure of the mind and its central dynamic aspects. Thus it was postulated that we all have ids, egos and superegos. That the dynamism of the unconscious stemmed from erotic and thanatotic (death) impulses or energies. These set up early crises such as the Oedipal crisis in all of us, whose resolution one way or the other profoundly affected our subsequent adjustment to reality.

On this issue of the supposed reality that patients were out of touch with, the analytic school split in a way that no other science has split. Comprehensively different depth psychologies emerged (the Jungian and the Adlerian) based on different paradigms. In these other systems, different motivational hierarchies are postulated. While they agree on the potential significance of dreams or latent content to behaviour, completely different interpretations to those offered by Freud may be put on the actual dreams or distressed behaviour. It is a truism that individuals undergoing a Freudian analysis have dreams laced with Freudian themes, whereas those undergoing Jungian and Adlerian analysis have dreams in which Jungian and Adlerian motifs appear. Unfortunately for the scientific status of all of these schools there seems to be no way of deciding who is right.

This rejection of the psychoanalytic paradigm by Jung, Adler and others should be distinguished from an acceptance of the psychological paradigm. All subsequent dynamic psychologies agree with the notion that clinical distress is meaningful rather than meaningless and, broadly speaking, on the existence of an unconscious. All agree with the notion that mental illnesses are states of mind. All implicitly suggest that if the patient appears to recover before that state of mind is explored, the recovery will be incomplete and the patient liable to relapse.

The depth psychologies have not been the only psychologies to consider mental illnesses a state of mind. Following Freud, the techniques of behaviourist psychology began to be applied to mental illnesses in the 1940s and 1950s. Advocates of this approach have scathingly rejected the claims of psychoanalysis. They have argued that one cannot be scientific about something that does not obviously exist. Likewise they believe that Freud's hypothesized constructs (ids, egos and superegos) are just so many incorporeal entities and that is exactly why their truth cannot be established reliably. Embarrassingly for the psychodynamic schools of thought, behavioural managements of many anxiety disorders are very effective. In current psychiatric practice, behavioural techniques, rather than an in-depth analysis, are turned to for the treatment of phobic and obsessional disorders.

For all their widely proclaimed opposition to psychoanalysis, however, behaviour therapy is consistent with the depth psychologies in seeing mental illnesses as states of mind. Thus they share the psychological paradigm. In this case an affected subject's mind is seen as being dominated by maladaptive reflex responses or habits that are appropriately managed by the kind of means one would employ to break any habit. If there really was anything wrong with the nerves of affected subjects, classic behavioural therapy would not hold. One cannot expect to be able to apply the results of stimulus–response learning experiments, that have been established on nerves working normally, to situations in which nerves are not working normally.

During the 1960s and 1970s when behavioural techniques were coming to be widely adopted, it seems to have been thought by many that the psychoses were simply a more difficult problem or intractable set of habits than the neuroses but that they too, under the influence of correspondingly radical behavioural interventions, would be open to reversal. Some support for this position could be demonstrated from studies which indicated that a good deal of the behaviour of chronic schizophrenic subjects appeared to result from institutionalization. This is necessarily something that is learnt by patients; a set of habits or a frame of mind.

Cognitive and interpersonal therapy

At present the hopes that one or other of these theories would account for all the phenomena of mental illnesses have been fading for some time. Psychodynamic treatment and behavioural management are both out of fashion for either the affective disorders or schizophrenia. But there have been other developments. While the earliest behaviour therapists denied the very existence of interior mental events, reducing behaviour to a collection of learnt reflexes or response patterns, current learning theorists have felt it necessary to concede the existence of some form of internal processing of information. This has been labelled the cognitive revolution in learning theory. Two sets of findings and schools of thought in this latter cognitive tradition have implications for any psychopathology of the psychoses, the development of cognitive psychotherapy by Beck and the demonstration of the phenomenon of learned helplessness by Seligman and colleagues.

Beck was originally a psychoanalyst specializing in the treatment of depression. He came to realize that in cases where he appeared to be successful he was doing something other than what analytic theory would have prescribed. In particular he was exploring the ideas his patients had about themselves, their world and their future and finding that these were profoundly negative and often seemingly unaccountably at odds with the evidence of successful lives.[10] These organized and entrenched negative thoughts he called schemata (a word close in meaning to habit). These schemata are maintained, he argued, by the subjects consistently misinterpreting what goes on around them. For some reason depressed subjects appear to distort the evidence that pertains to the question of their worth in a way that normal subjects do not. They appear unable to assess current events in a balanced way, reading too much significance into things said by others or seeing issues in absolute terms of black-and-white where others can tolerate ambiguity.

The mental analysis that revealed schemata was something different to the analysis one gets in psychodynamic psychotherapy. It did not probe the hidden depths of the personality. Schemata were not something arrived at with great difficulty. The mental events involved were something lying there on the surface, such as repeated unprompted self-denigration, or else they were easily brought there. They were easily recognizable by both patient, therapist and external observers. As such these mental events were unlikely to draw the wrath of behaviourists as quickly as the hypothetical constructs of analytic theories. Furthermore, what Beck did was in many respects close to what behaviour therapy did. He suggested that depressed subjects habitually turn to negative thoughts. Because these thoughts are at odds with the evidence one can manage them in ways not dissimilar to the way behaviour therapy manages unreasonable levels of fear that are at odds with evidence.

The relevance of this to the affective disorders and schizophrenia (the functional psychoses) is that, unlike behaviour therapy or psychodynamic psychotherapy, cognitive therapy is demonstrably effective in one of the functional psychoses, major depression (melancholia). Initially Beck saw his method as being of use for neurotic depressions – those depressions where the affected subject seems more to be demoralized by personal problems rather than afflicted out of the blue with an illness that responds to antidepressant treatment. But the surprise from recent research has been that cognitive therapy also appears to work for the kind of depressions that antidepressants also help. Indeed in many cases these subjects show a quicker and cleaner response than neurotic depressives. However, unfortunately for the cognitive therapy theory, melancholic subjects often get well after a brief exposure to cognitive therapy, too brief to have allowed the uprooting of any entrenched negative schemata or to have allowed the reversal of any propensity to illogicality.

A further complication for cognitive theory has been the development and apparent success of interpersonal therapy. This method of therapy claims its inspiration from therapists such as Harry Stack Sullivan and Karen Horney. In the 1920s these therapists moved away from Freud's concentration on intrapsychic disturbances to focus on the interpersonal relations of manic depressives and schizophrenics. Based on their work Gerald Klerman, Myrna Weissman and colleagues at Yale and Harvard devised a treatment package for depression that focused on the significant interpersonal relations of subjects with depression.[11] Commonly these are found to be disturbed and working on them produces clinical improvements. But again the surprise has been that using this treatment major depressive disorders (melancholias), the supposedly antidepressant responsive depressions, appear to also do well, if not better than subjects with chronic and obvious interpersonal problems.

Learned helplessness

Learned helplessness is a behavioural phenomenon that was first demonstrated in the 1940s. In 1967 it was demonstrated with a difference by

Overmeier, Seligman and Maier.[12] Like others before them, they showed that the behaviour of animals experimentally exposed to inescapable shock changed radically. They lost motivation, became listless and emotional and appeared to have difficulties learning. The significance of the 1967 studies of Seligman and coworkers lay in their interpretation of what was happening rather than in the redemonstration of this phenomenon. Their analysis of the findings suggested that the behaviour of helpless animals could not be explained simply in terms of learning laws, as these had been conceived by strict behaviourists. Instead they postulated that all animals must analyse events rather than simply respond to them and that the analysis of helpless animals must yield the idea that they have no control over what is happening. As a result they lose motivation because nothing is worth doing, they learn poorly because if there can be no control over things there is not much point in learning and as a result they are emotional.

Two implications were drawn from these findings. One was the support they offered in favour of the cognitive revolution in psychology which said that sophisticated behaviour is not just a set of sophisticated reflexes but involves mental representations of events and modification of those representations in the light of experience. The other applied directly to psychiatry. Seligman and coworkers were quick to draw attention to a resemblance between depressed humans and their helpless animals.

Had something similar to exposure to inescapable shock happened to people who were depressed? In very many cases, it seemed that something had; that these subjects had been exposed to life events. But we all are exposed to such events so why should some people be made helpless by them? To explain this, helplessness theory turned to attribution theory and postulated that when things happen to human beings they ask what has caused this to happen and they make a causal attribution (Chapter 5). In the case of depression, helplessness theory suggests that subjects liable to become depressed are also liable to attribute responsibility for unfortunate events to themselves. Holding themselves responsible for many things that go wrong they develop a belief that things are more uncontrollable than they actually are. Believing this they become depressed.

The significance of learned helplessness to the issue of whether mental illnesses are all states of mind is that animals made helpless appear in many ways to have what we will later call a psychotic depression (melancholia) rather than a neurotic one. Given that behavioural problems that stem from altered states of mind without any nervous disorder are neuroses and that Seligman's claim was that helplessness was learnt, to be theoretically consistent Seligman and others have had to claim that learned helplessness is an animal form of neurotic depression. That is, it is a state of mind, which can be treated by psychological means, forcibly reteaching animals control over what happens to them. But these animals also eat and sleep poorly and show many biological alterations similar to those found in human subjects who have melancholia (psychotic depressions). They also show a good response to antidepressant medication. Does the phenomenon of learned helplessness mean that psychotic depression is also just a state of mind? If it does, one implication is that mania and schizophrenia might also, despite appearances, be states of mind rather than biological illnesses.

Both helplessness theory and cognitive therapy differ as radically from psychoanalysis as behaviourism. But like behaviourism, they have a central feature in common with the psychodynamic schools of thought on mental illness. Both see depression as being primarily a disordered state of mind. The attempts of both these theories to answer the question of why depressed subjects should begin to do either of these things illustrate further the family resemblances they bear to psychodynamic theories.

Both of necessity have to postulate that something must have gone wrong in the past for depressed subjects (this is usually taken as meaning in their childhoods). Without the distorting influence of past trauma there would be no easy way to explain why life events should precipitate only some of us into the habit of being negative or handling self-related evidence illogically, or should make only some of us liable to misattribute responsibility for ongoing events in a way that makes life appear uncontrollable. Therefore, just like Freudian theory, both of these latter theories postulate that depressed subjects have suffered some form of loss event in their past. Furthermore in cases of quick or antidepressant-assisted responses, they leave the impression that if the influence of these hypothetical prior traumata is not countered the subject is not truly cured. In addition, holding either of these theories appears to commit the holders to the position that antidepressant- or ECT-assisted responses are in some way a papering over the cracks.

Thus with Freud two paradigms were established. The primary one was that mental illnesses made sense and all psychological theories of mental illness have ever since shared this paradigm. The second paradigm related to the kind of sense to be found in mental illness. This paradigm has not been universally accepted. It has fostered revolutionary revisions. In the main, after lengthy battles, these have succeeded in that psychoanalysis has lost the pre-eminent position it held in psychiatry until relatively recently (mid-1960s). However, as of yet no one revision has replaced it.

THE JASPERIAN PARADIGM

As outlined above, Freud established the paradigm for a new science, dynamic psychology. The essence of this was that many things that had hitherto seemed meaningless or whose meaning was indecipherable were shown to have meanings. This paradigm has coloured popular thinking about mental illnesses ever since. But at the same time as Freud was establishing his paradigm, another paradigm was being set up that has not penetrated popular thinking so extensively but which has provided the cornerstone of much of medical thinking on mental illnesses. This latter paradigm was principally articulated by Karl Jaspers and notably developed by Kurt Schneider.

Unlike Freud, whose life, struggles for recognition and principal ideas are well known from many television series, numerous Hollywood movies, several popular biographies and incorporation in countless novels, dramas and works of literary criticism, Jaspers' life, significance and principal ideas are probably not familiar to the reader. This is likely to be the case, whether the reader is a layperson or a mental health professional. Accordingly, a short biographical note seems necessary.

Jaspers was born in 1883 and was therefore considerably younger than Freud. He studied law, then medicine and psychiatry before finally settling on philosophy as a career. Having graduated in medicine in 1909, he studied psychiatry at Heidelberg. His first contribution to psychiatric thinking was an influential article on morbid jealousy in 1910. His major contribution to psychiatry, *General Psychopathology*,[13] was published in 1913, when he was only 30. This latter underwent seven revisions between 1913 and 1959, but these affected matters of detail rather than orientation. In 1915 he left psychiatry. Unlike Freud, Jaspers was not a lone genius attempting to establish his own vision against opposition. He was a product of and contributor to the Heidelberg school of brain research, established by Wundt and Nissl. His contemporaries there were Wilmanns, Gruhle and Mayer-Gross, and later Kurt Schneider. Heidelberg offered a basic continuity of psychopathological thinking that Jaspers' book did much to articulate but for

which he was not solely responsible. Furthermore, Jaspers' paradigm
built on the foundations set by Emil Kraepelin in 1896. That is, he
accepted that the varied clinical manifestations of the major psychoses
represented only two mental illnesses, manic depression and dementia
praecox (schizophrenia).

General Psychopathology was not translated into English until 1963.
It has not had a wide readership outside Germany partly because of its
size – 900 large pages much of which is small print – but also because
of its content and style. Despite his wish to be 'of service to all those
who make mankind their theme', Jaspers' work and book were soberly
scientific and concerned with the correct methods necessary to arrive at
the answers to psychiatric illnesses rather than visionary declarations of
hidden significances in human living. As a consequence, his ideas lacked
marketability outside psychiatric circles. In particular, they did not
inspire fresh approaches to literary criticism, new philosophical movements, or suggest the outlines of new plots for plays or novels.

However, perhaps the most important reason for its neglect lay with
the fact that psychiatric thinking in the English speaking world and
particularly America had fallen under Freudian influence. Even in a
marketable version, his ideas had little impact. Where Jaspers' writing
tended to the comprehensive and explicitly tackled philosophical issues
head on, in a way that most psychiatrists find uncomfortable, his most
notable follower Kurt Schneider was famous for his succinct and laconic
style. His book *Clinical Psychopathology* in 1959,[14] encapsulated the
Jasperian approach, but only ran to 200 pages despite illustrating the
issues with telling clinical and literary vignettes. However, it was equally
poorly received outside Germany, going out of print on its first edition.
In an article to the *American Journal of Psychiatry* in 1950, Schneider
outlined the essence of this alternative to the Freudian paradigm in only
two pages. He concluded with the remark that he realized that all of
this would be very different to the way his readers were accustomed to
view the issues, but that he felt sure that they would prefer to be exposed
to a novel approach rather than simply have repeated in a slightly
different format what they knew already. Kuhn might have predicted
that this was a serious mistake.

Initially Jaspers' thinking took the framework set by Kraepelin as its
basis. But this was before psychoanalysis took hold. Increasingly thereafter his presentation of the issues took the form of an opposition to
the dynamic psychopathologies being developed by Freud and others.
In contrast to dynamic psychopathology, the form of psychopathological

theory espoused by Jaspers came to be termed descriptive psychopathology. This is a slight misnomer as arguably descriptive psychopathology culminated with Kraepelin. Thereafter the second generation of psychopathologists were doing something other than just describing mental illnesses.

Reasons and causes

As outlined in some detail earlier, the basic Freudian position is that there is a reason for behaviours. However, this cannot be true for all behaviours. If we see an old man collapse at a crossroads, we wonder what has happened. Has he burst a blood vessel? Did he have too much to drink? Has he had an epileptic fit? In other words, we speculate on what has caused his loss of consciousness. On the other hand if we have seen him being assaulted and stabbed by a younger man, we will know what has caused the loss of consciousness. But we are not likely to think that the younger man's behaviour is caused. We will speculate on his reasons for assaulting the older man. Is he trying to rob him? Does he know something about the old man that we do not? Or is the old man's name Laius and did he insult the younger man and is the younger man's name Oedipus?

Freudian psychopathology is concerned with the *reasons for mental illness*. In essence, the Jasperian position is that the *major mental illnesses have causes but not reasons*. In depression and schizophrenia, the argument is that something goes wrong with the way the brain works. On this line of thinking the depressed person would be more like someone suffering from a mild form of concussion or an unnoticed intoxication than someone who is motivated in some abnormal way or whose behaviour needs to be interpreted.

Much of our behaviour lacks reasons, it simply happens. For example, we may have reasons for eating particular things, but swallowing and breathing are acts that happen automatically and not voluntarily. Consciousness itself simply is there for no apparent reason. Waking up in the morning happens, although we may need reasons for getting out of bed. Posture involves an immense amount of co-ordination of muscle groups without which we would be unable to move about purposefully or to execute our wishes. These involuntary and automatic behaviours act as a background tone to purposive behaviours and function much as organ pedals and stops function in the playing of organs. They are necessary but not directly related to the wide variety of tunes that may be played.

It is the wide variety of tunes that is of interest to the composer and to audiences, but when organs break down it is a matter of repairing stops and pedals not musical scores. In the same way, it is the wide variety of reasons we have for our behaviours that distinguishes humans from animals and makes human behaviour so interesting. In the case of the major mental illnesses the Jasperian approach is that it is breakdown of the stops and pedals that is involved. Some of these automatic behaviours have gone wrong. In contrast, for Freudian and subsequent psychological approaches, mental illnesses are a matter of some strange dissonant tune being played.

While always disagreeing with Freud as to what precisely underlay the neuroses, Jaspers argued that in many cases of mental distress it is appropriate to look for the unrecognized sources of the distress and by a creative articulation of the problem to the sufferer to set them free from their distress. He accepted a psychological but not psychoanalytic paradigm for the neuroses. But he objected to its extension to the psychoses. The Jasperian paradigm concerns the psychoses rather than the neuroses. In the case of the psychoses he argued that at some point they become non-interpretable and that attempts to interpret the behaviours in question in terms of reasons and motives are all unpersuasive at some point in the analysis. For example, bearing in mind the possibilities of hysterical fainting and malingering and the possibility that subjects may not recognize what they are doing, in the case of loss of consciousness it strains credulity in most cases to attempt to interpret the behaviour in terms of recognized or unrecognized motives.

This may seem relatively easy for most readers to concede. But in the case of persons with major (non-neurotic) depressive disorders, a typical experience is regular early morning wakening (03.00–04.00 hours). Is this caused or does it happen for a reason? Unquestionably, sleep disturbances can happen for a reason. We all have had difficulties falling asleep when we have had things on our mind and we are worried. Such anxieties may lead to broken or light sleep. But regular early morning wakening? Freud postulated that there was a reason for this phenomenon which was that the persons affected were trying to escape from threatening dreams. Here Jaspers and Schneider disagree and argue that it seems more reasonable to account for what is happening in terms of dysfunctional sleep centres in the brain.

Similarly in major depressive disorders, loss of appetite is a common finding. One might ascribe refusal to eat to a recognized or unrecognized wish to die. But this simple interpretation ignores the fact that it appears to be loss of appetite rather than refusal to eat that affects depressed subjects. Nor can the failure to uncover the motives for depressive loss of weight be put down to a blind attempt to see the problem as medical, when the very same medical approach has little difficulty in recognizing and conceding that the anorexia of anorexia nervosa is motivated. And in conceding that any encouragement to anorexics to abrogate self-responsibility by suggesting that what is happening to them is out of their control would be counter-therapeutic.

Features which resist explanation in terms of reasons and appear better explained in terms of causes were taken by Jaspers to indicate a psychosis. In depression these were early morning wakening, loss of appetite, profound loss of interest and energy. In mania, sustained sleepless activation and a speeding up of thought processes, called flight of ideas. In schizophrenia, a certain incoherence of thinking and feeling. The central behaviours involved are typically automatic and involuntary ones. And it is disturbances of these behaviours rather than the presence of delusions or hallucinations, lack of insight or poor reality testing that lead to a diagnosis of psychosis. In the absence of such features, bizarre behaviour and utterances lead to a diagnosis of neurosis rather than of psychosis. Indeed the most bizarre behaviours found clinically are hysterical in origin rather than manic depressive or schizophrenic.

For Jaspers therefore, one had a psychosis when one had a disorder some of whose clinical features involved cerebral disturbances. This clear statement marked the establishment of a new paradigm and again as with the revolution in the understanding of neuroses, the words at the centre of the revolution underwent a complete change of meaning. Whereas before neuroses and psychoses were partial opposites, the former implying a disorder of nerves and the latter a mental disorder, with Freud the neuroses became mental disorders and with Jaspers and Schneider the psychoses became truly nervous or cerebral disorders. Following Jaspers, one could have a psychosis without any evidence of 'insanity', delusions or hallucinations. Ever since, at least in European psychiatry, a depression with early morning wakening and loss of appetite has been classifiable as a psychotic depression, even though there may be no trace of delusions or hallucinations or gross loss of contact with reality.

In the case of depression, mania and schizophrenia, while some cerebral dysfunction must occur, Jaspers left open the issue of precipitation. It might be organic or psychological or both, just as both organic and psychological stressors can give rise to duodenal ulcers. He also endorsed the notion of a functional psychosis for these disorders, as the central disturbances had a coherence not found in organic disturbances. The latter produced more disjointed and random changes in behaviour. It was also noted that the functional psychoses often remitted without any interventions to correct presumed organic imbalances.

As categorized by Jaspers there were essentially three functional psychoses, epilepsy, manic-depressive illness and schizophrenia. The reclassification of epilepsy as a functional psychosis and its replacement of paranoia, which for Kraepelin was a psychological disorder rather than an illness, as the third functional psychosis indicates the terminological shift that Jaspers was aiming at. As the epilepsies are never now referred to as functional psychoses, this indicates that he did not bring off a change in the meaning of the term psychosis in the way that Freud had changed the meaning of neurosis.

Mental illness post-Jaspers

A rarely recognized consequence of the Jasperian revolution was a potential change in the concept of mental illness. Both Jaspers and Schneider argued that the normal use of the word illness implied that something physical must be disordered. Although not demonstrated in the case of the psychoses, such a disordering could be presumed as some of the clinical features did not seem reasonably interpreted in terms of motives. The difference between a psychosis and a neurosis was that nothing about a neurosis needed to be explained in terms of biological disruption, as Freud would have argued, and Jaspers and Schneider agreed, and as Thomas Szasz and others have never ceased to point out.

Are the neuroses therefore not illnesses? In response to this medical opinion has divided. Where most follow Jaspers' paradigm up to this point, many appear to think that something must be wrong if the neuroses suddenly are not to be classified as psychiatric illnesses. Schneider at least had no difficulties with the issue and one of his most famous dictums was that there are no neuroses only neurotics. Failure to accept this point has obscured a further one, that if the neuroses are not illnesses and as the psychoses are mainly physical rather than mental illnesses (even if psychologically precipitated) are there any mental illnesses? A conclusion that the Jasperian revolution points toward is that there are no mental illnesses; that mental illness is a logical impossibility.

As noted above, revolutions give rise to terminological difficulties. This is very clear at present with regard to the words psychosis and neurosis. Initially a neurosis implied a disorder of nervous function and was contrasted with the word, psychosis, which meant a disorder of the mind, rather than a nervous disorder. There would appear to be a need for two such contrasting terms. But if the term neurosis now also means a disorder of the mind and if psychosis has not taken its place as implying a disorder of nerves that affects behaviour, what current relation have these two terms to each other or what exactly is the current usage of the term psychosis? There are several different answers to this, depending on the framework one adopts and a good deal of mutual incomprehension is generated by the use of these terms in a number of different senses.

The least satisfactory but commonest use of psychosis now is to indicate what, in effect, is a severe neurosis. That is if there is evidence of a severe disturbance of *mental* functions. In particular if the patient seems to have poor contact with reality, or a lack of insight, they are likely to be labelled psychotic. Typically, the presence of delusions or hallucinations will bring an instant diagnosis of psychosis. There are a number of intractable problems generated by this usage. For example, if a psychosis is a severe disorder of the mind, how is it that antidepressants or ECT may be effective in its cure? Typically they, and other psychotropic agents are ineffective for the treatment of classic neuroses, which respond preferentially, as one might expect of a disorder of the mind, to talking therapies or relearning therapies. How could antidepressants or ECT possibly affect contact with reality or restore insight? Yet this is what current definitions of psychosis must imply they do.

On the other hand if a psychosis has a central physical disturbance at its core, does it make sense to talk about loss of contact with reality or loss of insight? Can one really make an assessment of a subject's capacity for insight or reality testing, given that they may be operating under the influence of a subtle cerebral disturbance about which they specifically lack insight? Unquestionably, a person who believes firmly that they are damned can be accused of being out of touch with the reality that most of us recognize. But what is commonly not taken into account is that the person expressing these beliefs is starting from a different data base to the rest of us. They are suffering from a clear impairment of performance which they cannot explain but must, for the sake of their sanity. Starting from a similar data base, current studies (see Chapter 5) suggest that it is not improbable that all of us might come to similar or equally extreme conclusions. This necessarily implies that the patient's reality testing is at least as good as that of the rest of us. Subjects with depression, mania or schizophrenia have never been shown by any form of testing to have any significant impairment of judgement.

Indeed, one can question whether reality testing in delusional depression or schizophrenic delusions is nearly so poor as that found in phobic states or, more particularly, in hysteria or in Kraepelin's paranoia or Kretschmer's sensitive psychoses. Compared to the neuroses and paranoia, the abnormal beliefs found in depression, mania and schizophrenia can be seen in one of two ways (Chapter 5). Either as rational attempts to account for an abnormal underlying physical experience or as a poor adaptation to affective or schizophrenic illnesses. That is those patients with affective disorders or schizophrenia, who become deluded, can be seen as handling their psychosis neurotically.

Furthermore, lack of insight is an ambiguous quantity. In practice, the presence of insight means that the patient sees their illness in the same way as their therapist. However, there can be no guarantee as to the validity of the therapist's insight, as therapists from differing orientations disagree strongly in most cases about what is going on in any psychiatric disorder. In many cases, one can question just who has the greater degree of insight.

Take a patient, suffering from depression, who insists that there must be something physically wrong with them. In almost all cases, such a patient will be diagnosed as severely lacking in insight. The patient may further insist that they have no significant emotional disturbance that they know of or at least none that wouldn't clear up if their physical state improved. In response to this it is likely to be suggested or thought that the patient is so heavily defended against emotions that he or she wouldn't recognize them if slapped in the face with them. But if the disorder is a genuinely physical one, as response to antidepressants would suggest it must be, such a patient is actually showing a great degree of insight to detect what may be quite subtle physical abnormalities. Indeed possibly a heroic amount of insight, if they maintain their point of view in the face of medical insinuations that they are neurotic. Much more insight than someone who is certain that they feel as they do because of some neglected problem or buried emotional complex.

CIVIL WAR IN AMERICA[15]

The Freudian and Jasperian revolutions were essentially European affairs. Indeed the Jasperian vision has never travelled beyond Europe. But the contradictions engendered by these competing visions have travelled. They are found in the difficulties encountered when trying to define the terms psychosis or mental illness. Not surprisingly there are moves afoot to resolve the confusion. Principally in the one place where one of these paradigms emerged undisputably victorious, America. While psychoanalysis never took over American psychology, it did triumph completely in American psychopathology. Until recently American psychiatric circles were its uncritical bastion.

However, American psychiatry has recently drawn up a new list of categories of mental illness, with strict definitions of the terms involved. The underlying philosophy, roughly speaking, has been that things are in such a mess that we will forget all theories and simply define words in a consistent way that comes close to popular usage. Holding these new definitions firm may help iron out some of the confusions that seem to stem simply from the incompatible use of words. The manual in which terms and definitions are set out is called the *Third Diagnostic and Statistics Manual* (DSM III).[16]

One of the most notable features of this manual is the almost complete absence of the term neurosis. This term was felt to imply an unproven Freudian aetiology to neuroses. Accordingly, it has effectively become a non-word, despite the protest of many behaviourists, who could never be called Freudian. The term psychosis is reserved strictly for disorders characterized by delusions or hallucinations. Underpinning these redefinitions is a professed agnosticism about the origin and causation of mental disorders. One can wonder whether this redefinition of words by committee will work. Intuitively, it seems an inherently unsatisfactory way to go about things and likely to lead to terms that are empty of meaning or at least stripped of historical resonance.

Many do not accept that the stated intention is one of scientific agnosticism, but see in the process an attempt to shake off the legacy of a Freudian past. Why such an upheaval? The stimulus almost certainly came from the introduction of effective psychotropic drugs for the treatment of mental illness. As outlined by Kuhn, a change in paradigms should not necessarily be taken to imply that a more complete and obviously correct view has replaced an older less adequate view. Initially new paradigms may explain little more, or even less, than the view they are replacing. But in some crucial way they will be seen as offering more research opportunities than the older view. As psychoanalysis has little to say about why antidepressants or neuroleptics effect the changes they do, the introduction of these agents could have been predicted to produce a revolutionary crisis. It is this crisis that underlies the attempted redefinition of terms found in DSM III.

Psychopharmacology – a sideshow?

In 1952 the first neuroleptic, chlorpromazine (Largactil) was tried out experimentally. By 1954 it was being used clinically. By the end of the decade it, and others (thioridazine/Melleril, haloperidol/Serenace, flupenthixol/Depixol), were being used widely in ever increasing amounts for schizophrenia and mania. Around the same time the large and overcrowded mental hospitals began to empty out their inmates and the emphasis on psychiatric treatment became one of getting people into hospital early and out again quickly rather than locking them up for lengthy periods of time as a final resort. The neuroleptics are often cited as permitting this change in practice. However, there has been much argument since that these developments stemmed from a change in custodial attitudes rather than any magic treatment of schizophrenia (Chapter 6).

In 1958 the first antidepressants (imipramine and amitriptyline, which were tricyclic antidepressants, and phenelzine and iproniazid, which were monoamine oxidase inhibitors) also came into use. By the early 1960s they had a proven place in the treatment of depression. ECT had been introduced before these two groups of drugs but did not seem to pose as much of a problem for the Freudian paradigm, as its mode of action could, at a push, be explained in terms of punishment or the crude obliteration of memories.

In 1965, Joseph Schildkraut formulated the catecholamine hypothesis of depression and a new era was born. This hypothesis proposed that brain levels of the catecholamine neurotransmitters were lowered in states of depression and that antidepressant treatments acted to increase them. Compared to the psychoanalytic hypotheses before it, this hypothesis was an extremely simplistic and one-dimensional view of depression. It was not particularly consistent with the known data of its time. Neither it nor any of its various modifications has ever been supported by experimental findings. But its significance lay in its offering a shape for hypotheses to come. This shape took account of cerebral factors in a better way than the Freudian hypotheses and legitimized research on the cerebral substrates of the affective disorders in a way that the psychodynamic hypotheses did not.

It has been a common complaint of psychopharmacologists, medically-oriented psychiatrists and philosophers of science that psychodynamic approaches to psychiatry were doomed to failure. They were, it is argued, intrinsically unscientific and hence of necessity doomed to replacement by the properly scientific (Chapter 3). The principal evidence of their unscientific nature is the inability to disprove the tenets of psychoanalysis. An inability that seems to stem not from their surviving disproof by being apparently correct, but by virtue of any attempted disproof seemingly running up against a phenomenon of shifting goalposts. This seems to be combined with an unwillingness on the part of the adherents of psychodynamic hypotheses to contemplate the possibility that fundamental tenets of their theories might be wrong. All of which Kuhn would argue is good scientific practice, even if not in accord with our notions of what that practice should be.

It is rarely noted that the catecholamine hypotheses have survived disproof of their initial premises in much the same way that the development of psychoanalysis was not deflected by the disproof of the occurrence of sexual traumata at the origin of the neuroses. Furthermore, that the catecholamine hypotheses appear to be as adept at shifting goalposts as the Freudian hypotheses before them. When no lowering of any catecholamine was found in depression, disturbances in catecholamine receptors were proposed instead. Likewise the inability to pinpoint any derangement of neurotransmitters was put down to biochemical or clinical heterogeneity. That is, it is argued that only some depressions involve a lowering of catecholamines and hence research on all depression as a block will miss those in whom catecholamine function is deranged. Or it is proposed that the crucial disturbance lies in the balance between catecholamine and other neurotransmitters. But no testable specification of the imbalance has ever been offered.

Research on the cerebral substrates of the affective disorders has not been characterized by any obvious interest in disproving the catecholamine hypotheses, as Karl Popper has advocated should be the goal of all rigorous science. Rather such research appears aimed at supporting some version of the amine hypothesis. Inconvenient results are explained away with an ingenuity entirely comparable to that of psychoanalysts confronted by awkward facts.

Interestingly it would be a mistake to think that because the catecholamine hypotheses are biological that they are necessarily Jasperian. One of the unrecognized ironies of the current state of affairs is that the catecholamine theories of depression have to date been crypto-Freudian in their psychopathology. As formulated by Schildkraut, the catecholamine hypothesis and its successors have appealed to notions of reward and punishment centres in the brain and implied that their biochemical formulations are consistent with behaviourist notions of depression involving a derangement of reward-seeking behaviours. This apparent consonance with a 'scientific' psychological theory has arguably been one reason why the catecholamine hypotheses have been so influential.

Along with an irrefutability that is comparable to that of psychoanalysis and a common psychopathological orientation, the catecholamine hypotheses have penetrated popular consciousness almost to the same extent that Freudian notions before them did. Where once mentally distressed subjects approaching psychiatrists expected to be told about latent psychosexual problems and unrecognized childhood disturbances, now many subjects will expect to hear talk of chemical imbalances. Popular magazines and daily newspapers will refer casually to the 'known' depletions of neurotransmitters in depression. For those to whom the idea of drug treatment is unappealing, foods in which the precursors of the relevant neurotransmitters can be found are recommended.

It was not until the early 1970s that a corresponding hypothesis for schizophrenia appeared, the dopamine hypothesis. This is based on the fact that neuroleptics, which are used widely in schizophrenia, have been found to have a principal action on the dopamine system in the brain. In contrast to the fate of depression after the introduction of antidepressants, which paradoxically did not become any more of a medical disorder but rather a psychological hypothesis cloaked in biological language, the introduction of the dopamine hypothesis in schizophrenia has had the opposite effect. Where once it was seen as at least partly a psychological disorder, at present schizophrenia is almost a parody of a medical illness with none of its significant clinical features being seen as anything other than organically caused (Chapters 5 and 6).[17]

Although twenty years later, they still offer a very limited view of manic depression and schizophrenia, these 'biological' hypotheses remain very much in the ascendant. As we have noted, the fact that they more adequately account for clinical responses to psychotropic drugs is one reason. But other factors seem suggested by the example of the adoption of theories of morbid heredity and degeneration in French psychiatry precisely 100 years earlier. At this time French psychiatrists were beset by problems. The public held them in low repute. The magistracy derided their claims to legal expertise. The profession was sharply divided along theoretical lines.[18] A situation similar to that faced by psychiatry, especially American psychiatry, 100 years later.

Under these pressures, the notion that morbid heredity and degeneration in the germ plasm of cells underlay mental illness became seemingly irresistibly appealing. This theory was never well defined. It always remained vague and flexible. As a result it had the capacity to accommodate widely differing points of view. It also offered intellectual legitimacy through identification with the established biological sciences. And as with 'biological' hypotheses of behaviour, it was deeply pessimistic,[19] which was also in tune with the spirit of the age.[20] All of which could be said about our current position and the role of the catecholamine and dopamine hypotheses also.

STALEMATE

Unlike the Freudian revolution, which on one level succeeded completely and on another immediately led to civil war, the Jasperian revolution has neither succeeded nor led to civil war, but has run into serious resistance. It has remained incomplete. Why?

The issues we have been considering have been issues of psychopathology rather than psychiatry. As mentioned in the introduction, psychopathology is the theoretical framework that specifies what mental illnesses are, how many of them there are and what the precise abnormality at the core of each is. Psychiatry is the practice of treating mentally ill subjects. While an idea of what is wrong with mentally ill subjects is obviously useful, psychiatry can be pursued without much reference to psychopathology. Much of current psychiatric practice consists of the application of treatments with a known effectiveness for certain loosely specified clinical conditions, but without much consideration of the underlying nature of the disorder being treated or much specification of first principles in the solution of particular clinical problems.

This neglect of theory is not peculiar to psychiatry. Much of medicine is practised because certain treatments are known to work, but little may be known about the true nature of the illness being treated. It is an approach that works passably in clear cut psychiatric cases but breaks down if the patient fails to respond to the treatment given or the clinical presentation is atypical. When therapists of differing orientations attempt to discuss these cases, incomprehension commonly results.

This pragmatic approach offered a way out of the clash between Freudian and Jasperian paradigms. It only became possible with the advent of agents or technologies that could bring about demonstrable clinical improvements. As such the modern practice of psychiatry has only developed, since World War II, with the advent of antidepressants and neuroleptics. Also important has been the advent of a number of specific psychotherapeutic procedures such as behaviour therapy for phobic or obsessional states and cognitive therapies for depression. Most practising psychiatrists will have recourse to these treatments because of their proven effectiveness, rather than as a matter of principle or philosophy. Indeed, therapists from quite different schools of thought will make use of them with little debate about whether the treatments work, as these issues have been settled or can be quite easily. There can, however, be heated debates among therapists using the same treatment as to how 'cures' come about or as to what is happening in cases that do not respond in the usual ways.

One reason why psychiatry is now so studiously pragmatic and almost totally neglects theory is that it might have been expected to take a considerable length of time to work out the implications of the introduction of effective psychiatric treatments. Almost inevitably the explosion of knowledge in psychopharmacology and behavioural biology has temporarily diverted attention from ambiguities in the psychopathological framework, into which such developments must ultimately be slotted.

All such developments have tended to reinforce the validity of the Jasperian position. Only the psychoses, in the Jasperian sense, show a response to psychotropic agents. This is not surprising as arguably only these are illnesses in the usual medical sense of the word. Using the word psychosis in its essentially Freudian sense, leads to the paradox that the effective agents we possess are only effective for the severe forms of mental illnesses and not for milder forms. Surprisingly this is rarely commented on. Probably because it is embarrassing. In no other illness does the severe form of the disorder respond to treatment and the mild form fail to respond.

A second important reason for the failure of the Jasperian revolution to properly take root lay in the domination of American psychiatry by psychodynamic schools of thought. A domination only recently shaken. But this shaking has not resulted in conversion from a Freudian paradigm to a Jasperian one. While the term neurosis has been dropped completed, because it was felt that it had too much Freudian baggage attached to it, the term psychosis has been restricted to disorders in which delusions and hallucinations are present. This gives it a meaning almost diametrically opposite to that found in Jaspers and Schneider. Ironically it gives it an almost quintessentially Freudian meaning, that of a severe neurosis. Given American dominance of the media, both scientific and popular,

America was a significant bastion of resistance when psychoanalysis held sway and also now when nothing holds sway.

A third reason that can be cited is that the Jasperian paradigm was never as communicable as either of Freud's paradigms. Compared to the concept of a neurosis, which was simply a disorder of the mind, that of a functional psychosis was much more complex. While cerebral rather than behavioural disturbances were at the core of these disorders, they did not entirely constitute them. Thus the clinical picture becomes a complex one. Because the cerebral disturbances are liable to give rise to strange experiences, reactions to those experiences will inevitably be unusual, even to a delusional extent. There is at present an almost complete failure clinically to distinguish the core of the affective disorders and schizophrenia from reactions to them. Both core and reactions are branded as organic in origin. If any of a patient's utterances are going to be seen as reactions to their illness, ironically it is reports of the very things that Jaspers and Schneider suggested were at the heart of a psychosis, such as difficulties with attention or of physical discomfort, that will get dismissed as 'neurotic'. This inversion of meaning is as commonly found in medical thinking which might be supposed to be Jasperian as in psychological theorizing.

Jaspers' ideas about delusions may have also added to the confusion. Where a majority of psychopathologists had seen delusions as psychological reactions rather than as stemming directly from an abnormally functioning brain, Jaspers left the distinct impression that he saw certain delusions arising directly from cerebral disturbances (Chapter 5). This central ambiguity, perhaps more than anything else, has obscured the thrust of the rest of his argument which was that manic depression and schizophrenia were more like epilepsy than any putative insanity. That their insane features were largely accidental.

One further possibility, whose weight is incalculable, is that the medical establishment was not happy to enthusiastically embrace the Jasperian view. One of the logical consequences of this view, we have suggested, was that only manic depression and schizophrenia were illnesses. The neuroses and personality disorders and substance dependencies were not. If not, the next question is should they be under medical jurisdiction? Have we not medicalized misery or socio-political problems? Fully embracing a Jasperian view would seem to commit the holder to answering yes to this question and to being prepared to restrict the sphere of medical responsibility for these disorders.

However, medical domination of mental illnesses has been hard won and has constantly had to be defended. The defence of this position has not simply been a matter of maintenance of prestige or income, but has been based on a genuine belief that a medical approach to mental illness is more enlightened and less moralistic than any non-medical one. It therefore seems unlikely that a large section of these gains would ever willingly be given away. Hence on the medical side of the argument, the Jasperian view would be one to cite selectively as authoritative but not to adopt radically. While on the non-medical side, these implications of Jaspers' views were never elaborated, presumably as brief acquaintance with his thought would give the impression that it was medical in the extreme.

These competing pressures have led to the demise of the broad church that was psychopathology. As the notion of a functional psychosis was at the start a tense one, holding together a complex of opposites, it was almost inevitable that it should have fallen casualty. We no longer appear to have any notion of an illness that could involve subtle disturbances of cerebral functioning, which might be precipitated by psychosocial stresses and might be responsive to psychotherapy. In medical circles ideas of psychological management seem to imply a desertion to the enemy rather than suggesting the height of medical skill, which traditionally has been taken to lie in the effecting of cures even when specific therapeutic agents do not exist.

Before going on to see whether a more nuanced view of the affective disorders and schizophrenia can be reconstructed in the light of recent advances and within the framework of mind, psyche and brain relations outlined in the last chapter, one more issue must be dealt with. Typically when Freudian/psychological and Jasperian/medical paradigms clash, the arguments are not about matters of fact. Rather the Freudian paradigm is criticized as being unempirical and unscientific. Psychological psychopathologists generally counter that the handling of human issues inevitably requires a different methodology to that found in the natural sciences. Therefore to dismiss interpretative approaches to the problem of human distress is mistaken. Accordingly, central to the issue of suspended revolutions in psychopathology is the issue of what a scientific psychiatry should look like. If all psychiatrists were being properly scientific would one or other of these paradigms vanish? To answer this needs some characterization of science.

TABLE 2. Changing meanings of neurosis and psychosis

	NEUROSIS	PSYCHOSIS
Initial Meaning	Disorder of nerve function	A spiritual disorder
Freudian Meaning	A psychological disorder	A severe neurosis
Jasperian Meaning	A psychological disorder	A disorder of brain functioning
DSM III	A non-word	A severe neurosis?

THREE   The Successors of Paracelsus

What makes science scientific? A widely cited answer to this question was that given by Herbert Butterfield,[1] who traced the rise of modern science to the development of an experimental tradition in the seventeenth century. He also pointed to the proscription by the Royal Society of debates on issues that could not be settled by observation or experiment. This edict owed much to Francis Bacon who had argued that scientists should only make inferences strictly from observations. The influence of Bacon and the practical effect of the Royal Society's edict was to remove philosophical and theological subjects from the scientific agenda. This removal, Butterfield argued, marked a turning point in human affairs as momentous as events such as the rise of Christianity. However there are problems with simply identifying the rise of science with an experimental tradition. For example, all the tools, reagents and interventions of the kind which were later to form the basis of chemistry, were present and in use long before the seventeenth century; why then was the rise of chemistry delayed until then?

Another problem is that science was flourishing before the advent of the great experimentalists such as Boyle. Its prior advance was largely a conceptual one, whose famous experiments occurred in the minds of its protagonists as in the case of Galileo, or were fortuitous occurrences, literally falling from above as with Newton. Such historical precedents are at odds with a picture of a strictly experimental science, which advances by piling one experimental result on top of the other and whose concepts should be ones that evolve. As we have seen, many historians of science influenced by Kuhn, in contrast, are now portraying science as a revolutionary process, whose concepts at any one time are often little influenced by experimental results or which are confirmed by subsequent experimental findings rather than resulting from such findings. Indeed, as in the days of Galileo and Einstein, new concepts often result from thought experiments or from mathematical juggling far removed from any laboratory. Furthermore, many of the great scientific revolutions, such as the Copernican revolution, have involved a triumph of reason over evidence in a manner that seems to make of science much more of a mystical or intuitive process than an empirical one in the Baconian sense.

However, there are problems for this account of science also. Arguably modern science does not just possess different concepts to Renaissance science, but is a radically different enterprise. For example, Galileo and Newton advocated a mathematization of nature. This might appear consistent with the widespread employment of mathematics in modern science. However, both Galilean and Newtonian mathematics largely involved the contemplation of abstract symbols, whereas the mathematics of modern science is quite different.

The role of measurement in science may make this clear. Ever more precise measurement is characteristic of modern science, but it is irrelevant to pure mathematics. Measurement did not greatly trouble Copernicus, Galileo or other early giants in physics. For Galileo and Newton mathematics involved pure concepts existing in intellectual space. For the modern scientist they are a technical instrument, necessary for measurement; this is particularly evident in the case of statistics.

An alternative to these conceptions of science has emerged recently. Central to this new view is the thesis that modern and Renaissance science differ radically.[2,3] That as well as the revolution that gave rise to science there has been a revolution that transformed it. Crucial to this transformation were the rise of probability and the development of the human or interpretative sciences. However, many still think of science as it was in the days of Newton and Galileo and require of scientists that they conform to these role models. It is in these terms that Freud is criticized. We will argue that Freud was very much a scientist in the Newtonian and Galilean mould, and that, paradoxically, it is precisely this that leads to the radically unempirical quality of psychoanalysis. To understand this requires a further look at the history of science.

SCIENTIA AND OPINIO[4-7]

There were two forms of knowledge at the time of the Renaissance, scientia and opinio. Scientia was derived from Aristotelian natural philosophy. It aimed at *certain* knowledge. Its paradigm was the syllogism, which could only lead to a single rational conclusion, given a common starting point. In this tradition, the actual material world was to some extent a set of appearances that were seen as concealing rather than revealing the true nature of things, their hidden essences. These essences were what Galileo, Newton and their contemporaries were hoping to get at, even while, in practice, they were breaking away from logic and metaphysics and beginning to practise science. In this tradition mathematics was seen as the queen of the sciences, in that it was a pure intellectual exercise concerned with divining necessary laws that were free from the corruption of appearances. Newton's deductions of the orbits of the moon and planets from his mathematical equations were seen as a stunning demonstration of the validity of this approach, revealing the *necessary* truths that lay behind the appearances of things.

But a syllogistic or deductive form of reasoning can only work when there is an agreed common starting point. That is, ineluctably correct answers are only ineluctable if the protagonists in a debate agree on certain basic premises. This agreed common starting point became an increasing problem as the hypothetical nature of the initial premises of scientific practice, as opposed to those of philosophical debate or mathematical demonstration, became obvious. Hence Bacon's insistence on working from agreed and reliable observations and only from those. From this hard evidence there appeared to be two logical steps that might lead to a single rational conclusion or certain knowledge. Following Bacon, one could proceed by induction based solely on the data. This is what most people understand by empiricism. But this approach has always been an ideal rather than common practice. More recently, following Karl Popper, one can deny the possibility of proof but assert that of disproof. Contrary instances provide a basis for a single rational conclusion, i.e. that the hypothesis in question does not hold.

Although a common starting point has become an increasing problem, the ideal of a single rational conclusion is not one that philosophers or scientists are happy to give up lightly. Arguably it is still single rational conclusions that many scientists think they are seeking. The problem for either of these approaches lies in explaining scientific advance – how are new data generated? Following Bacon or Popper, scientists might avoid drastic mistakes, but are they going to make any great leaps forward?

In addition to scientia, a body of knowledge termed opinio developed. In contrast to scientia, opinio took the appearances of things very seriously. Appearances were signs. Opinio was about interpreting these signs or determining their significance. Initially the signs in question were the views expressed by authorities but during the Renaissance there was a shift. Men such as Paracelsus began attempting to read the book of nature rather than the books of old masters. Signs were about everywhere, from the fever on a brow to the arrival of a comet.

Renaissance medical scientia took its agreed common starting point from Galen. In the second century AD, he had argued that all diseases stemmed from malfunctioning of one of four humours – phlegm, melancholy, sanguine and choler. Before Paracelsus, taking the Galenic approach with its a priori humours, Renaissance physicians made necessary deductions from them – if possible in a way that could be reconciled with the appearance of their suffering patients. In contrast Paracelsus started not from a position of already knowing the essences of illnesses or from an agreed starting point, but from one of wanting to find out. The appearances of the patient were signs or evidence to be used for a *diagnosis* and a *prognostic* opinion not for the demonstration of necessary laws. Patients rather than Galen's books were what needed to be read.

As the term opinio suggests, this approach led to something much less certain and much less respected than true knowledge. Paracelsus nowadays reads more like a mystic than a rational investigator. The practitioners of opinio as opposed to those of scientia were typically medical practitioners and alchemists. Generically, they were characterized as magi (magicians). Reading the signs was something done for the purpose of intervening in nature to cure illnesses or to transform base metals into gold rather than to find out essential truths.

The problem with signs lay in their interpretation. Some were more trustworthy than others. So grew the notions of confidence in particular signs and attempts to assign the significance of signs and to assess the frequency of their associations. Initially, the credibility of opinio stemmed from God being the ultimate guarantor of the meaning of the signs. This appeal to belief and trust was obviously a good deal less rational (in the sense of logical or necessary) than what was being offered by scientia.

But it became rational in a sense different to that of the necessary rationality of philosophers and 'scientia-ists' with the discovery of probability. A notable feature of the scientific revolution, only recently emphasized, is the complete absence of a modern idea of probability before 1660. With the introduction of the notion of probability and a mathematics to quantify levels of probability, given a large enough sample of signs, it became possible to make a rational stab at probable, if not certain truth. The interpretation of signs became less a question of healing magic and more a repeatable intervention.

The development of probability gave a whole new meaning to the rationale for experiments. For Galileo or Newton, experiments were secondary to ideas, optional extras rather than the means to discover new truths. They were a means of demonstrating or illustrating hypotheses or showing what flowed necessarily from them. But the dynamic of scientific advance lay in conjecturing. The usefulness of experiments was uncertain as the wrong result could always be explained away as the consequence of poor instruments or the influence of distorting factors. Historians of science have pointed to the fact that there were many natural observations or inconvenient experimental results that did not fit in with Newton's hypotheses. But in practice these inconvenient observations were of no importance, so that while Newton's laws may have been testable in principle they were irrefutable in practice. Indeed Newton's hypotheses are rarely thought of as hypotheses. Rather they immediately assumed the status of necessary laws and, in so doing, gave scientists the impression that science was all about discovering laws.

With the rise of probability, there emerged the possibility of diagnostic rather than demonstrative experiments. For example, it could be established if successive throws of a die were probable or not. If not, the question arose as to whether the die was loaded. Dissection of the actual die was one way to settle the issue – to diagnose what the state of affairs was. In contrast to a demonstrative experiment, which ideally was a magnificent demonstration of a necessary truth, a diagnostic experiment proceeded from ignorance to knowledge. It set a new prognosis based on the revealed state of affairs. But such prognoses were only probable opinions. Thus if future events deviated systematically from the prognosis (if the throws of the die still seemed improbable) the diagnosis was called into question and further analysis was required. This conjunction of diagnosis, prognosis and experiment has an inbuilt dynamic of advance that aims at ever more probable truth and leads methodically to discoveries. This, it can be argued, rather than isolated conjectural or experimental advances or even any beliefs in the value of being empirical, is what is responsible for the progress of modern science.

Medical opinio
The rise of a probabilistic approach to scientific knowledge was strongly resisted. The greatest names in science, even in the twentieth century, condemned the turn to probability and statistics as a resort to second-

grade knowledge, to mere opinion. In extreme cases, mathematics and physics were seen as the only proper or high sciences. They were distinguished from the lower sciences, which only deserved the term science in so far as they adhered to the methods of physical science. These latter became synonymous with empirical methods. The biological sciences such as physiology or anatomy were variously thought of as being a high or low science depending on the point of view of the commentator.

Medicine, however, quickly became the exemplary opinionated or low science, as its use of the terms diagnosis and prognosis might suggest. As medicine was a practical art rather than a purist's contemplative exercise this was perhaps understandable. But the intimate conjunction of medical practice with the development in the seventeenth century of a modern conception of probability is worth noting. It is no accident that at the end of the seventeenth century a physician, William Petty, could be found exhorting his contemporaries to conduct controlled experiments to discover 'whether of 100 sick of acute diseases who use physicians as many die in misery as where no art is used, or only chance'. In this quote can be seen the seeds of a distinctively modern form of rationality.

As befits a low science, developments in the rational application of opinions were intimately linked with money matters. In particular they were linked with the need for seventeenth and eighteenth century States to raise money. This was done through the issuing of annuities and insurances. In order that the State would make a profit from such enterprises, while at the same time giving its subjects a fair return on their money, it was necessary to determine the life expectancy of the population and also the relative risk of mortality of various applicants, according to age and social class. This practical necessity harnessed many of the best minds of the time to solving the mathematical issues involved. It led to the development and widespread application of statistical techniques.

The rational basis for annuities and insurances also required reliable data. Hence began the process of notification of deaths and of diseases. This information became the data of the insurance industry. However, these data were collected not for the purposes of demonstrating necessary truths but for the purposes of diagnosing the state of affairs, based on which a rational prognosis could be made. In this way the necessary expertise to handle complex problems was built up. The notion grew that scientific prediction based on a rational analysis of data was not something that stemmed necessarily from those data but could be something that held true, other things being equal.

These developments were essential to the evolution of the modern concept of a disease. This is a complex concept rather than an entity which has a necessary essence.[8] A disease does not simply start with the entering of a bacillus into a person; in many cases we appear to be able to live quite happily with our bacilli. Rather the biological disordering which bacilli may initiate also depends on other factors such as the general state of health of the person and probably their state of mind, as well as on the particular strain of the bacillus in question and on whether that particular individual and this particular strain of bacillus have had prior contact. Once biological disruption takes place, the course of the disease depends far more on a variety of host factors than on the vagaries of the infecting organism. Many of these factors will be accidental, such as where in the lungs the infectious process took root or whether the individual had prior exposure to this or other related organisms. In addition there is the further set of accidents that are the way the individual responds to being ill – whether they seek help or not, and if they do, whether they are given an appropriate treatment or not.

Hence specifying the *essence* of tuberculosis or syphilis is just not possible in the way that a high science might like. Once a disease becomes established a process has been instituted in which a great number of things may be going on. This process may present clinically in a great variety of ways, and is liable to run a variety of courses and to have a number of possible outcomes. An analogy can be had with weather forecasting and hurricanes. Weather is something that more or less informed opinions can be given on. The best opinions stem from the closest observation of signs. Hurricanes crystallize out of weather but they are not just one immutable entity and they can arise in a variety of ways.

Furthermore many diseases can be and have been handled without knowing that much about them, never mind their putatively essential natures. All very well it may be argued, but surely their essential natures are discovered at post mortem? Not so. Post mortems are apt to reveal what people can live with just as much as they reveal what we die of.

In contrast to the development of physics, the development of medicine suggests that central to the development of modern science has been the progressive replacement of the high science methods of conjecture and demonstration by the methods of diagnosis and prognosis found in the low sciences. From this point of view physics has been one of the last sciences to become modern. It survived in a realm of certain truth until the advent of quantum mechanics. This was probably because the triumphs of Newton and Copernicus led to a belief in the power of the human intellect to grasp truth beyond the evidence. The introduction of probability schedules into the heart of physics with the quantum revolution, and the realization that even physics only offers relative and probable truth, mark the final triumph of opinio over scientia and a final nailing of science to the mast of concrete detail.

Philosophy of opinio

Both the philosophy and mythology of science have until very recently concerned themselves with scientia rather than opinio. They have considered the dynamics of progress in physics rather than in medicine. Their rational archetypes have been Copernicus and Newton rather than Paracelsus and Pascal. Theory has been pre-eminent over practice and experiments have been seen as a method to test theories rather than as a source of knowledge. To this day one is more likely to be offered research funds if one can specify what hypothesis one is testing rather than simply in order to do something that has never been done before.

This happens despite the fact that, classically, scientific advance happens when improvisation is called for, such as during wars or in situations where the experiments are adventures unlinked to hypotheses, as in the course of space programmes. For example, a considerable degree of modern technology and observations central to the twentieth century development of physics occurred as the result of an international race to produce a temperature of absolute zero. This race was spurred by a motivation akin to that of mountain climbers faced with an unclimbed peak and had little to do with the supposedly rational testing of conjectures.[9] Similarly many of the most progressive branches of science (thermodynamics, biochemistry and neurobiology) are or have been technically led, with concepts being conjured up perforce to label new and unsuspected phenomena revealed by the application of new diagnostic techniques to old problems.

Nevertheless, the suspicion still lurks that necessary truths rather than best possible opinions are the material of science, that scientists are critical thinkers rather than critical doers and that rational advance is a matter of some form of logic rather than of method. If the alternative, methodical doing, appears to make scientists out as practitioners or technicians rather than natural philosophers, then one might reflect on the fact that technicians do not suffer from crises of confidence about the reality of their concepts or about how empirical they are being. Neither are they only happy when things go wrong and conjectures are refuted.

Several features of a science dominated by probability and experiment deserve note. Probabilities and correlations derive from signs. They are not mental fictions, hypothetical entities or pure conjectures. In a systematic fashion appearances, impressions and local variations yield methodically to probable correlations. Many may guess at what underlies the correlation of rats with plague, for instance, and particular conjectures may be demonstrably more likely, but the actual correlation is not hypothetical. It is real. Correlations cannot be refuted by single contrary instances as, for example, can Karl Popper's conjectures.

What may well be incorrect is our image of what underlies the correlation. There is nothing unreal or hypothetical about the differential functions of quantum mechanics. However our *images* of little balls spinning in space and hopping between electron shells may be unreal and may bear no necessary correspondence with reality. But when atom bombs explode or men land on the moon the correlations and functions of relativity and quantum mechanics are borne out beyond reasonable doubt. If the lasers of some strategic defence initiative destroy nineteen out of twenty incoming missiles, the fact that one missile gets away is unlikely to cause the survivors of the holocaust to doubt the correlations of the photon theory of light. Although if they are physicists, they may still wonder about whether light comes in waves or packets.

Another aspect that is notable about an opinionated science is the combination of universalization and specialization that results. Probability methodically systematizes appearances and impressions and leads to universal generalizations. Not the universal and necessary truths of a scientia but generalizations that hold across specified ranges of concrete conditions and under the proviso that other things are equal. Whatever light is, the photon theory of light is obviously something that has got pretty close to it, if the understanding of light that results from this theory can be used to deploy light so effectively. The fact that we cannot usefully *imagine* exactly what it is that could wreak as much destruction as a laser should not obscure the fact that this theory has got very close to the concrete nature of light – as opposed to its necessary nature.

While permitting such universal generalizations (prognoses), the process of diagnosis is one that attends ever more closely to material detail. As more and more material details are found out, the practice of science becomes ever more specialized as individual scientists can only be expected to master so much detail.

Following from both of these points, we can suggest that modern science involves an ascent to the concrete. Its progressive nature stems from the fact that learning commonly occurs through action and mistakes rather than by contemplation. In contrast to scientia, opinio is ever seeking to interpret signs and make diagnoses in order to intervene or offer prognoses. It starts by looking at the signs, not with conjectures – some of which may be ethereal. It is forced back to the signs if its prognoses deviate systematically from expectations. One may become certain that particular problems respond to specific interventions, but unless they respond with a very high degree of frequency (95 per cent), one is left with the knowledge that the scientific intervention is less than specific or the particular problem is compound.

One may then experiment with the signs in order to refine their significant component or to discover the source of anomalies. But opinio sticks to the problem at hand and is inhibited from making unwarranted deductions from particular successes and applying them to analogous situations by strings of failures, loss of business or deaths of patients. This has the merit of throwing up fresh problems because as soon as one responds to a new regime its removal makes others more salient. Testability is just a surface feature of this process which is characterized by engagement with the real world of material presentations. Progress is born of constant attention to concrete detail rather than from internally coherent conjectures, even though they resonate with the music of the spheres.

Empirical opinions

A final aspect of opinionated science refers to the issue of being empirical. If science is about attention to detail and the generation of new details rather than induction from established details, then being empirical must be something that pertains to the scientific community rather than to individual scientists. This is a notion that is resisted strongly by many philosophers of science for whom being empirical is still a matter of individual honesty or heroism.

Individual genius is unquestionably solely responsible for grasping the possible relations between various sets of data. For example, how a hidden weight might account for the results of the die. But many possible Eurekas are simply dreams of the night that do not hold in the cold light of morning, i.e. in the face of further data. Flushed with excitement of discovery, one may overlook this and even by force of personal enthusiasm or persuasive powers cause others to overlook it. But finally, given a large enough number of people, someone will raise the issue of available inconvenient data or will generate awkward new data. Not necessarily because this someone is particularly open and critical, ready to rigorously test every conjecture and to refute if possible, but rather because anomalies will inevitably come to light through the deviation of actual results from the expected frequencies.

Such an arrangement is important in science as the *tabula rasa* of universal doubt in individual scientists is an impossible ideal. We all bring to the data our preconceptions and biases. Indeed these 'faults' may be happy ones leading on to discoveries against current odds. When not so happy, modern scientists, as opposed to philosophers of science, can be characterized by their trust in the activities of their guild, rather than in logic, to bring such inevitable human errors to light.

What follows from this is that Newton was not necessarily any more empirical by nature or training than many people who may be detained in mental asylums. Indeed other than when his hypotheses were subject to the scrutiny of fellow scientists, it appears that he was liable to eccentricities and to beliefs in mysticism and Rosicrucianism that many people would find quite at odds with the evidence and with the picture of scientists as soberly rational individuals. This also appears to hold true for many of the greatest names in science so much so that one might wonder whether the capacity for vivid imaginings rather than for Baconian empiricism is what is necessary to make a pathbreaking scientist. Scientific fantasies differ from others in being subject to the scrutiny of others. They only survive when they become common fantasies.

This lengthy attempt to establish that modern science is all about holding best possible opinions and attending ever more closely to concrete detail, and that it does so empirically by virtue of this attention being a collaborative exercise, has been undertaken because this is exactly the characterization of scientific psychotherapy that will be offered in Chapter 7.

PSYCHOLOGICAL SIGNS

The history of science is littered with hypotheses that appeared to survive apparent refutation by the observations. One of the most notable was that of Prout who hypothesized that all elements were integral multiples of hydrogen. Experimental attempts to demonstrate this repeatedly turned up evidence in favour of the hypothesis being wrong. Prout later turned out to be correct. Many other hypotheses as we have noted in the case of Newton have had a practical irrefutability. Despite the historical evidence of Newton and Prout, philosophers of science commonly all agree that psychoanalysis is not scientific because it is irrefutable.

Some suggest that it is intrinsically untestable as its data are internal or subjective. Others concede that it is testable in principle but irrefutable in practice. They point to the fact that typically attempted refutations are put down by psychoanalytic practitioners as a manifestation of unconscious resistance to the truth by objectors. Given the survival of other scientific hypotheses, despite practical untestability or in the face of the facts, why has psychoanalysis been so singled out for opprobium? It seems somewhat unfair as nowhere are any hard criteria spelt out for degrees of irrefutability or reasonable shelf-life for a hypothesis.

The issue of testability in principle, turns on whether internal or subjective signs are proper material for scientific investigation. Do we ascend to the concrete when investigating them? As such data had not been the subject matter of scientific investigation before Freud, he must either have established a new science or else his enterprise was radically flawed from the outset. Given that psychology is now a flourishing science and that even introspection is once again a respectable method in its armoury (Chapter 4), it would seem that this question has been answered in favour of Freud's having established a new science, clearly differentiated from neurology or philosophy. As such he set a paradigm, in a manner comparable to Newton's fathering of mechanics.

Unlike Newton, however, the initial subject matter of his science was clearly material fitted for a low science, material fit to be a matter of opinion. Like Paracelsus, he was an interpreter of signs. Signs, such as recurrent dreams or lapses of memory or some physical symptoms, were guessed to be indicative of underlying disturbance or as indicators of Pascal's 'reasons of the heart which reason does not know of'. If the low sciences are now the modern sciences, why is it that he is singled out as being unscientific?

Furthermore, given that medicine was born of the attempt to interpret signs, it seems somewhat ironic that it should have been, and should still be, so hostile to someone who opened up a whole new range of signs for interpretation. To understand why this was so requires some more detail on the role that signs played in medicine before Freud. From Paracelsus until the end of the nineteenth century medical signs were essentially fevers on brows, casts in urine, heart murmurs and breath sounds to which were later added the demonstration of micro-organisms in body fluids. These were the signs in which medicine dealt rather than any verbal reports by patients.

This was as true for psychiatry as for physical medicine. The initial medical approach to madness looked for signs of the type found in general medicine and illnesses were named accordingly. Thus mania became the illness characterized by an observable increase in activity. Melancholia was the illness of decreased activity. Whether the patient was happy or sad was not an issue. Anyone with decreased activity was liable to a diagnosis of melancholia – even if they had reduced activity by virtue of being paralysed with obsessions rather than because they had the disorder of mood we now call melancholia. Thus what was being looked at was the *form* of behaviour or speech (e.g. incoherence); in contrast to Freud's later interest in the *content* of behaviour or speech.

In general medicine, however, there was progress from an exclusive reliance on the signs of altered physical form. Physicians became increasingly likely to pay heed to the symptoms of the patient and take these as signs. Thus a pain in the chest reported by the patient to be gripping and to radiate up to the throat or down the left arm became a clinical sign by which one could diagnose cardiac problems, even in the absence of traditional signs. Differences between this kind of pain and chest pains that seemed worst on inspiration allowed differential diagnoses and the possibility of a prognosis as to what would happen based on what the patient said, rather than on altered physical forms.

It is only recently, however, that this willingness to contemplate signs that have no existence independent of the verbal reports of the patient has been thoroughly exploited. Until recently physicians preferred conditions that looked painful rather than reports of pain. They felt more comfortable with patients who came to them with areas of their body inflamed and tender than with patients who had pains in their low back region but with no objective signs such as diminished reflexes.

Current work on pain, however, increasingly suggests that the verbal reports of the kind of pain a patient has are very good indicators of what the underlying condition will be. If they are of a certain kind, it is now reasonable to pay heed to them, regardless of whether physical investigations supplement verbal reports. That is the patient has the ability to report on certain signs hidden from the physician's gaze beneath the opacity of the body's surface.[10] In these cases, however, the alteration in content of a subject's report signifies an alteration in form, rather than an alteration in content of the type Freud was interested in, where by definition there was no disorder of form.

In the case of psychiatry, a further factor inhibited the turn to the subjective. This was the general belief that there was no point in talking to the insane – that their discourse was intrinsically unintelligible. Given this there seemed little point in paying heed to and classifying delusions as general physicians had begun to pay heed to and classify pains. Anyone who was deluded must essentially have the same illness, insanity. It was only during the nineteenth century when it became legitimate to pay more heed to the content of delusions, that it was found that they could be classified. Certain delusions occurred in melancholia such as delusions of guilt or doom, while others occurred in mania such as delusions of grandiosity, and in other cases delusions appeared to consume the patient's personality as in paranoia. While increased attention was paid therefore to verbal utterances, these were still only taken seriously where they were thought to refer to occult disorders of form.

In response to the Freudian paradigm that saw sense in mental illness and the diagnostic opportunities in paying heed to 'subjective' signs, Jaspers made two distinctions. One was to draw attention to the importance of phenomenology in psychopathology (Chapter 4). The other was a distinction between understandable and non-understandable clinical conditions. Depression, mania and schizophrenia, he argued, were not understandable in the sense of being interpretable. This was because the diagnostic signs involved, whether verbal reports or behavioural observations, stemmed from organic disorders which made them meaningless from the interpretative point of view. That is they were indications of caused behaviour rather than motivated behaviour; disorders of form rather than of content.

Understanding and explaining
Disorders of form, he argued, could ultimately be explained, even if they were established by subjective reports, as at the end of the day they were just another set of physical phenomena. This was not the case for disorders of content. These could only be understood. The distinction between erklaren (explaining) and verstehen (understanding) arose with the hermeneutic revolution in Germany in the second half of the nineteenth century. This will be considered below. Both Jaspers and Freud saw this issue as central. In making the distinction Jaspers arguably displayed a hankering after scientia. Freud for his part attempted to construct an explanatory depth psychology rather than an understanding

one and in so doing, I will argue, he constructed a psychological scientia rather than an opinio.

Explanation in the physical sciences is usually contrasted with understanding in the human sciences, against a background of claims that only the methods of the physical sciences are truly scientific. Only the kind of explanations offered by the physical sciences are true or definite knowledge of causes.[11] This is because they are established by discovering causal connections between events, in a way that is quite impossible for the interpretations achievable in the human sciences. One way of putting this has been to point to the fact that the products or concepts of the natural sciences are expressible in mathematical (and hence precise) terms, whereas those of the human sciences are not. This dichotomy between understanding and explaining is still commonly invoked in psychiatric textbooks, in order to dismiss psychotherapy. As understanding or interpretation is an inferior and less scientific form of knowing to explaining, it is argued, psychotherapy cannot be a science. At most it can be an art.

Before arguing that the distinction between understanding and explanation is misleading, it is worth noting what has happened to so-called explanation, since Freud and Jaspers were concerned with the issue. In 1900, the natural sciences, in contrast to the human sciences, did seem to offer definite and reliable knowledge and explanations of natural phenomena. However, since then, the quantum revolution has brought the realization that the apparently invariant laws of physics rested on statistical regularities rather than on necessary causal connections or immutable entities, forever free from the vagaries of interpretation. While such regularities often point strongly to the presence of novel phenomena or entities, when it comes to individual and particular cases or events, reliable knowledge has to yield to probability estimates.

It has become clear that the so-called iron laws of physics only hold good in experiments, where all factors in the experiment can be controlled or a sufficient number of comparable events can be investigated so that extraneous influences can cancel each other out. If neither of these conditions can be met one has an open system. The art of experimentation in the natural sciences that has led to the ability to make predictions has been one of establishing closed systems. A less abstract way of putting this is to note that single instances of anything are necessarily shaped by a considerable number of accidental or random factors which only hold at the time of determination of that instance. As any science demonstrator well knows an experiment based on an established iron law of physics or chemistry is quite likely on the day to turn out other than the law would predict.

Even the bastions of pure mathematics, free from the corruption of appearances, have crumbled. It has been realized that the necessary explanations of mathematics are relative. That its axioms only follow on from initial arbitrary starting points. Thus the crowning glories of mathematics, far from being the discovery of immutable truths, are products of the human mind no less than great works of art. However, they are products that are immensely useful, not because of their truth but simply because they work.[12]

THE HERMENEUTIC REVOLUTION[13-16]

When the issue to be investigated is one of establishing what has happened to someone, however, one only has a single instance or a single chain of events to work from. As in quantum mechanics nothing terribly definite can be said about one event or one happening. Even summating a series of such concrete instances should not necessarily yield laws. Inability in such cases, however, to provide a closed system should not be taken to imply that certain things to do with human beings will forever remain barred to scientific investigation or that they can only be investigated by some sort of second class scientific activity. The reason why not lies with the development of hermeneutics.

The term hermeneutic comes from Hermes, who was the messenger of the Gods for the Greeks. Hermeneutics is the science of reading messages in signs. It became a science rather than an art with the development of history as a science. In the case of history, the signs to be investigated were the signs left by men rather than the signs from the book of nature. Those black marks on white paper or hieroglyphs on walls, the monuments, ruins and alterations to the landscape that men leave after them. An awareness of the possibility of reading such signs, of becoming scientific about man's historicity, first arose clearly in Germany in the latter half of the nineteenth century.

From the outset, it was inevitable that any such science was going to be a low science, a matter of opinion. One obviously could not expect definite, necessary or causal knowledge about history. Accordingly if history was to be given the title of a science it seemed obvious that it must be a very different science from that of physics or chemistry. Hence the distinctions that are drawn between the human and the natural sciences, which imply to this day that these are two very different enterprises and that only the natural sciences are the real thing.

The development of the hermeneutic method stemmed from the work of Droysen. History before Droysen had been a matter of chronology and of preserving in authentic form the texts that had been handed down. This latter concern had been a very real one in the study of European medieval history as the honesty and competence of the compilers of source materials for the political and ecclesiastical affairs being studied was open to question. Droysen, however, argued that although concern for the reliability of texts is crucial to a successful historical project, there was another task for the historian. That he has to advance beyond this concern to an interpretative grasp, a verstehen (understanding), of what was happening in history. Understanding in this sense meant getting inside the mind of the person who wrote the text. It meant being aware that any text might tell as much about its author as about the events it purported to be recounting faithfully.

History, he argued, was not just a case of taking a good look at the facts or of letting them speak for themselves, but of going beyond the facts. Not just a matter of making sure the signs on the piece of paper were kept the same, but of looking at them, reading them and seeing what their likely correspondence to events of their time was. An analogy may be had in the interpretation of a sentence. Simply understanding the meaning of the words may not yield the sense of the sentence. Rather that sense may determine which of the possible meanings that a word may have is operative in this particular case. The sense of the sentence as a whole, however, is constrained by the words used, which provides the basis for self-correction of the interpretative process. This analogy with a sentence and its words indicates the hermeneutic circle of understanding as proposed by Droysen. He argued that one can only understand a text in the context of what was known of the times in which it was written, but correspondingly close attention to a text may alter our ideas of what was happening at the time.

Furthermore, just as the same sentence can mean two things to two different people or to the same person at two different times, so also historical verstehen may yield a different understanding of what was happening at a particular time than that held by participants of those times and written up in histories or memoirs. For example, someone in 100 years time, working back from texts containing the word psychosis, could conclude that in the 1980s there must have been a crisis about its meaning. They could conclude this from inconsistencies in its usage. They would be correct, even though none of the users of the word may have realized that there was a crisis. Similarly, clinical history taking may lead to a different idea of what has been happening to someone than they appreciate themselves.

This appeal to hermeneutic *verstehen* may appear unempirical in its avowed going beyond the facts. But even in the natural sciences, it is now commonly conceded that creative progress involves going beyond the known facts and proceeding on the basis of intuitive or diagnostic hunches. It is subsequent congruence of the facts with the hunch rather than inferences based solely on established facts that gives rise to scientific advance. What must be kept in mind about the so-called facts, in the case of history, is that it is a fact that they are signs but their relation to what happened in the past is an ambiguous one. Hence there is a need to decode rather than to simply read the message.

This point is made clear when, as often happens, one set of signs and one set of facts contradict each other. For example, two of the four Gospels give Jesus brothers, two others do not. Did he have brothers? What other evidence can be brought to bear on the issue? Has the meaning of the term brothers changed since the time of writing? Or, for example, modern reconstructions of what the Gospel according to John means, emphasize that it must have been written by several different authors, adding bits at different times, seemingly in response to political issues occupying the minds of those likely to read the text.[17] The text therefore contains a story about what was going on at the end of the first century among Christian communities as well as one about what had happened fifty years earlier to a man called Christ. Working on the meaning of signs rather than simply accepting them yields a different story to that obtained from a straightforward reading of the text. Arguably a story that will be closer to the truth of what happened, but certainly one that will reveal more of what actually happened.

The second enlightenment

Droysen's arguments may not seem all that radical, but they were for the nineteenth century. With the rise of the science of mechanics in the Renaissance, many traditional assumptions had been challenged. This challenge led to Descartes' famous methodological dictum 'doubt everything'. Far from being a method of universal doubt, however, as it might seem on the surface, Descartes meant something like 'do not too hastily accept the judgements of authority'. Radical doubt was a product of the eighteenth century and constituted what is now known as the enlightenment. It was caught in Kant's methodological precept to 'have the courage to make use of your own understanding'.[18]

Where Renaissance science was symbolically pitted against the authority of Aristotle, Galen and the scientists and physicians of antiquity, enlightenment science was pitted against the authority of the Bible and traditional Christianity.* Before then what was written down was seen as necessarily true. It was a difficult task to realize that it might be untrue. Particularly in the case of the Bible. It took great critical effort to realize that we are almost inevitably prejudiced in favour of what is written down. And from this to learn to distinguish between an opinion from the past and what had probably happened. Once the breakthrough was made, however, a prejudice against prejudices arose. This led to the positivist conception of history, whereby everything was scrutinized relentlessly.

Droysen and later scientific historians stood this positivist conception of history on its head. They argued that in order to establish what had happened in history, one had to get inside the mind of one's source. And to do this one had to be *sympathetic* to one's sources. There had to be willingness to do justice to the author or society being studied. This could only properly happen if one was prepared to concede that differences between then and now were not a matter of differences in rationality but stemmed from cultural or situational factors. Accordingly, the primary concern was to avoid the misunderstandings that might easily arise from failure to recognize cultural or situational differences.

The hermeneutic method was subsequently adopted for more general use in the human sciences by Dilthey and later Husserl, who realized that not only could one reconstruct what had happened in the past but one could also reconstruct what has been or is happening in the lives of individuals and of communities. Max Weber took the methods into social science. Since then they have been adopted widely in psychology and in anthropology.[19,20] These disciplines have all, under the influence of the hermeneutic revolution, taken an anthropological turn.[21] There would seem to be no good reason why such methods should not also be applied to the interpretation of what is happening to mentally distressed individuals (Chapter 4). They are not applied at present.

---

* During the writing of this chapter the controversy over the book *The Satanic Verses* arose. This illustrates the point being made, and the depth of feeling involved in these issues.

So much has this methodological requirement to have sympathy now been accepted in historical circles that Gadamer has recently argued that in order to be properly scientific about anything, far from having the *tabula rasa* of the Baconian scientist, one must be working from inside a tradition.[22] Such talk of interpretation and tradition seems all very well for literature, but surely not for one of the natural sciences? Recent developments in the history of science, to which Thomas Kuhn has been a notable contributor, support Gadamer. They indicate that the physicist and the chemist, no less than exegetes and anthropologists, operate from within a tradition and that effective physics and chemistry require an appreciation of the appropriate traditions.

The deductions of the orbits of planets from Newton's laws of motion once appeared to many to be a clear and certain knowledge of a different order to that found in the humanities. However, the subsequent displacement of Newtonian physics by quantum mechanics and general relativity indicates that far from being necessary truths free from the vagaries of tradition (prejudice), physical theories are no less a construction of the human mind than literary works. Their key terms can be as creatively ambiguous as any found in art. Far from existing free of prejudice, the successful operation of science depends on prejudice and authority. For example, to be a modern physicist requires a prejudice in favour of quantum mechanics. Articles that are not suitably prejudiced when submitted to journals simply will not be published, no matter what their content is. It is this rehabilitation of prejudice that has been termed the second enlightenment.

Empiricism revisited

As practised initially by Droysen and by historians since, the hermeneutic method was and is empirical. This holds if by empirical we mean an orientation that attends to the evidence, where possible without preconceptions and without reading more into the data than the data can bear. Remaining empirical is something that is achieved by an insistence on adhering to data rather than to conceptual systems. This insistence means that interpretative constructions prove open to revision as others point out data not accounted for. As in the natural sciences it is only through collaboration with others that a properly empirical stance is achieved. Also as in the natural sciences, historical science today is methodical and progressive, yielding cumulative and related results. This is to be expected of an empirical science, as ever more attention to the data reveals fresh possibilities and successful interpretative constructions point to fresh sources of data. Thus close attention to detail may yield information about the site of some buried city. Archaelogical investigations may uncover the city with perhaps a library in it and further texts to shed further light on the original text.

Given these developments the distinction between erklaren and verstehen (explanation and understanding) has become somewhat artificial. Both natural and human scientists understand and do so by similar intelligent operations. One and the same type of insight grasps the possible relations between the data and one and the same critical judgement decides which of those insights most probably explains the relation. And, as mentioned, both divisions of science can be empirical, methodical and progressive. Both appear to be ascending to the concrete. The differences lie in the problems being tackled. The prototypical natural sciences operate on problems that come in multiples and continue to happen, so that constructs can be erected that will hold valid for a specified set of conditions. In contrast, the prototypical human sciences are concerned with things that have happened and are unlikely to recur. Therefore, they do not aim at prediction and are not concerned to develop closed systems.

These differences in subject matter provide the basis for a different distinction to that between eklaren and verstehen – a distinction between nomothetic and idiographic sciences.[23] The idiographic sciences are concerned with establishing as much as can be established about unique events or individuals, the nomothetic sciences are concerned with what holds, other things being equal. While the subject matter of the idiographic sciences does not permit the generation of universal generalizations, it should not be thought that such generalizations are the sole aim of science. Rather they result, almost as a by-product of the application of probability assessments to problems. The primary aim of such assessments, however, is ever greater attention to detail. This can be achieved without the application of statistical methods.

Indeed the empiricism of the human sciences has laid the basis for an epistemological revolution equal to that that was stimulated by the development of the natural sciences. It has become increasingly apparent that the empirical quality of empirical methods depends on the investigator using a particular method and using it in collaboration with others. This is more important than any intrinsic quality of particular individuals or of particular methods or whether or not the results of certain methods permit mathematical formalization. If a process of submitting one's hunches and hypotheses to the critical scrutiny of others is what makes for being empirical, it would seem that there is no a priori reason to believe that mentally ill patients cannot be empirical or that the process of psychotherapy cannot also be empirical.

Crisis of historicity

The hermeneutic revolution is now well established. But it has only become so during the course of this century. Indeed, the early years of this century, when Jaspers and Freud were struggling with these issues, were a time of particular crisis for hermeneutic disciplines. It was slowly being realized that historical truth was a construction of the human mind as much as a reading of what was there on the page of history and that historical concern had to be confined to the world of experience, just as the natural sciences were.

In addition the revolution in history was paralleled by a revolution in geology that, along with the development of the theory of evolution, had brought a growing realization of the nature and extent of time. Where once Pascal, faced with developments in physics, had stood terrified at the prospect of 'les espaces infinis', opening up in the seventeenth and eighteenth centuries, the end of the nineteenth century brought the no less terrifying prospect of an infinite regress to history.[24]

The terror of history lay not just in its extent but in its accidental quality. In many ways it seemed a matter of luck that things had turned out one way rather than another. That history is the outcome of cock-ups rather than of conspiracies. Had the Falkland's War not happened and not been brought to a successful conclusion, would Margaret Thatcher have won a second term of office? And if not re-elected would Britain be the same now?

Stephen Jay Gould has documented how difficult it was for geologists to face up to the idea of the accidental; as difficult as it had once been to doubt the Bible.[25] The natural response was to seek for some pattern underlying events. Geologists sought evidence for a cycle in time. They competed to be the Newton of geology; the person who discovered the necessary and invariant laws behind geological events. They sought a scientia. In history, the scientia was provided by Hegel who envisaged a rolling process of thesis meeting antithesis and leading on to synthesis, operating behind the appearances of history. For Hegel the interpretation of history was a priori and abstract. The actual details of history only mattered in so far as they fitted into his previously established framework. In great part, the empiricism of the German historical school and awareness of man's actual historicity developed as a reaction to Hegel.

Freud's approach to history, I will argue, was essentially Hegelian. In many ways this was inevitable as, being a man of his times, he had recourse to many of the same strategies when faced with history as his contemporaries in biology and geology faced with indications of evolution and of deep time.[26] The general response to the appearances of history was to look for what was timeless and invariant: the kind of thing found by Newton to lie behind physical appearances. Ironically only a few years later, it would become clear that even Newton's eternal verities were historically relative, only applying to certain concrete, specific and accidental states of the universe.

FREUD'S SCIENTIA

Recognizing that the process of interpretation can be as empirical as any other scientific pursuit, many psychotherapists have suggested that psychology should abandon the attempt to copy the methods of the natural sciences and wholeheartedly embrace hermeneutic methods. Does this not return us to Freud? Are we not, when faced with a patient, faced with the need to read the message in the clinical signs? There is intense medical resistance to this point. Interpretative psychology is contrasted with supposedly scientific psychology which medicine is prepared to make use of. This roughly translates as behaviourist psychology.

There are many ambiguities here. Historical reconstructions inevitably form an essential part of psychiatric practice. However, they are frequently undertaken so naturally and automatically that few realize they are taking part in a scientific experiment. One is aiming at an understanding of what has been and what is happening in a person's life, what has been going forward and the relation of that interpretation to the clinical presentation. This seeking after evidence may range from the detailed life histories, accumulated during a course of psychotherapy, to more pointed clinical interviews in outpatient departments. In difficult cases, the opinion of a colleague may be sought. The details can be presented at a ward round inviting critical scrutiny, or as a last resort a case conference may be held to see what can be gained by bringing to bear on the case the cumulative experience or particular diagnostic abilities of different colleagues.

To refuse to concede an empirical and scientific character to such clinical history taking would seriously undermine the therapeutic enterprise. Just such a refusal, however, is offered by medical psychopathologists. Clinical history taking is presumed to be a matter of simple empathy rather than of interpretation. Medical hostility to the depth psychologies is so deep that *anything* that smacks of interpretation is deemed suspect. Hence the distinction between empathy and interpretation.

Being empathic alone would obviously not be scientific. But as practised clinically, so-called empathic understanding is no less interpretative, in the sense of constructing what is going on, than the 'interpretative psychologies'. When practised properly, however, it differs in the kind of preconceptions of what is going to be found and its willingness to avoid misunderstanding. As such it can be empirical and open to radical revision. This revision can occur as new facts become available or as different clinicians put fresh constructions on the data. Likewise by virtue of different experiences they may ferret out further relevant data.

In contrast to such diagnostic interviews and historical reconstructions, psychoanalysis has a priori conceptions about what such interviews must reveal. Ids and egos are at war, whether or not the patient or anyone else agrees, in much the same way that under the Galenic system all illnesses resulted from disturbances in four a priori humours. In psychoanalysis, necessary deductions are made ineluctably from basic premises in a way that would have delighted Newton or Galileo. Just as in the Galenic system, the deductions are made in a way that is as consistent with the clinical appearances as is possible. But if there is a conflict, the appearances are sacrificed rather than the supposed iron laws that underlie them.

Far from ascending to the concrete reality of individual lives, psychoanalysis brushes material details aside as it seeks for the essence that lies behind such details. The true or essential significance of behaviour or neurotic conflicts is held to have been established. Just as with Newton's laws, inconvenient data does not stimulate critical scrutiny. Thus, while being in the business of reading signs, the psychoanalytic approach to clinical histories can be legitimately accused of being non-empirical just as the Hegelian approach to general history is accused.

Why did Freud take an Hegelian turn? After all psychoanalysis started life as a historical science concerned to determine the truth about past events from present signs. Distinguishing between the apparent and latent content of what patients had to say was justified in terms of sympathetic listening. The proof of this methodical pudding was in the unearthing of buried memories, whether the buried traumata of hysteria or the buried forbidden pleasure in the case of obsessional disorders.

However, Freud met with a crisis relatively early in this exercise. He came to doubt that some of the traumata or pleasures reported by his patients actually happened. At this juncture, he made a fateful change of direction. If his patients were not telling him something about their past, he argued, they must be telling him something about their present. And as what was being reported was not actual in the present either, it followed that a patient's communication was principally concerned with present fantasy. He therefore moved from attempts to reconstruct past happenings to an attempt to determine the structure of present fantasy. Under the influence of this new orientation, it would appear that he neglected compelling evidence of sexual trauma and incest in the past of many of his patients.[27]

As present fantasy became the object of investigation, the problem became one of corroborating data to support the analyst in this investigation. While details of the public past of patients can be checked by asking informants, present fantasies are a different matter. They are a particularly difficult problem. Fantasy as we all know seems chaotic, seething with details, details that are often accidental. One way out of the problem would be to give fantasy a structure, to which the course of an analysis could be held to correspond. From this need arose concepts such as ids, egos, superegos and libido. Thereafter, actual facts increasingly became subordinate to the structure of fantasy. More importantly, where sympathetic listening had once been the order of the day, aimed at determining what the actual facts were, suspicious listening became so as fantasy had to be strapped to its Procrustean bed.

Freud was keenly aware of the novelty and potential importance of what he was doing when he postulated his structure for the psyche. He liked to say that there had been three important scientific revolutions that affected man's vision of himself; the Copernican which displaced man from the centre of the universe, the Darwinian which displaced man from the pinnacle of creation and his own in which reason, usurped by the forces of the id, had been displaced from the centre of the individual's stage. In contrast, what is being suggested here is that Freud, who did so much to further the revolution in the human sciences, stumbled over its central scientific obstacle, which was the issue of handling what was specific, idiographic and accidental.

This point is marvellously illustrated by Robert Darnton in a comparative study of psychoanalytic and historical interpretations of fairy tales.[28] The analytic interpretations he uses are those of Erich Fromm and Bruno Bettleheim of *Little Red Riding Hood*. That these analysts differ in their interpretation of the story will come as no surprise to those who are

97

cynical about psychoanalysis. That their interpretations focus on sexual matters, virginity and Oedipal themes, will be no surprise to anyone; this is a consequence of having an a priori view of what the material *must* reveal. What Darnton shows is that both analysts have no interest in establishing accurately the original versions of the story and no interest in the context in which this story and other folk tales arose. Had they done so, their interpretations would not have been possible as the details they rely on for their claims were not part of the original. Taking an anthropological approach, Darnton indicates what can be said about these texts and supports his interpretation with a great deal of corroborating evidence. In contrast to the timeless *Little Red Riding Hood* of the analysts, his fairy tale reads as specific to a time and place and set of historical accidents.

Psychoanalytic concepts

To the charge that its concepts are a priori and non-scientific, a counter charge is often made in defence of psychoanalysis. Why it is said does postulating ids and egos make psychoanalysis unempirical? Surely if anything they resemble the natural sciences even more by having such concepts. Both physicists approaching new problems and psychoanalysts approaching clinical material bring scientific concepts with them. To accuse psychoanalysis of being unscientific by virtue of bringing to particular problems the accumulated wisdom of past solutions, as espoused in its concepts, is to condemn it to an inability to progress. All sciences organize their gains or accumulated knowledge in terms of constructs and many of these constructs are not directly testable, even in physics.

Two points can be made to counter this. One is that as a matter of scientific practice, not all branches of science aim at universal generalizations. As noted above, sciences using the hermeneutic method aim instead at greater comprehension of particular stories. By definition individual cases do not support the sort of statistical manipulations that are necessary for the determination of generalizability.

Second, and related to the first point, is the question of the nature of the concepts used in the natural sciences. Such explanatory constructs are not simply concepts evoked at will or based on plausibility in a handful of instances (as were the psychoanalytic concepts). Even when intuitively appealing and held a priori to the investigations in hand, as in the case of the concept of the atom, the concepts of those sciences aiming at universal generalizations are such that they ultimately yield to correlations derived from material details. Otherwise they are abandoned as, for example, was the concept of the ether. Furthermore, while scientific enterprise has not abandoned the concept of the atom, it has radically altered its meaning such that atoms are now whatever it is that corresponds to the differential functions of a calculus or a matrix. The character of Freudian constructs, in contrast, is deeply non-empirical in this sense. They are radically a priori. As a matter of historical fact, they have not been provisional concepts open to revision or abandonment, other than at the whim of the master.

Freud's process of diagnosis and prognosis, therefore, never became rational in the modern sense found in the historical or ideographic sciences. Neither did it become rational in the sense of aiming at a probable accuracy as is found in the nomothetic sciences. Rather it was rational in an older Newtonian or Galilean sense of either resting on the authority of a master or as being a necessary deduction from a set of first principles. Like Paracelsus, Freud straddled the divide between Renaissance magus and modern physician. Cures were brought about but uncertainty was left as to how they had been achieved. The components of the therapeutic process were not broken down and experimented with to see if the schedule of probable outcomes could be altered thereby. His discipline therefore did not develop an 'opinionated' character although it has been struggling to do so ever since.

While therefore the first to read the psychological signs, Freud's new science was a scientia in the classic tradition and not an opinio. A set of sublime conjectures from which logical conclusions inexorably followed once the initial premise was conceded. Id, ego and superego are not correlations. They do not have a provisional character open to progressive development based on discrepancies between actual and observed frequencies. They are the primary qualities, the immutable entities, without which the logic of a high science does not work. Freud created a science in the mould of Galilean physics, 400 years too late. Ironically, just when physics was about to finally divest itself of the straitjacket of scientia. As a matter of historical record, however, it should be noted that it was only toward the end of Freud's life that physics itself finally came to grips with the accidental and specific.

Despite an orthogonal existence to the kind of data a low science needs to work, one could argue that this new science of fantasy might be valuable and prove itself, if it worked. Whether it does or not is a matter of dispute. If it does, given its present constitution, one cannot be sure what it is that brings about recovery. Furthermore, it appears that fantasy can have many structures read into it. Each of these may be as effective as psychoanalysis, but none are as effective as the behaviour therapy programmes for the treatment of most neurotic conditions in which fantasies are taken into minimal account.

The issue of whether psychoanalysis works or not, however, reveals one further aspect to psychoanalytic concepts. Psychoanalysts just like physicists wish to use a body of knowledge and the interpretations based on it to effect change. On this point as well as on the question of interpretation, Freud was not engaging in a literary exercise. He was aiming at a science closer to what he conceived the natural sciences to be. In the case of historical interpretations one might be able to get at the truth of what happened in the past but one does not effect change. Psychoanalysis was about effecting change and appeared to require 'technical' concepts rather than just interpretative methods. What about the capacity of an interpretative psychotherapy to effect change without such concepts?

Rightly or wrongly, the summit of medical wisdom has traditionally been seen as an ability to effect change when a recourse to specialized remedies or concepts is not available. In principle, as we have noted, taking a clinical history may lead to different interpretations of what has actually been happening to people in distress than those interpretations actually held by the sufferer. This happens routinely in good psychiatric practice and it used to happen routinely in good general practice.[29] Frequently a correct interpretation of what is happening will considerably alleviate distress and restore a subject to their usual level of functioning.

Even Jaspers, the supposed hammer of interpretative psychotherapy, was a strong advocate of the potential therapeutic benefits to be derived from this kind of psychotherapy. Such a hermeneutic approach seems called for and seems to be effective in many cases of anxiety.[30] Paradoxically, it may have been the influence of Freud which has undermined the ability of general practitioners, and indeed of all of us, to listen empathically because we now suspect that there is something we should be listening for and we do not know what it is.

In anxiety states, however, what is involved is understanding another person's understanding, even if all that is to be understood is that their distress is a matter of habit. The physiological discomforts of the state are no hindrance to understanding what is happening. On the contrary they are evidence that the physiology in question is carrying out its normal understandable functions – to prepare the subject to flee from some threatening situation or to confront an aggressor. Once the state of mind changes, whether that state of mind has been shaped by complex inhibitions or is dominated by maladaptive (neurotic) habits, the physiology will change. Thus reading and interpreting the signs of altered physical form and subjective state can scientifically effect change.

However when one comes to depression, mania and schizophrenia, Jaspers and medically-oriented psychiatrists insist that reading the signs is only of diagnostic usefulness. It properly should lead to a prescription of a physical treatment, albeit supplemented by a general supportiveness toward the patient. Interpretations of what is happening to the patient cannot, in principle, cure. Indeed far from leading to a cure, they are generally held to be misguided.

The substance of the following chapters is that this attitude is mistaken. That depression, mania and schizophrenia, no less than anxiety can be expected in most cases to respond to interpretative interventions. These interpretations, however, will differ radically from those offered in the psychodynamic therapies. We have said a lot about the spuriously technical concepts of dynamic psychopathology to date and of the belief among medical psychopathologists that only a nomothetic science will meet their needs, which leaves them awaiting the coming of a Messiah from among the natural sciences.

The reader may, therefore, be surprised to hear that in order to explain why depression, mania and schizophrenia should respond to interpretative interventions, we have to turn to an idiographic natural science and a nomothetic human one. To an account of the currently flourishing science of neuropsychology (Chapter 4) and to recent developments in dynamic psychology, which has lately acquired a set of statistically-based technical concepts (Chapter 5). Putting these developments in place may then allow us to construct the general outlines of a scientific psychotherapy (Chapter 7).

FOUR The Romantic Science

> Among the windings of the Violins
> And the ariettes
> Of cracked cornets
> Inside my mind a dull tom-tom begins
> Absurdly hammering a prelude of its own
> Capricious monotone
> That is at least one definite 'false note'.
>
> 'Portrait of a Lady', T. S. Eliot

Jaspers' classification of depression, mania and schizophrenia as functional psychoses, rather than neuroses, hinges on their fundamental non-interpretability. What is at stake, he argued, is not some disorder of the content of a subject's communications or behaviour, but a disorder of form as is found more generally in medical illnesses. General medical practice does not call for historical reconstructions but looks for signs indicative of disordered physical functioning such as fevers on brows and casts in the urine. Clinical skill involves the ability to detect ever more subtle manifestations of disordered form, not easily detectable by the unskilled observer, such as heart murmurs or minimal disorders of co-ordination. While recently there has been increased willingness to make diagnoses based on what people say, rather than to exclusively depend on visible disorders of functioning, physicians do so only in so far as what they say seems likely to refer to a disorder of form. In contrast the neuroses, by definition, involve individuals saying or doing unusual things without there being any physiological disorder to account for what is happening.

In the heyday of the depth psychologies, it was often argued that disorders of form were just another disorder of content. That is that holes in the gut or cardiac arrests were primarily communicative acts –

that in view of their consequences were obviously disordered. Holes in guts and heart attacks do not look much like normal behaviour or communication. Yet many of us have in the past been prepared to see them as disorders of content rather than of form, as mental problems rather than physical ones. So what odds are there on our being able to reliably distinguish nervous disorders of form from disorders of content? The difficulty here is that disordered form in the nervous system will both give rise to disordered behaviour and to altered physical functioning. For example, raising my arm abruptly in the presence of someone else may either have an angry content to it or be a contentless disorder of form, a tic.

In the case of depression, there can be obvious gross mental and physical slowing, in the case of mania an overactivity and in the case of schizophrenia an incoherence of thought and speech. These for Jaspers were clear indications of disordered form. But for many psychotherapists, they have typically been seen in terms of communicative acts whose content, a regression to a fetal position, a frantic defence against depression through activity or a regression to childish ways of thinking and speaking, indicates why there are visible changes in functioning. If these behaviours are contentless, does this imply that the 'medical' approach to depression, mania and schizophrenia sees little point in paying any heed to what subjects say other than for diagnostic purposes?

Neuropsychology

Disturbances of brain functioning are now termed neuropsychological disturbances. Neuropsychology is one of the newest sciences. At the end of the nineteenth century the first neuropsychological disturbances were described. These were the dysphasias (disturbances of speech), dyspraxias (disturbances of action) and agnosias (disturbances of recognition). As a matter of historical interest, while he was still a neurologist, Freud was among the first to study such disturbances systematically, publishing a book on aphasia.

In the case of the dysphasias, subjects are often left unable to speak and hence to give a subjective account of how they are. In the case of the agnosias, one of their peculiar properties is that affected subjects are often unaware that there is anything wrong. Accordingly, given the way these two neuropsychological disturbances affect people and the fact that they were typically noted as sequelae of illnesses such as strokes or tumours, the psychiatric importance of such disturbances did not immediately become apparent. Instead, they were seen as falling within the province of neurology. As further signs to go along with the alterations of tone or power in limbs that these illnesses also provoked and which in conjunction with disturbed tone, reflexes and co-ordination might permit a more precise localization of the disturbance in brain functioning.

Now, however, alterations of power and muscle tone in an arm or a leg are conventionally thought of as neurological deficits, but alterations in the capacity to speak or do things are commonly designated as neuropsychological disturbances – even though both result from brain dysfunction. The latter are typically seen as disturbances of higher functions. In many cases of more localized brain disturbance than that found after a stroke, there may be no alterations in peripheral signs such as grip strength or limb reflexes and muscular tone, but there may nevertheless be a complete inability to carry out an action (dyspraxia). (That is, peripherally everything may be normal so that actions could be carried out but the area of the brain responsible for putting the components of a skilled movement together appears to have been disturbed.) Similarly everything else may be normal including eyesight but the patient may be unable to read anymore (dyslexia) or to write (dysgraphia).

More subtle deficits may involve the ability to speak but not to be able to recall the names of common objects (nominal dysphasia), or the ability to repeat comprehensibly complicated statements but not to say even simple things comprehensibly in response to a question (transcortical dysphasia). Some subjects may comprehend readily but be unable to speak. Others may be able to speak readily but to produce answers to questions that indicate that they are unable to comprehend what it is they have been asked. Or subjects able to recognize things may be unable to recognize their colour or to say what their function is (various forms of agnosia). Some disorders may lead to an inability to recognize parts of one's own body (somatagnosia) or to recognize faces, even one's own (prosopagnosia). Some subjects may be found who are able to initiate actions they have been asked to do but who are unable to stop so that they go on repeating what they began long after they ought to have stopped (perseveration).

Oliver Sacks in a fascinating book entitled *The Man who Mistook His Wife for a Hat*[1] has offered a set of clinical vignettes of patients suffering from a variety of neuropsychological deficits. The pertinent point to most of his vignettes, in contrast to the earliest neuropsychological disturbances of agnosia and dysphasia, is that, in most of them, the affected subjects are able to vividly describe their experience of their brain not working correctly.

Yet until very recently nothing was heard of neuropsychological disturbances in psychiatry. Why should this be, if brain disorders are supposed to give rise to the central disturbances of the affective disorders and schizophrenia? One reason may be that the science of neuropsychology has only been an independent science since the 1940s. It therefore arose only after the major psychopathological formulations were established. While dysphasias and agnosias were described at the end of the nineteenth century, they remained isolated neurological signs rather than providing the basis for a new science.

Nothing new was methodically erected on the basis of these signs, until Alexander Romanovitch Luria and colleagues in the Soviet Union began to appreciate how such signs might tell more about how the brain functioned.[2] Normally 'mental' functioning is such a smooth performance, such a seamless garment, that we are unaware that overall coherent performances are constructed from the interactions of sub-systems. That there were a multiplicity of interacting sub-systems, only gradually became apparent with the description of a multiplicity of dysphasias, agnosias and memory problems. Luria and colleagues began to systematically catalogue normal and pathological functioning, in memory, speech, writing, recognition etc, in order to pick up the deviations from normality that might indicate how normality was constructed. Increasingly subtle deviations soon came to light and have been steadily recognized and intensively investigated ever since.

One of the most striking and profound of such deviations from normal was described by several different authors, among them R. W. Sperry in the 1950s.[3] In the 1940s the operation of dissecting the corpus callosum came into use for the control of intractable epilepsy. The corpus callosum is an enormous mass of tissue in the brain, at first thought to be there simply to support the ventricles, which are cavities in the brain filled with cerebrospinal fluid, but later found to be composed of fibres coursing between the left and right cerebral hemispheres. A reasonable assumption was that these fibres were involved in interhemispheric communication.

As epilepsy often involves an electrical disturbance which starts on one side of the brain and then spreads to convulse the whole brain, it also seemed reasonable to think about sectioning the tracts between the halves of the brain. This would hopefully safeguard the electrical integrity of at least half of the brain. This daring operation also seemed reasonable as comparable operations on animals in the 1940s had revealed no apparent behavioural changes or disturbances of function. Furthermore it appeared that some individuals were born without a corpus callosum and suffered no obvious loss as a consequence. All these reasonable assumptions were borne out and the operation of division of the corpus callosum was a great success for intractable cases of epilepsy.

Sperry among others was to show that beneath the apparent normality of patients who had had this operation lay a very strange reality. In brief, it appeared that when information was directed to one hemisphere in a way that excluded the other – for example, information sent from the extreme left of the visual field enters the right hemisphere of the brain first – in these patients the stimulated half of the brain learnt and the non-stimulated half did not. Normally entry into one hemisphere first is a matter of convenience and only the prelude to the sharing out of information through the whole brain.

After the operation of corpus callosum division, it appeared that each hemisphere could build up its own store of memories and learning. Indeed it had to live its own life as it was cut off from its fellow hemisphere. This was not apparent unless looked for as, in practice, information is rarely presented exclusively to one hemisphere. Our eyes scan the visual field rather than simply stare straight ahead as they are required to do for such studies. Further testing revealed that the 'personalities' of each hemisphere free from the influence of the other differed. These differences have entered into popular mythology as a matter of the right brain being more intuitive, artistic and romantic and the left being more analytical and abstract.

Another notable aspect of this work is what happens when the right hemisphere is given instructions to do a task. It seems that the left hemisphere can be puzzled by what's going on when the physical musculature swings into action. Either the subject says something like 'Now why did I do that?' Or they come up with some plausible reason to explain what had happened. For example, if the right hemisphere is given the instruction to rub a leg and the subject is then asked why they rubbed their leg, a typical answer might be because they had an itch. As this example illustrates, overall coherence of behaviour is not something readily given up.

These studies raise profound questions. Normally it would appear that both hemispheres operate in parallel or one dominates depending on the requirements of the task at hand. The interaction of the two hemispheres seems normally seamless leaving us with the impression of a coherent self. But the above findings suggest our idea of what we are is more ambiguous than many of us suspected That we may even potentially have more than one self. A supposition supported by work on multiple personality disorders and hypnosis.[4] However, self in this context appears to mean a centre of self-consciousness, which we have argued in Chapter 1 is a psychological capacity. Several selves are compatible with one mind, one striving for authenticity, one person.

This is a point made often by Luria in relation to other disturbances of psychological functioning, such as complete amnesia or loss of the capacity for abstraction. A moral being (in the sense outlined in Chapter 1) remains and it is often possible to overcome devastating neuropsychological handicaps by appealing to the innate drive for self-actualization. This, we have argued in Chapter 1, should to some extent be independent of its underlying psychological constituents and can potentially harness other capacities and skills to substitute for the missing function.

Another subtle and unusual neuropsychological disorder has recently been uncovered by L'Hermitte and coworkers which they have called the environmental-dependency syndrome.[5] This appears to happen as a result of dysfunction of the frontal lobes of the brain, an area that it has often appeared possible to destroy entirely without causing dramatic behavioural disturbances. Injuries to the frontal lobes typically fail to result in gross neurological signs. L'Hermitte found, however, that many frontal lobe disordered patients showed a loss of 'free will'.

In order to elicit the features of this syndrome, patients had to be put through a rather odd non-interview. Brought into their examiner there initially was no dialogue between interviewer and subject. During this silent period the examiner was entirely neutral to the patient but made several movements of his body or gestures such as thumbing his nose (not at the patient) combing his hair, singing a well known tune or doodling on paper. Normal subjects reported their amusement or perplexity at this behaviour but did nothing in response to it. Children sometimes copied the examiner, but with some report afterwards such that the examiner was a very funny man. But patients with a frontal lobe disturbance copied the examiners' movements and gestures, even if told not to. This imitation could even be elicited in a room of twenty people, in response to the examiner's imitation of urinating against a wall. The particularly interesting thing about this was that when asked afterwards why they did so they reported that they felt compelled to do what the examiner had done. Recovered subjects afterwards noted their loss of critical ability during the period of their illness. They felt unable to restrain purposeless gestures or to prevent themselves from imitating ridiculous acts. The experience was described as one of loss of autonomy or free will.

This unusual syndrome fits in with hypothesized roles for the frontal lobe, one of which has been termed the supervisory attentional system. Disorders of this have been hypothesized to produce what we commonly see as absent-mindedness. For example, putting shaving cream on the toothbrush or pulling the cord to turn the bathroom light on on our way into the bathroom, even though it is already on. Or more dangerously accelerating in our cars when waiting at a traffic light, in response to a slight movement forward of the car in front.

Instances such as these have led to the conclusion that normally a large amount of behaviour is organized such that once initiated it follows on automatically, according to script. Only if there is a serious mismatch between the target of a behaviour and the result of its execution – such as ending up in a dark bathroom – is attention called to the task in hand. Supervising all these dedicated operations, there must be a system which monitors mismatches. Failure of this system appears to result in a failure of strategic planning and a capture of activity by dedicated programmes that may be inappropriate to the task in hand. The subjective correlate of this is one of a lack of 'free' will or of alien inputs to the willing and execution of action, thoughts and emotion. All of which, interestingly, comes pretty close to some of the central experiences of schizophrenia.

Romance
These syndromes along with others described in Chapter 1, such as the phenomenon of blindsight, the distinction of memory into habit systems and cortical memory systems, and the investigation of imagery and imagining, constitute some of the current areas of neuropsychological research interest. The findings have been startling and the implications for our ideas of ourselves are only slowly beginning to feed into other areas of psychology as well as into philosophy. There are other implications pertinent to psychopathology that may be generally thought of as romantic.

From the very start Luria described neuropsychology as a science requiring a romantic approach, something more than scientific detachment.[6] Why? One of the reasons that can be offered is that its subject matter has a strangeness about it that is comparable to that associated with talk of black holes and mirror-image universes found in modern physics. In both cases inverted worlds are the subject of scientific attention. The utter strangeness of such worlds and their mysteriousness offering not just more of the same, but the promise of something radically novel seems to contribute to the generation of a certain romance that some other disciplines lack. In the case of neuropsychology there is even specifically the vision of a hitherto unsuspected romantic self locked inarticulately in the right hemisphere.

These are not the only senses of romance, however, to which Luria was referring. A good deal of neuropsychological investigation has depended on working with subjects of brain illness or injury. Because no two injuries, tumours or other lesions are quite the same, involving precisely the same area of brain, most investigation has to be of single subjects. Much of neuropsychology has been built on the brilliant and detailed investigation of single subjects. Thus neuropsychology, although rooted in biology and hence a natural science, has also been largely an ideographic science.

In the extreme such investigation has involved close observation of a subject over thirty years or more in order to determine as precisely as possible the parameters of a disturbance, its true effect on a subject's life and the responses called forth in subjects forced to live under the constraints of their particular disability. Extensive investigation of this sort inevitably approximates to a biography of the experimental subject as was brilliantly illustrated by Luria in two books *The Mind of a Mnemonist* and *The Man with a Shattered World*.[7,8] Biography is essentially romantic – in the oldest sense of that word, which means a story.

Being able to accurately judge what is happening also requires a great deal of sympathy with the affected subject. Sympathy rather than supposed sober scientific detachment is what leads to insight on the brain mechanisms involved and derangements thereof. First, because the resulting experiences are often so unbelievable that they strain credibility and are likely to be dismissed if the investigator is not committed to rather than detached from his/her subject. Second, because many of the disturbances being investigated are so subtle that they could be taken as normal unless we pay heed to the insistence of the subject that what is happening is not normal.

In such cases the investigator depends critically on the subjects' reports to distinguish events that behaviourally ('objectively') may all look the same. As L'Hermitte's environmental–dependency syndrome demonstrated, in order to understand what is happening in many of these neuropsychological disorders, investigators must have recourse to the experiences of the subject. Mere recording of behaviour observed is not enough. Without the report from the patient that they were imitating their examiner because they felt obliged to do so, the environmental–dependency syndrome would be emptied of its significance. Thus investigation becomes a collaborative enterprise.

This is wonderfully illustrated in another of Oliver Sacks' books, *Awakenings*.[9] This gives an account of what happened when the drug l-dopa was given to patients with a profound Parkinsonian stupor, lasting in some cases up to forty years. They had entered this state following on their having encephalitis lethargica in the 1920s. As is now well known the use of l-dopa in Parkinsonian states can arouse a patient from a state of immobility to one of activity, but often at the cost of forcing unwanted activity and movement on them. As opposed to just replacing the loss of dopamine thought to be at the heart of Parkinson's disease, it would appear that treatment is a matter of striking a balance or of maintaining a balance on what is a rolling log.

What Oliver Sacks' book demonstrates is that this balance is not just a question of finding some optimum between physical immobility and overactivity. Of far more importance is the balance between the *experience* of psychic retardation and that of forced and overwhelming experiences. Successful treatment involves getting a balance for oneself. And this is something that fluctuates in response to changing environmental circumstances and social pressures. It does not just depend on brain dopamine levels.

Therefore, selves as well as diseases have to be managed. This is made very clear in Sacks' account of a patient with Gilles de la Tourette syndrome[10] but even more so in the book *Ivan* by Ivan Vaughan, who suffered from Parkinson's disease.[11] In these cases not only is the examiner dependent on what the patient has to tell him/her, but also the patient becomes what can best be described as the principal investigator of their own condition. An investigation that can be assisted but not undertaken or directed by a sympathetic examiner. This extends to the point where only the patient can be said to be really able to diagnose what the current state of the illness is and where in many cases prescription of medication seems best left to the patient.

What is involved in these cases can be termed an exploration of inner space. Of the images and experiences that can vanish from normal living or irrupt into it threatening its coherence. The empirical investigation of such inner space has, however, since Descartes, been fraught with difficulty.

PHENOMENOLOGY

Following on from Droysen and Dilthey's establishment of empirical interpretative methods and the possibility of empirical human sciences, one of the pressing issues became that of whether one could be empirical about internal psychological events. This issue was put on the scientific agenda by Franz Brentano who argued that its subject matter formed a separate branch of science, phenomenology, also called subjective psychology. Initially for Brentano, phenomenology literally meant the science of appearances. Rather than sterile philosophical debate about the possibility of knowledge or the coherence of logic, Brentano wanted a science of concrete human living.

He pointed to all that was being ignored by philosophy. For example, facial gestures. Smiles differ from frowns, scowls, glares and laughs. These differences in facial gestures are easily perceived and Brentano wished to record appearances such as these. He wanted to determine the number of different facial or other gestures, as well as the many other events, which make fleeting appearances in human living comparable metaphorically to the fleeting appearances of sub-atomic particles in cloud chambers, and which like these sub-atomic particles are the constituents of concrete reality, despite anyone's theories about that reality.

To his early concern with determining accurately the appearance of things, Brentano, and later Edmund Husserl, added that such appearances meant something. They were intentional events. For example smiles mean something. Not something that can be easily analysed into discrete particles, but something definite nevertheless. The proof of this is that we do not go down the street indiscriminately smiling. And it is the meaning of a smile that makes it visible. Thus there are an enormous range of smiles and some may be bare flickers but, despite the diversity of facial conformations involved or the evanescence of some of them, we see them because they are meaningful events.

As thus defined, phenomenology might seem ideally suited to be an opinionated science as described in Chapter 3, where it was argued that opinio in contrast to scientia took the appearances of things very seriously and the sciences that stem from it have been seeking by one means or the other to come as close as possible to the full concrete reality embodied in appearances. This would present no problem except for the fact that phenomenology was concerned with describing mental states or the mental event of perceiving patterns in appearances.

This led to a crisis. When describing the appearances of a scene or an activity, investigators effectively paint a picture which can later be checked against the original scene or activity in order to determine the accuracy or goodness of fit to the original. In the case of internal pictures, however, how does one decide on the accuracy of the picture painted, given that no one else has access to the original landscape or mental acts.

For Wundt and the earliest psychologists, this was no problem and they seem to have assumed that the study of images and the other flora of the mental garden were the natural subject of a psychology.[12] But for others, notably the British philosophers Wittgenstein and Ryle, the possibility of being scientific about seemingly immaterial subject matter was seriously in doubt.

It became fashionable to talk in terms of mental imagery and events only having sense in terms of the behaviour in which they were embedded. For example, if I claim to be in pain, no one can tell what is going on inside of me and hence there is no independent check on my claim. But the claim to be in pain may receive support from my behaviour. Thus if my general behaviour and demeanour, or the six-inch gash on my leg, fits what would be expected by others from a person in pain, then my claim may be credible. Unsupported by other evidence the status of pain statements or statements about mental imagery or emotions was reduced to one of fictions, and it was simply not possible to be meaningfully scientific about fictions. In taking this eminently 'empirical' approach the ghosts of Descartes' dualism, which phenomenology had raised, could it seemed be safely bypassed.

In response to this crisis, Brentano and Husserl paid less and less heed to the cataloguing of mental appearances and more and more to the philosophical issue of how meaning gets into mental pictures. They did so to the point where phenomenology was almost stillborn as a science and became instead the archetype of a turgid philosophy. The difficulties phenomenology ran into had serious consequences. Shorn of a cogent scientific basis all branches of psychology dependent on introspection withered and were replaced by behaviourism. Behaviourism also eschewed all talk of mental imagery and events and, in the extreme, it aimed at accounting for all behaviours in terms of chains of stimulus–response reflexes. Rather quickly, it became the norm to regard behaviourism as an objective psychology and phenomenology as a subjective one.

This was further reinforced by the separation out from phenomenology of gestalt psychology. Gestalt psychology is also a psychology of appearances, but in this case the appearances are those perceived by all subjects. A gestalt involves the perception of a whole or an assembly among constituent parts. As, for example, when faced with certain arrangements of dots on a piece of paper, it is common to see faces, figures or other objects. That is we fill in the missing detail to complete the picture. In such cases, we may therefore seem to see what is not there. This has disturbed many philosophers. But the fact that all of us typically see the same thing is sufficient to protect the scientific credibility of gestalt experiments.

The stripping out from the body of phenomenology of gestalt psychology left so-called subjective psychology as a ghostly subject dealing with ghostly realities. Something to be left to existential philosophers and various literary artists. The scientific approach to the psyche was to analyse it anatomically at post mortem, determining its electrophysiological properties by work on animals and assessing its behavioural outputs either by the methods of behaviourist psychology or by trained and restrained observation of behaviour. That this may sound to many readers like an appropriately scientific way to handle a tricky and dangerous subject attests to the recent paradigmatic dominance of linguistic philosophy and behaviourist psychology. For almost fifty years hardly a voice protested that this was not science magnificently surmounting difficulties but academic capitulation following the line of least resistance.

Time and the development of neuropsychology has caught up with this long-standing dispute. Neuropsychologists have had to practise an older innocent phenomenology. They have had to have recourse to introspection by force of necessity. The impressive results they have achieved have effectively cut this particular Gordian knot. If recent neuropsychological research means anything, it seems to indicate that Brentano and Wundt were correct in the first place. Imagery really does seem to function as pictures flashed up on a mental screen rather than as some linguistic or verbal ploy. Pain really is registered intrapsychically such that the different descriptions of pains can lead investigators to detect their source, even if it is hidden from public scrutiny. Indeed, it now seems as if Brentano was correct in a very primitive sense in so much as mental events and objects are as much *material realities* as any other events or objects and their appearances matter as much as any other set of events and objects. And that a science of the psyche depends critically on getting the correct description of such events and objects. Of course, correct description is not a final scientific statement and the early phenomenologists seem to have been relatively unaware that there is no such thing as pure description, that theory shapes critically what is seen. Nevertheless, the best possible description of psychological elements would seem to be a prerequisite to an adequate explanatory psychology.

THE ECLIPSE OF PSYCHOPATHOLOGY

In particular, one might have thought that best possible descriptions of internal mental events would be the central subject matter of any theory of mental illness. This certainly was the view of Jaspers. The classic descriptions of mental illness until then had been those of Kraepelin and Bleuler who had described the appearances and behaviour of manic depressives and schizophrenics in searching detail, but from the outside. Their descriptions were so good that in many cases it is possible to retrospectively make a neuropsychological analysis of what must have been going wrong in the brains of their patients. In contrast, Jaspers devoted a substantial section of *General Psychopathology* to illustrating the need for phenomenology in psychiatry.

The description of Parkinson's disease from the inside by Ivan Vaughan can now be held to be a description that any comprehensive theory of Parkinson's disease should be required to account for. In much the same spirit, Jaspers used the notebooks of the Russian artist Wassily Kandinsky as a source of descriptions of aberrant psychopathological phenomena from the inside.

Based on Kandinsky's reports, he distinguished between images, pseudo-hallucinations and hallucinations. Images are unremarkable internal percepts. Pseudo-hallucinations are remarkable internal events, which have the character of images but are not recognized as such by the subject. Hallucinations are perceptual events thought by the subject to have an external reference. Put more concretely, in some cases the voices heard in a psychiatric illness are located by the subject inside their own head but not recognized to be their own auditory images or thoughts (pseudo-hallucinations). In true hallucinations the voice seems to be coming from outside. This distinction has been upheld ever since. It is one routinely sought in practice, but seemingly without stimulating many to account for why some voices should be located in internal space and others externally. Jaspers argued that such distinctions, once made phenomenologically and upheld, become the data that any cognitive or psychological theory must be able to account for, if it is to give an adequate account of mental illnesses.

Following Jaspers, Schneider made use of phenomenological methods to pinpoint the first rank symptoms of schizophrenia. He took the reports of schizophrenic patients seriously rather than just observed their behaviour. Through paying attention to them he gradually came to realize that certain reports characterized schizophrenia. Bizarre utterances can be found in a wide variety of psychiatric illnesses, from hysteria to the affective disorders and paranoid psychoses, as well as in schizophrenia. But the bizarre reports of feeling alienated from one's own thoughts, feelings or even bodily functions, which suggest a frontal lobe disturbance, appear to be relatively specific to schizophrenia.

These early phenomenological distinctions of Jaspers and Schneider have not been supplemented by anything more recent. Psychiatrists today prefer to rely on the words of old masters rather than to discover new truths. The discovery of further mental elements, Jaspers believed, would be an essential prelude to the construction of proper explanations in psychopathology. Classic psychopathology, however, is now so lacking in confidence that it has moved on to neither fresh descriptions nor explanatory syntheses. The best contemporary descriptions of the inner life of the mentally ill can be found in authors like Ronald Laing,[13] whose very name is anathema to orthodox psychiatry. Some descriptions of schizophrenia from within can be found written by sufferers. But these are seen as being of peripheral interest rather than as source material for a science of psychopathology. Thus they are used as helpful supports to give to someone who has the illness rather than as data that any theory of schizophrenia must account for.

Phenomenology has been reduced to an activity of describing a patient's visible appearances for the purposes of diagnosis. And even this is restricted to supposedly trained empirical observers. Schneider's first rank symptoms are used widely for diagnosis, but few clinicians wonder exactly what mental process could give rise to such experiences. Instead Freudian psychopathology appears to have obtained squatter's rights on the whole notion of explanation in psychopathology, with medical psychopathology referring to itself as descriptive psychopathology in contrast to dynamic psychopathology (which offers explanations). Ironically, medical psychopathology seems to have become not only incapable of explanations but also less and less capable of the only descriptions that really matter. Arguably it is the drying up of the phenomenological reservoir that has led to the drought in psychopathology that we find today. Perhaps it was only to be expected that psychopathology's day should turn in to night, along with those of the other branches of the psychological sciences which depended on introspection, during the eclipse of phenomenology by behaviourism.

The very comprehensiveness of Jaspers' psychopathology also made for confusion. He distinguished between objective, subjective, empathic and interpretative psychologies, where phenomenology was synonymous with subjective psychology. Jaspers himself had no problems with the idea of a subjective psychology being empirical. He remarked tartly that all the findings in so-called objective psychology depended on subjects at some point. But others, as we have seen, had problems with this point. Problems that he may have contributed to as he, himself, inveighed so damningly against the interpretative psychologies, which for many were the epitome of a subjective, introspective psychology. He also may have caused further problems by failing to distinguish between the phenomenology he advocated, which was an early form of phenomenology, concerned only with the appearances of mental events, from the later forms of phenomenology.[14] The latter went on to become a particularly impenetrable branch of philosophy which psychiatrists as doers rather than thinkers quickly decided they could do without.

More importantly, however, the results of the phenomenological method never found a local habitation or a name. If hallucinations, pseudo-hallucinations and the alienation of thoughts, feelings, volition and bodily functions were disorders of form as claimed, they shed little light on what exactly psychiatric disorders of form were. We have argued that seeing the effective disorders and schizophrenia as disorders which involve some hardware dysfunction rather than just software errors amounts *now* to saying that they involve neuropsychological disturbances. But this characterization was not open to Jaspers or Schneider, for several reasons. The first was that there was no such thing as neuropsychology, when they were trying to pin down their psychopathological framework. Although Schneider stressed that the bizarre reports that constitute the first rank symptoms of schizophrenia involved *experiences* of alienation of will, emotions, thoughts and bodily functions, or the experience of these functions not working normally, he had difficulties making this clear that he possibly would not now have had. As things stand, the vast majority of psychiatric practitioners see the first rank symptoms of schizophrenia in terms of delusional ideas, which cannot be neuropsychological in origin, rather than in terms of odd experiences.

Another reason may be that psychiatric disorders of form have gone their own way for so long now without being seen as neuropsychological in nature, that sheer inertia keeps them apart from the mainstream of neuropsychological disorders. In addition, psychiatric expectations of what neuropsychological deficits should look like have been heavily coloured by the type of deficits produced by strokes or tumours. These are commonly irreversible, whereas the functional psychoses follow a remitting course. Furthermore strokes and tumours produce fairly complete loss of function or, alternatively, a lack of awareness that there is anything wrong. If all neuropsychological deficits entailed a lack of awareness or an inability to express their awareness on the part of the patient, they certainly would not do as the concrete specification of psychiatric disorders of form. If this was the case Schneider's subjects would not have been able to offer him their first rank symptoms. In addition, it would seem that in at least some cases behavioural factors should be able to precipitate them.

This is not now an impossible prescription for neuropsychological disturbances to fill. But it was up until a few years ago. Now we know that brain disorders such as Parkinson's disease or infectious illnesses such as influenza lead to subtle and reversible disturbances of brain functioning. They also leave affected subjects quite able to describe their own impairment of functioning. And in the case of disorders of form, at least of other organs, there are precedents for the disturbance arising in response to behavioural stressors. For example in the case of ulcers, very clear holes in the lining of the gut may be precipitated by behavioural factors.

The specification of psychopathological disorders of form in terms of neuropsychological disturbances would have a number of radical and dramatic advantages. First, it would confer greatly increased comprehensibility on psychiatric illnesses as it would locate the core disturbances of depression, mania and schizophrenia within a range of phenomena, of which some have been well characterized. Failure to make this identification risks leaving psychiatric disorders of form in some ghostly realm, that can never be properly investigated scientifically.

Second, as neuropsychological research has indicated, such an identification might have the added benefit of rehabilitating the psychiatric patient. It would enable them to become empirical investigators and managers of their own disorders rather than to have them condemned to the outer darkness of insanity. Perhaps, paradoxically, it is this spectre of the abolition of insanity that most militates against psychiatric disorders of form being seen as a set of neuropsychological disturbances.

PSYCHOPATHOLOGY AND NEUROPSYCHOLOGY[15-20]

What are the neuropsychological disturbances in the affective disorders and schizophrenia?* In the case of depression, there are disturbances of sleep, typically an unaccountable early morning wakening, disorders of appetite, especially loss of appetite, and loss of libido. Both medical and psychological psychopathologists are happy to concede that these are unmotivated; that they stem from disturbed brain functioning. Accordingly they would meet criteria for a neuropsychological disturbance. Typically, however, they are termed neurovegetative changes rather than neuropsychological changes. But the latter is arguably a generic term that subsumes the former. Strokes and tumours can equally give rise to neuropsychological deficits that affect vegetative functions. However, even where these vegetative disturbances are seen as arising because of cerebral dysfunction, they are commonly seen even by medical theorists as somewhat incidental to a *mood* disorder and as such, although prominent, do not seem the right candidates for the core disturbances of depression.

The other prominent clinical features of depression are hopelessness, guilt and thoughts of suicide. These cannot be neuropsychological disturbances. No abnormality of brain functioning is needed to account for hopelessness in the way that one is needed to account for an environmental-dependency syndrome or the constriction and expansion of experiential fields found in Parkinson's disease. One can be hopeless, guilty and think of suicide without one's brain working abnormally. This follows from the relative independence of psyche from brain outlined in Chapter 1.

There is a further group of grey symptoms – loss of energy, loss of interest, loss of concentration, a strange affective state difficult to put

---

* From here until the end of the book, it will be assumed that the affective disorders involve disturbances of circadian rhythms. Such a lesion would give a core experience in depression that many readers will have shared when they have been jetlagged or following shift work. While a good deal of evidence points toward circadian disturbances in the affective disorders, whether they are the pertinent disturbance is not the issue at stake here. If not circadian rhythms, then something giving similar experiences is at the heart of the affective disorders. The choice of the circadian system has been made in order to put fleshy details on the bare bones of what would otherwise be a very abstract argument.

In schizophrenia, it will be assumed that some disturbance of frontal lobe functioning has occurred, which gives an experience not unlike the environmental-dependency syndrome of L'Hermitte. On a technical point, when the first rank symptoms are mentioned experiences of alienation are meant.[21] Experiences of influence do not count. These are often taken as first rank symptoms but are non-specific to schizophrenia.

in words and an obvious physical and mental slowing (psychomotor retardation). Instinctively most of us seem to think of loss of concentration, energy or interest and a slowing up in ourselves as being the kind of things that happen to us when we have a problem on our mind or we are demoralized. But as a matter of fact, influenza or disturbances of circadian rhythms can also lead to loss of interest, loss of energy, a strange mood hard to put in words and poor concentration. So it would appear that these central disturbances could either be a matter of disordered content of behaviour or the expression of neuropsychological disturbances. Why opt for one or the other?

The empirical patient

One reason that the neuropsychological option has been neglected has been that we do not believe that psychiatric patients can be empirical about their disabilities. Many depressed patients repeatedly tell their therapists that there is no reason for their loss of interest or their loss of energy. That they cannot understand why their memory or concentration has been so poor lately. That what they feel is something different to sadness and unhappiness and much more like something physical. We typically ignore or even fail to hear them say this. Partly because ninety years of depth psychology have persuaded us that there wouldn't be a problem if the patient knew what was wrong with them (see below). But also, as we have noted, sufferers from pain disorders are liable to have their reports treated as second-class evidence as to what is happening in them, unless the reports can be supported by other signs which do not depend on the affected subject's observations. So also the reports of depressed, manic and schizophrenic subjects are not likely to be given a central place in any theory about what happens in these disorders. Even though what they may be reporting may be central to the disorder.

Paradoxically, this is most likely to be the case in psychiatry of all medical specialties, even though it, more than any other specialty, seemingly pays heed to what patients say. This attention, however, is attention trained not to take at face value what a patient says. Rather the clinician is attempting to diagnose irrationality, in which case an affected subject's statements become essentially meaningless. Where Ivan Vaughan, describing Parkinson's disease from the inside, causes irritation to many medical practitioners, partly by illustrating how they fall short of the mark, he and other sufferers from neuropsychological disorders are increasingly likely to be paid heed to because they are not insane. Not so the psychiatric patient. Mental health professionals do not have to accept being taught their job by their patients.

Yet even a superficial scrutiny of clinical material should be sufficient to indicate that these attitudes to patients are misguided. Take the phenomenon of psychomotor retardation in depression. This is a reversible impairment of functioning, whereby affected subjects appear slowed down in their mental and physical activities. For example, asking questions elicits answers after a noticeable delay. This may be observed and rated by clinicians with some degree of reliability. But it can also be observed by the affected subjects themselves, who in response to the question 'Are you slower in yourself?' will answer 'Yes'. Indeed it can arguably be more sensitively rated by the affected subject. Many depressed subjects report being slowed down, when this is not apparent to the clinical observer. However, such reports do not lead to a note in the chart that the subject has psychomotor retardation, unless the clinician can also see it. We simply do not trust our patients as observers.

In the case of schizophrenia, the visible disorders of form affect the form of thought and of emotion. When clearly present, the patient may be unable to keep to one topic of conversation or may talk at length without saying anything substantial. Emotionally-affected individuals may appear to be unable to prevent their emotions veering all over the place, so that their emotional state may be incongruous with what is going on. Alternatively, they may be unable to shift emotion at all so that they appear to be almost emotionless.

Just as with psychomotor retardation in depression, these disorders are not reliably observed unless present in a severe form. As in the case of psychomotor retardation, one might expect patients to be able to observe that they are having difficulties conversing or maintaining rapport. Yet when patients report that thoughts come into their mind unbidden, or that they are unable to summon up thoughts, or that impulses come from nowhere or that they have become emotionless, it is commonly either thought that they are in the throes of a psychological (neurotic) crisis or that they are deluded. It does not seem to occur to anyone to diagnose schizophrenic thought disorder on the basis of what the patient says, i.e. to let the patient make the diagnosis.

A wealth of information could follow from letting the patient make the diagnosis. For example, in a set of studies of the concentration problems of depressed subjects, Fraser Watts and colleagues in Cambridge have found that their loss of concentration on objective testing is much more like the kind of problem that occurs after a mild concussion than those that occur when someone has another problem on their mind. This is consistent with concentration problems having a neuropsychological rather than a psychological origin.

The really interesting finding, however, was that affected subjects appeared to be able to distinguish between varieties of concentration disturbance. Some reported going blank and others that their mind wandered. Clinicians only observing the outer form of behaviour miss these distinctions. But it appears that the distinctions are valid ones. Patients who go blank do poorly at some tests that those with mind-wandering do well at, and vice versa. Likewise it seems that schizophrenics when they have 'neurotic' complaints perform poorly on tests of frontal lobe functioning.

Reasons and causes[22,23]

There is another reason why the neuropsychological option is not taken. In general, when reconstructing behaviour, it makes sense to ask for a subject's reasons or intentions, or their understanding of what was happening, and to piece the story together in terms of recognized and unrecognized motives. All fragments of behaviour, even down to the minor facial twitchings of a smile, mean something. While ordinarily we do not think as much about the reasons for behaviours that are involuntary or automatic as we do about supposedly voluntary or intentional behaviours, we are quite ready to read motives into such behaviours, when necessary. This is because while such functions are largely involuntary, they may be brought to some extent under intentional control, even down to such things as heart rate or the amount of gastric acid secreted. And, in general, they may be modified by habit. We hold ourselves responsible for them. As we noted with corpus callosal lesions earlier, responsibility for behaviours is not something we give up readily.

Behaviours have to be grossly abnormal before we suspend our instinctive search for motives. Even epilepsy was once seen as a spiritual affliction and still has some stigma attached to it. Ninety years of depth psychology has changed our ideas of what kind of motivational aberrations might lie behind strange behaviours, but not our propensity to look for motives. In particular mental health professionals, whether or not they adhere to Freud, assume that the behaviour of their patients means anything but what it appears to mean on the surface.

For example, we have mentioned earlier the somatagnosia that can occur after strokes. In such cases, affected subjects apparently disown their paralysed left limbs. Subjects have even been observed to ask who the strange person sleeping in the bed with them is, in apparent reference to the parts of their body they are disowning. Under a Freudian influence to make sense of such a behaviour no matter how odd, it was common during the 1930s, 1940s and 1950s to hear this behaviour being interpreted in terms of the subject being unable to face up to the reality of their illness, even to the extent of denying the evidence in front of their eyes. Thus many such patients were referred for psychotherapy. It is now known that loss of brain cells from the parietal lobe of the brain causes this syndrome.

Stammering is another instructive example. This speech defect typically has its onset around the age of four or five. There is commonly a history of stress occurring in the home at time of onset. Once established, it frequently gets worse under stress. The age and circumstances of onset, and its worsening under pressure, made it for a long time a battleground on which competing psychologies fought. The depth psychologies argued that it represented some blocking of affective development. That it was a neurosis that could only be relieved by analysis. In behaviourist terms, it was interpreted as an attempt by the child to gain attention and therefore was best treated by ignoring him/her. Like depression and schizophrenia it became a disorder of many theories – the same ones that have sought to explain what is happening in these latter illnesses.

Current understanding is that, although this disorder may be precipitated by stress, once established it is effectively more like somatagnosia than a behavioural disturbance in a problem child. Something goes wrong in the speech centres of the brain at a critical stage during the development of fluent speech. It appears that the brain is programmed to acquire various skills at sensitive points. When these skills are not learnt at the optimal time, whether because of interference by stress or otherwise, they can be difficult to learn at other times. This it seems is what happens in cases of enuresis (bedwetting) and stammering. When finally learnt it is often the case that a compensatory skill rather than the original skill is acquired or that the skill is not learnt as securely as skills acquired at the appropriately sensitive stage. In the case of stammering this disorder does not clear up during analysis or behavioural programmes of rewards and punishments, except co-incidentally. But it can instantly be overcome by standing behind waterfalls or by wearing earphones that block out the sound of the speaker's own voice. With time and practice it also can be controlled by a variety of compensatory speech therapy techniques.

Despite longstanding folklore awareness of the benefits of standing behind waterfalls, or that stammering does not happen while stammerers are singing, there has always been a tendency to interpret it in terms of motives or reasons rather than to see it as a medical disorder. The tension between these competing views of the disorder have existed since Hippocrates, with the difference that dynamic or behaviourist views have possibly been less harmful than earlier interpretative views, which saw the disorder in terms of a spiritual problem. In general, interpretative views have always tended to prevail, presumably because speech is such a 'mental' act. But also, presumably, because even in acts that are not so 'mental' we tend to ascribe personal responsibility for them to someone rather than to see them as involuntary. Commonly this even applies to such involuntary functions as micturition and defecation, such that subjects who defecate and urinate under excitement or stress feel ashamed of what has happened. Or parents toilet training a child will often see lapses on the child's part as evidence of wilfulness.

Another aspect of reading motives into behaviour becomes apparent in the case of autism. This is a disorder of childhood where from the earliest age a child displays a complete lack of social interest. They occupy themselves with their individual worlds, display an extreme preference for familiar routines and react with great distress to change. This disorder is now seen as the result of brain damage acquired perinatally. But until quite recently it was common to hear it being interpreted as the result of parental coldness leading to the child's withdrawal from reality. In the case of autism what becomes apparent is that over-interpretation is not harmless. Many parents have been distressed greatly to learn on the highest authority that it is they who are responsible for their child's disturbing state. Doubly so as taking such information to heart and attempting to radically restructure their lives in terms of it only had the effect of leading to an even greater sense of failure as no improvement in their child's condition resulted.

INSIGHTS AND INVERSE INSIGHTS

Given that we have difficulties in recognizing that disturbances such as convulsions, somatagnosia, stammering, eneuresis or autism are caused rather than motivated, what odds then our interpreting, in terms of causes, the lack of energy of depression, the overactivity of mania or the inattentiveness or seeming wilfullness of schizophrenia? Can any principles be offered to guide our interpretations of what is happening in these disorders?

As noted in the last chapter a cardinal precept of modern hermeneutic method lies in the approaching of a to-be-interpreted subject with sympathetic understanding. This methodological precept stands in marked contrast to the negative critical approach which antedated it in historical studies. It also stands in contrast to the suspicion which has dominated dynamic interpretative approaches. Obviously scrutiny of any individual's behaviour is liable to lead to conclusions that they have both recognized and unrecognized motives. Accordingly, some suspicion of their utterances is appropriate. But in contrast to modern hermeneutic methods, psychodynamic interpretations are relentlessly suspicious. Nothing can be taken at face value. Cynically one might add that no motive remains unscrutinized until it conforms to what the analyst knows beforehand is the operative motivational pathology. Even when these buried motives are uncovered, if the patient fails to get well the adequacy of the analytic interpretation does not come under question. Rather unconscious resistances to recovery are postulated.

In contrast, hermeneutic methodology now advocates making allowances for the different circumstances of others when interpreting their behaviour, particularly when that behaviour appears alien. It counsels the need to be acutely aware of the possibility of misunderstanding the subject, the necessity of being prepared to refrain from premature conjecture or closure on an issue and a willingness to give the subject the benefit of the doubt. Being the victim of disordered neuropsychological functioning effectively puts a subject in different cultural circumstances. Putting on the mind of such a person involves realizing that they have been and are being subjected to a host of unusual experiences. Also that they will almost certainly be tempted to account for these in the usual way, in terms of motives. And that in doing so they will be incorrect. What is needed is not an insight into their motives but the inverse insight that there are no motives.

Inverse insight

In general, insights grasp relations between data that make sense, whether those relations concern the physical features of the world or details of the historical record. By inverse insights I mean that kind of insight that grasps that there is no relation to be grasped of the type being sought. For example, in mathematics most of the numbers we use mean something or correspond to something in our worlds. Thus the integer 1 can stand for 1 apple or 1 star and the fraction ½ for ½ an apple or ½ a star. But other numbers not in common use are recognized to be incommensurable, others to be irrational, or surds (e.g. $\sqrt{2}$). For a long time equal status with the integers was denied to such numbers because of their lack of understandability and their lack of obvious relation to our world. The problem of the irrational numbers caused almost insuperable difficulties in the past. But mathematics now proceeds happily juggling mixtures of integers and surds or rational and irrational numbers and compounds of these numbers. In the final analysis this happens because these numbers are useful. Equations and calculations which use them work.

Similarly in physics, insights grasp the relations of things to each other. But an appreciation of Newton's first law of motion requires an inverse insight as it is counter-intuitive in its statement that bodies persist in motion unless acted upon. That is that rest rather than motion requires the action of an external agency. Similarly in biology, insights grasp the progression of organic forms displayed in the fossil record and can explain this progression in terms of evolution of functions. But to attempt to account for all the details of the record in terms of developmental process is doomed. One must also postulate external catastrophies, events that make no developmental sense, in order to maintain that there is development.

In the same way, insights grasp the relations between events that make sense of human behaviour, even though that behaviour may have arisen in response to very different exigencies and in quite different cultural situations. Where insights grasp the reason for the behaviour in question, inverse insights assert that there is no reason, that the normal process of rational behaviour has been suspended. For example in a temporal lobe automatism, there may be relatively complex behaviours carried out by a subject totally out of their control.

The surprise engendered by an inverse insight indicates that it runs counter to our spontaneous anticipations of intelligibility. Inverse insights are difficult to grasp. Not only it seems in human behaviour, when they involve interpretation in terms of causes rather than reasons, but also when they are called for in the natural sciences. However, just as insights occur in both the natural and human sciences and inverse insights occur and can be managed in the natural sciences, so inverse insights must be expected in the human (or interpretative) sciences. Indeed they may have as useful or as necessary a role to play there as they do in the natural sciences.

Inverse insights and functional psychoses

Reformulating the interpretative problem that faces us in the case of determining the meaning of mania, depression or schizophrenia, it can be suggested that insights alone cannot piece together an understanding of what has been happening. That both insights and inverse insights are needed to handle the complex of intelligibility and inverse intelligibility that constitutes these illnesses. The disease processes provide an ongoing set of stimuli that can only be interpreted counter-intuitively. This brings us back to the cardinal point of hermeneutic method which is to avoid misunderstanding by giving the to-be-interpreted subject the benefit of the doubt as a rational human being. *Particularly when the behaviour under investigation appears to fall short of rationality.* Autism, stammering and somatagnosia indicate how easy it is to misinterpret neuropsychological disturbances. Only a methodical awareness of the bias involved in spontaneous interpretations can hope to avoid misinterpreting the even more ambiguous deficits found in depression, mania and schizophrenia. Two examples may help bring home the value of such a methodical awareness.

The first concerns a middle-aged lady who took an overdose of tablets that would have been expected to kill most people. When she was later admitted to a psychiatric unit, it was quite clear that she was seriously depressed. She was eating and sleeping poorly, was slow in herself, complaining of poor concentration, had lost interest and energy, was wracked with guilt and wished she were dead. Straightforward depression except for one other complaint she had, a vaginal pain. This she had had for twenty years. It had started several months after the birth of a child, one night while having intercourse with her husband. From the very start it was an extra-ordinarily severe pain. It made driving in a car difficult as every bump in the road registered. When particularly bad, even sitting comfortably in a seat was difficult. Not surprisingly further intercourse was prohibited.

However, when she went to have it investigated at the hospital nothing abnormal could be found. She had had an episiotomy during the birth but the episiotomy site looked normal. Nevertheless in response to her insistence that the pain was at the site of the scar, the gynaecologists excised her scar and did a fresh repair. To no avail. Over several years she visited a number of different doctors, specialists, faith-healers, hypnotists and others but with no relief. Some alleviation of her pain was obtained fifteen years after its onset by a procedure which involved freezing her vagina. But when she had begun to get depressed several months before her overdose the pain got much worse again.

How should this pain be interpreted? In most psychiatric units worldwide, such a case would be thought of as crying out for a dynamic interpretation. It would seem to be almost too Freudian to be true. (A real life 'White Hotel'). In the unit she was treated on, most of the staff saw relations between this woman and her husband as poor. He had threatened to kill her on more than one occasion. She wished to divorce him but given the severity of her pain was incapable of an independent life. In the past, on occasions when her pain had abated somewhat, he had arranged vacations for them both but every time just before they were about to set off her pain got much worse. Most of the staff thought her pain was being used as a defence against a normal sexual exchange. In support of this interpretation it was noted that there were episodes from her past, before she had met her husband, that caused her guilt and which bore on her relationship with him. Further facts that might be pertinent to the case were that her mother and a sister had died from genital tract problems.

In response to having all this pointed out to her, this particular lady insisted that her pain was real, that it did not come on as a defence against sexual intercourse and that she and her husband had been planning on having a further child. On issues unrelated to the pain, the lady in question seemed very reasonable, thoughtful and warm, if somewhat guarded. In most psychiatric units or outpatient clinics, however, her apparent reasonableness would not be enough to prevent therapists queuing up to sort her out. Neither would failure to be sorted out make much difference to the matter. It would simply be interpreted as entrenched resistance to the truth. Yet modern hermeneutic methodology suggests that every effort should be made to interpret this story as though this lady was no less rational and capable of being empirical than her clinician.

Starting from this point of view one could immediately account for current poor relations between herself and her husband as the almost inevitable result of twenty years of living a torture. While he had threatened to kill her, the fact that he was still with her twenty years later despite repeated advice from the experts that she was putting all this on could be taken as indicating a very real love on his part. Her wish to divorce him, likewise could be seen as guilt on her part at having inflicted all she had on him and a wish to set him free rather than herself free. A clinician really sympathetic to her might have recognized that the pain she complained of bore resemblances to other pains occasioned by nerves being damaged, such as phantom limb pain or causalgia. In these cases there may be no obvious inflammation at the site of the wound; the pain may be among the most severe known and it may persist for years.

As it turns out increasing numbers of such pains are being reported after episiotomies in recent years, but as yet few medical practitioners, whether general, neurological or psychiatric know of this condition. In this particular lady's case a detailed and sympathetic examination should have forced some such conclusion on her clinicians, even if they were unaware of the existence of post-episiotomy pain syndrome, as she also had a pain in her big toe. This she rarely mentioned as it seemed irrelevant. But in fact the vagina and the big toe share the same nerve root, in the same way as the heart and the inside of the left arm do. This leads to pain in the heart often being experienced as pain down the left arm. Naturally only real cardiac pains cause this. In just the same way only a real pain in the vagina, especially one involving the nerves to the vagina, would be likely to cause a pain in the big toe too. But so seductive was the possibility of making a dynamic interpretation in this lady's case, that even this fact was dismissed by the clinicians treating her.

Apart from this specific source for this lady's pain there was another general one. Most depressed people when asked how they feel find it hard to put in words what it is that they feel. Some say a sadness beyond tears or an emptiness, such as one might expect of a major psychological loss or a dark night of the soul. But many others deny being particularly unhappy except as a result of their poor sleep, appetite and energy. Their denials are commonly not believed. Yet it seems that over a third of patients presenting to general practitioners with an illness that meets criteria for being regarded as depression, present with a principal complaint of pain of some sort rather than unhappiness or sadness. These subjects are commonly seen as somatizing their emotional problems and as being individuals who wouldn't recognize an emotion if hit across the face with one. (There is no evidence that this is the case, just suspicion.)

Increasingly, however, it seems that there is an intimate connection between pain and depression.[24] There have been repeated indications that there is something abnormal in the pain systems of subjects who are depressed. If this is the case and if the pain that accompanies depression is in many cases a subtle one that amounts to little more than a physical discomfort such as one gets with jet lag, then it makes eminent sense that subjects should find it hard to put in words how they feel and that many of them should present with primary complaints of pain. In this case, seeing this particular woman's condition as involving reactivation of a disturbed pain system by a further pain would help make sense of what was happening to her. (This is a common finding in subjects who have nerve pain syndromes, the old war wound acting up again.)

If this were the case strictly physical treatment of her depression could be expected to alleviate this lady's pain. As it turned out, her pain abated and her sleep and other disturbances cleared up with ECT. A more detailed investigation of her condition and those of many others who present with pain, founded on a willingness to let such subjects interpret their own state even when it goes against our instinctive interpretative grain, would be a useful scientific exercise.

The second example concerns a large number of subjects, perhaps even millions. Depression, schizophrenia and many other conditions can be extremely disturbing and can lead to states of severe tension and agitation. The appropriate pharmacological intervention is with neuro-leptic drugs such as chlorpromazine or haloperidol. These, when they work properly, induce a 'what if' feeling, a feeling of indifference, which subjects often find protective. Typically many patients are interviewed at length only once during their stay in a psychiatric unit, right at the start of their admission. They are then slapped on neuroleptics within hours of that interview.

Many treated in this way, however, do not get better quickly. Indeed they may appear to get worse, as indicated by restless pacing and worried expressions. As a result their drug regimes are increased, commonly without further consultation. If interviewed such patients will commonly complain about their drugs, saying that they do not think they are doing them any good. Saying something like this also leads to drug levels being increased with the further instruction to nursing staff to make sure that the patient is actually taking their medication rather than just appearing to.

This scenario suggests that there have been several failures to grasp what is happening when inverse insights are called for. First, as the illness is thought to produce abnormal behaviour, more abnormal behaviour is interpreted as a worsening of the illness and hence as an indication for more of the drug. However, in a large number of cases neuroleptics may also cause motor restlessness, a wanting to jump out of one's skin, or a feeling of being chemically strait-jacketed. In either case an apparent worsening of behaviour can be expected that is not related to a worsening of the illness. Whether increased restlessness or a therapeutic indifference is caused seems a matter of individual wiring and side-effect profiles of the different neuroleptics. Changing from one to another neuroleptic based on what the patient says the effects of the various drugs on them are, would be a way to overcome the problem. Philip May and colleagues in California have shown that a subject's initial reaction to the neuroleptic medication they receive correlates very well with their subsequent outcome on these drugs.[25] Those who like what they feel after the first day of medication do well and those who dislike what they feel do poorly. Yet we never, in practice, pay any such heed to what our patients say.

A second failure to show inverse insight is the failure to appreciate that while a certain amount of a drug may be useful, more of it may not be. It is not uncommon to find patients in psychiatric units who are receiving over 2000 mg of chlorpromazine per day or up to 200 mg of haloperidol. However, recent research indicates that amounts of chlorpromazine above 400 mg/day cannot be more therapeutic as all the brain receptors that chlorpromazine acts through are blocked by 400 mg.[26] The comparable figure for haloperidol is 40 mg/day. Going above these levels can only induce side-effects, some of which may be permanent. Yet on many hospital wards it is probably uncommon to find many acute patients on less than 400 mg/day.

In such cases, even where the initial effects of neuroleptics may be appreciated by patients as therapeutic, this effect is likely to be counteracted by the side-effects produced at the higher dose. In these instances, patients almost certainly are correct when they say that they would be better off without their drugs. Heedless to the experience of patients under these regimes imposed on them, it is common to find clinicians bemoan the lack of compliance of schizophrenic patients as regards taking their medicine. Furthermore this lack of compliance is taken as additional evidence in favour of the deep seated, although rarely vocalized, belief of many clinicians that mental illnesses at heart involve manipulation of some form.

Inverse insights and empirical method
It can be noted that in each of these examples, inverse insights have the effect of bringing us closer to the concrete details of people's lives. Indeed, these examples may help illustrate why approaching the concrete is so closely linked to the question of being empirical. Empirical methods

require that *all* the data pertinent to a particular problem be accounted for by any proposed solution to that problem. One cannot arbitrarily select from among the data and still maintain that one is being empirical. In this case the data that are typically neglected are the data of what depressed, manic and schizophrenic subjects actually say. This neglect is commonly justified by claiming that what such subjects say is really a defence against what we know they need to say or by appealing to their current irrationality. These latter justifications, however, in actual fact are hypotheses just like any other and therefore stand in need of confirming evidence – evidence that is totally lacking.

The consequences of neglecting these data necessarily provide further data. Data which embarrassingly offer considerable support for the antipsychiatric proposals that medical handling of mental illness is dehumanizing and even that the medical establishment creates mental illness. In the case of our woman with perineal pain, taking seriously what the medical profession told her created problems where none existed before. In the case of schizophrenic or manic patients treated insensitively with neuroleptics the story is similar. The antipsychiatric line of thinking in turn, however, also fails to make appropriate inverse insights when they overlook the data offered by patients that can only be interpreted counter-intuitively in terms of an illness.

Both psychiatric and antipsychiatric approaches, therefore, currently fail to take all the data into account and fall down on their handling of the data supplied by patients.

Perhaps the most damaging legacy of the Freudian revolution is a certain atmosphere of suspicion. This particularly applies to mental illness, where patients become suspect individuals, by definition. Behavioural formulations differ little from psychodynamic ones on this point. They see the pertinent pathology in terms of patients who in some way are getting something out of mental illness that they should not be getting and/or that others have not noticed. This suspicion of patients seems equally held by both medical and anti-medical practitioners. The same degree of suspicion is never applied to the therapists. One could argue that therapists' motives for being in the mental health business are dictated more by the need to solve their own problems than by selfless concern for those who are suffering. One could point to the not so hidden rewards that therapists get out of mental illness – money, mystique and power. One could suggest that there is a certain irony in the latest fashion, cognitive therapy, in which the least scientific of scientists urge their patients to solve their problems by adopting a scientific attitude toward them.

These suspicions and ironies are well grounded in current realities but are usually kindly left unvoiced or suspended in practice. The same courtesy is not given to patients. Yet there is not one jot of creditable scientific evidence to suggest that suspicion of patients' motives is warranted or helpful. Does illness warrant such overt suspicion more than making money or achieving social status out of its treatment? It was this sense of double think about mental illnesses that angered Jaspers about Freudian psychopathology leading him eventually to characterize the whole of psychoanalysis as a 'pseudo-belief . . . a giant process of self-deceit . . . calculated to destroy what appears to be of most value in man'.

The need to grapple with these issues can be avoided by scientists or philosophers of science, who wish to return to the womb of Newtonian physics, where science is a matter of soothing certainties, rather than an attempt to avoid misunderstanding. A critic will almost certainly enquire 'What mathematics might be suitable for an inverse hermeneutics?' In reply to this something odd about the mathematics of modern science can be noted. In the first place the whole process of ever more precise measurement can be seen as an effort to avoid misunderstanding.

More tellingly, however, the application of probability theory to science, as found in statistics, rests on a related set of inverse insights. Statistics are an application of inverse probability.[27] Their application hinges not on degrees of certainty about what is known but on the quantification of uncertainty. The distribution of measurements around a mean is not what is of interest. Rather it is the distribution of errors made in measuring. What is significant about the correlation of two measurements is not the likelihood of their being associated, but the unlikelihood that the findings arose by chance. That inverse insights are not just some soft psychological option can be seen from the fact that it took a century from the discovery of modern probability to get to the notion of inverse probability. Repeated attempts to put the quantification of certainty to use failed until Bayes and Laplace independently realized that what was needed was a quantification of uncertainty.

FIVE The Dynamics of a Psychosis

> Lovers and madmen have such seething brains,
> Such shaping fantasies, that apprehend
> More than cool reason ever comprehends.
> One sees more devils than vast Hell can hold:
> That is the madman. The lover, also frantic
> Sees Helen's beauty in a brow of Egypt.
> Such tricks hath strong imagination,
> That if it would but apprehend some joy,
> It comprehends the bringer of that joy.
> How in the night imagining some fear,
> How easy is a bush supposed a bear!
>
> *A Midsummer's Night Dream*, Shakespeare

I have been arguing that individuals who are supposed to be mentally ill are not suffering from any mental or even psychological disorder, but have a neuropsychological disturbance. I have contended that they remain capable of being rational and empirical and that the best hope for the treatment of their condition would seek to exploit their rationality and empiricism. A moment's pause for thought, however, should suggest that one of the characteristics of the so-called insane, in contrast to the picture just painted, is that they are at least on occasion insane. This is not a judgement that many depressed, manic or schizophrenic subjects would argue with as almost all on some occasion will have thought they were going mad. Can these pictures of empirical and insane patients be reconciled?

There are two ways to appear insane/eccentric, which apply equally to Newtonian planets and to man. One is to have a genuinely eccentric orbit. And the other is to appear eccentric because of the influence of some other agency. Thus it was that eccentricities in the orbit of Neptune led to speculation about the existence of Pluto. Recently, anomalies in the electromagnetic radiation arriving on Earth have generated interest in the possibility of locating black holes.

In this chapter it will be argued that the neuropsychological disturbances at the core of the affective disorders and schizophrenia provide a disturbing external force. One that arises from within. In response to it, judgements about what has happened are dominated by uncertainty as to what will happen next. Where will this new orbit take us? What lies in our path? What correcting action should be taken if we know neither the consequences of this change in orbit nor the likely effects of any compensatory manoeuvres? Dynamic psychology is now in a position to answer how we are likely to respond to problems such as these. Along with the growth of neuropsychology, one of the newly flourishing areas of psychology has been the assessment of risk-taking behaviour and of the factors that shape judgements made under uncertainty.[1]

Three developments catalysed growth in this field. First, there was the recognition, by Paul Meehl in the 1950s, that clinicians, faced with the need to offer prognoses for clinical conditions, make predictions that differ radically from the predictions that would be made based simply on statistical considerations. For example, take a psychiatrist who has examined a number of subjects who have just been admitted with schizophrenia and who is asked to predict the likelihood of recovery of the patients in question. Outcome studies repeatedly give the outcome for schizophrenia as 33 per cent fully recover, 33 partially recover and 33 per cent fail to recover. But our psychiatrist faced with a particular patient will not give a such a neutral probabilistic answer. He or she will be more likely to be pretty confident that this particular patient will either do well or poorly. If asked why he or she is so confident about the outcome, the answer is likely to be in terms of an intuition or a hunch.

This mode of operating differs little from that of the gambler, who feels sure they have a 'system' that will defy the odds. Commonly subjects of such experiments, even when they feel they have done a good job at predicting, get the actual outcomes badly wrong. The surprising thing is that feedback seems to be of very little use in helping to correct and improve performances. It seems that in areas we think we know something about, we persist in thinking we have personal insights that will take our performance beyond the average.

Another input came from the study of subjective probability and the introduction of the Bayesian paradigm to psychology by Edwards.

According to this view, probability is not a question of what the world is probably like but is one of what we the knowers know. Changing probability estimates, therefore, involves not just demonstrating certain facts about the world but of overcoming *sets* of beliefs or hunches the subject may have. Thus experiments that demonstrate that 95 per cent of the outcomes appear inconsistent with a particular hypothesis may not lead the subject to rationally reject that hypothesis if it involves important beliefs for them. This is because these beliefs are supported, at least indirectly, by other evidence.

For example, the weight of evidence that smoking causes cancer commonly does not lead people, even medical people, to give up smoking. Why not? Because the evidence presented is not the only evidence on the subject that a typical person has. They may have a grandparent who lived to be a hundred and smoked forty cigarettes daily. Or they may associate smoking with being virile and being virile with longevity. For the subjective estimate of probability to change, a whole set of beliefs must change rather than just knowledge of what studies on smoking have shown. Conversely beliefs only shakily supported by the evidence are taken up enthusiastically rather than cautiously by subjects who have other beliefs congruent with the ones in question. This applies to scientists and lovers as much as to madmen and gamblers.

The third influence on recent dynamic psychology came from attribution theory, first developed by Heider. According to attribution theory when things happen, and in particular when they happen to us, we must come up with answers as to what is happening and why. There are certain answers we seem prone to, it could be argued almost evolutionarily predisposed to. Chief among these is our propensity to attribute causal agency to dispositions rather than to situations. This has been termed the fundamental attributional error.

These three inputs combined have led to the study of man, the 'lay psychologist'. It has become clear that in daily life we are not particularly rational, in the sense of estimating statistically valid probabilities. Indeed it would appear that we use some very simple predictive strategies and on many occasions use them to our detriment. These have been called heuristic strategies or biases.

The hypotheses and concepts we derive from such strategies, however, are often ones we do not easily give up. They appear capable of surviving potent logical and empirical challenges. Experiments suggest that they can even be bolstered up by contrary evidence or the total destruction of the evidential bases on which the belief was founded.[2] Such studies have shed much light on the generation of social prejudice. They would seem to have an obvious relevance also to the question of the origin of delusional beliefs – which is the central question in the psychopathology of the psychoses.

Bias of representativeness

This bias refers to our liability to be over-influenced by individual items of information or our familiarity with certain situations to the neglect of a balanced view of the whole scene. Thus, given descriptions of a person's personality as shy, retiring, bookish and asked to judge whether the person involved is a nurse or a librarian, most people plump for the librarian label. Despite the fact that there are far more nurses than librarians. Even when provided with the information that the personality profile was selected from a group of ten profiles eight of which were nurses and two librarians, experimental subjects defy the odds. It seems that we assign an occupational label to the personality profile based on our intuitions of what nurses and librarians *should* look like. We feel more confident with stereotypes than with a rational analysis of the probabilities of a situation.

This thinking by stereotype happens all the time in daily life. Thus given some ethnic or social groups we dislike for some reason, we are likely to seize on a press story featuring a member of that group engaged in unseemly behaviour as evidence for the unsavoury nature of all members of the group. No matter how large the group or improbable the likelihood that so many people could be so perverted or uncivilized. Single examples of crazy people are frequently enough to tar all sufferers from mental illness with the same brush – they are all unstable and liable to violence!

This bias is also shown in the case of our beliefs regarding things that may help our physical or nervous ailments. Thus many people take herbal preparations or old country remedies on the basis of a confident assurance by a friend or neighbour that it did wonders for someone else they knew. We often believe more in this wondrous cure of one than in the many cured by more orthodox treatments. This form of thinking does not only affect lay people. Many psychiatrists have their favourite antidepressant for example, often based on one dramatic response to the drug in question, despite the weight of evidence that all antidepressants are about equally efficacious. Many psychotherapists are similarly convinced of the efficacy of their brand of psychotherapy, based on a handful of dramatic cures. The point behind all these examples is that one dramatic example is likely to speak louder than a large number of unremarkable examples.

We are also quite likely to draw exactly the wrong lessons from experience, based on this preference for dramatic examples and stereotypes rather than a balanced view of the overall picture. Kahneman and Tversky provide a good example of a flying school and flight instructor. If the instructor praises a particularly good landing, what is the likely outcome going to be? Well in the nature of things, exceptionally good performances are followed by performances that are not so good. Both instructor and pupils may draw from this the lesson that praise for good performances is a bad idea. Equally both may be readily convinced of the usefulness of bawling out poor performances.

In both cases such instinctive responses would be wrong, as all that is happening is that by the law of averages two exceptional performances are unlikely to succeed each other. Failure to take this into account may lead to beliefs that the human condition is such that you will get the best out of people by being hard on them or that rewarding people for good performances will lead to disappointment. This line of thinking can get even more destructive if you begin to speculate on their motives for disappointing you.

Bias of availability

Another bias stems from the availability of pertinent examples in our own experience. In general, we appear to estimate the frequency of particular events or conditions by the ease with which examples come to mind. Thus if one comes from a family in which there have been a number of people treated for heart attacks or mental illnesses, one is likely to overestimate the risk to oneself of having a heart attack or becoming mentally ill, as well as the incidence of these conditions in the population at large. We all tend to think that common things in our own experience are common generally. This kind of thinking can be seen in the case of a depressed person, who has a number of relatives that committed suicide. The expectation that the current sufferer will go the same way may be overwhelming on the part of both the subject and surviving relatives. This expectation may, in a real sense, be self-fulfilling.

In the case of our health, it is current levels of performance that are most readily available and most likely to influence us. For someone who is depressed, current poor performances typically outweigh the evidence of a lifetime of solid achievement. In manic states present levels of energy and drive are often expected to last forever, despite the evidence that several weeks previously it may have been hard to get out of bed. In schizophrenic states current bizarre experiences are likely to lead to the conclusion that the world is a dark and shady place despite all previous assessments to the contrary. However, it is not just the depressed, manic or schizophrenic person who makes this mistake. All too often those who are involved in the care of depressed subjects are misled by the patient saying that their marriage is terrible. For the patient, this judgement comes from the current strains being experienced, but one would imagine that therapists would be able to stand back and assess the overall picture. Unfortunately, faced with one strained interview involving both partners, they all too readily seem to take that as indicative of the entire marriage.

Drawing conclusions about themselves, their relationships and life that are influenced heavily by current problems, schizophrenic, depressed or manic subjects often arrive at answers that are inconsistent with their past. When this happens, the original assessment of the past is often revised. Thus what formerly would have been described as a happy or unremarkable childhood becomes an unhappy one. An average marriage, in retrospect, seems flawed from the start. This is termed retrospective falsification. But far from being the point at which insanity enters into the picture, such rewriting of the past is consistent with good scientific practice. If a new view becomes dominant all the evidence that it explains suddenly gets noticed. Equally, awkward pieces of evidence not easily reconciled with the dominant view, somehow seem to slip out of sight.

This rewriting of history is based on the need to maintain consistency. Whatever happened in the past, there is no doubt about current poor performances. The past, therefore, must also have been less adequate than one might have thought. On reviewing it, both patients and therapists all too easily find it possible to come up with evidence that can be used to support the new version of history.

While this may be regrettable and is unrealistic in the sense of not being probable, it is not insane. Plausible stories are created, and plausible stories rather than scientific accuracy are all that most of us need to get by. However, thinking this way and spinning stories that are at least as consistent with the evidence as the myths that keep most of us going, is not allowed the mentally ill. Thinking this way, we will argue, is precisely what leads to a diagnosis of insanity.

Illness behaviour

These heuristic biases apply to situations where we are called upon to make judgements when in possession of an incomplete set of facts. Falling ill is such a situation. In the case of the regularly occurring minor aches and pains, the thousand natural shocks that flesh is heir to, we may not heed too much if they occurred before and proved to be inconsequential. Even so if we can explain them we will.

This need of ours to get a grip on uncertainty shows up clearly in drug trials that involve placebos. It is the common experience of many researchers involved in such trials that a number of patients have to be withdrawn from research projects because of severe side-effects. Both patient and researcher may be convinced that the new drug is responsible for the effects reported. However, when the double-blind coding is cracked, it frequently turns out that the patient was on a placebo. What is happening? A simple explanation would be that during the period on the placebo, some unusual physical sensations, discomforts or changes would have occurred. These, or similar anomalies, may have been suffered or endured in the past or they may have led to an appointment with the doctor and by the time of the appointment may have cleared up. However, in the new situation of trying out an unknown compound, the obvious temptation is to leap to the conclusion that this must account for what would be otherwise inexplicable.

The concept of illness behaviour was recently developed by David Mechanic to account for just such experiences.[3] A typical population for which it was described were medical students. An averagely rational group. It seems, however, that medical students become more hypochondriac than the average, when they start doing pathology. This is the subject that exposes them for the first time to illnesses and their symptoms. At this time they usually also start seeing real patients and illnesses such as multiple sclerosis. What is happening? Like any other group it can be hypothesized that they have aches and pains. But unlike others they have a fund of recently acquired dramatic stereotypes to choose from, when faced with the need to determine the significance of what is happening to them. They develop 'illnesses'. Multiple sclerosis is particularly common. It has the advantage of frequently presenting with a seeming innocuous ache or pain or episode of blurred vision. The consequences of these innocuous presentations, however, are dramatically horrifying.

While illness behaviour can occur in the absence of an illness, as the multiple sclerosis example indicates, it is particularly likely if there is some real but vague or indeterminate disturbance. In the case of broken legs or heart attacks, it is usually clear what is happening. Thereafter there are only a limited number of rational responses. But the opposite is true in less clearcut cases. The less clear cut the case the more the scope for, or *necessity* for, individual ingenuity to come up with the rational answer to what is happening. Rational here implies the answer that best squares with the facts, or to which the facts can be squared.

A range of behaviours may cluster around an illness. In contrast to the illness behaviour that can exist in the absence of an illness, there is also the illness behaviour that consists of an inappropriate lack of illness behaviour. Some subjects on being informed that they are ill, respond with a complete denial of the illness and its implications. Other behaviours may involve catastrophic reactions or frankly hysterical reactions. While we have suggested that illness behaviours are most likely to be unduly prominent parts of the clinical picture in cases where the core disturbance is vague and indeterminate, brief episodes of 'lunacy' can also occur in clearcut illnesses such as broken legs.[4] As Dennis Potter remarked in *The Singing Detective* 'when you lose your health, the entire medical profession takes it as axiomatic that you have also lost your mind'.

In all these cases, however, nothing need be presumed wrong with the brains of subjects behaving oddly. These reactions are the normal reactions of subjects with a physical illness and an uncertain future. They also occur in subjects with brain illnesses, such as Parkinson's disease or brain tumours. This being the case they can also be expected to happen in the case of the affective disorders and schizophrenia, especially if these illnesses, as we have been arguing, have a physical core. This means that these illnesses should, on inspection, show signs of brain dysfunction and signs of normal psychological reactions. However as both brain dysfunction and psychological reactions give rise to altered behaviour, the disentangling of illness behaviours from illnesses in these cases can be expected to be more complicated than in other branches of medicine. Even something such as the response to pills will not help us tease these elements apart in any foolproof way, as both sets of behaviour can be expected to clear up if the pills cure the core disturbance.

Fundamental attributional error
I will argue that the greater part of the affective disorders and schizophrenia involve illness behaviours, clustering around a core neuropsych-

ological disturbance. But there is one further bias that is particularly likely in the case of these illnesses, that makes their illness behaviours quite different to those of other illnesses. This stems from what has been called the fundamental attributional error. I touched on this when I distinguished between reasons and causes in Chapter 4. It involves attributing to persons and their dispositions what is better explained by situational factors. That is when trying to work out what has happened or why it has happened, we are more likely to think that the people involved in a situation influenced the outcome more than any character-istics of the situation. We look for the reasons rather than the causes.

Experiments such as the following indicate what is involved. A group of persons may be split up into three; questioners, answerers and observers. The task of the questioners is to think up general knowledge questions for the answerers to answer. The task for the observers is to rate the levels of intelligence or general knowledge held by the ques-tioners and the answerers. What is surprising about these experiments is that both observers and answerers end up rating the questioners as extremely intelligent and widely versed in general knowledge. Even though both groups know that the questioners have had the advantage of making up whatever questions they liked. The answerers in particular end up rating themselves as of less than average intelligence and general knowledge.

Situations like this are similar to therapist–patient interviews. The therapist sets the questions and determines what the correct answers are. Inevitably, simply by virtue of training and situation the therapist will know a lot of relevant information that the patient won't know. However, the conclusion drawn by both sides, typically, is that there is something more than situational factors involved. That the therapist is dispositionally superior to the patient. That they are more psychologi-cally integrated than the patient and less liable to human failings.

This, rather than the mysterious action from a distance exerted by a buried Oedipal complex, can explain why patients tend to fall in love with their therapist. Particularly if they are of the opposite sex. In actual fact, both patient and therapist are making the commonest mistake of normal thinking, attributing to personal qualities in each, what is much better explained as a function of the situation in which two people find themselves. A similar dynamic comes into play when the therapist then goes to visit a lawyer or bank manager, except that the roles are reversed. However, Oedipal complexes are rarely invoked to account for the interpersonal dynamics occurring in such situations.

Why make such attributional errors? The answer is that common sense biases us this way. We are all necessarily on the look out for trouble. If there are no earthquakes, volcanoes, plagues or wars happening or threatened, experience has taught us that the most likely source of trouble is other people or ourselves. If the external situation looks stable and if we are not physically sick, but nevertheless things are not going right we look for the person responsible. This is a good bet. It is common sense. However, we appear to credit others with too much trouble-making potential, to the neglect of the intrinsic difficulties of situations. For example, we routinely attribute social messes to the evil machinations of politicians rather than to the technical difficulties of organizing and catering for millions of people. The definitive example of this bias lies in the shooting of messengers who bring bad news.

When applied in error this bias can lead to the conjuring up of the truly bizarre from the ordinary and everyday. Paul Barber, in a recent study of vampire mythology, gives many detailed examples of this.[5] It would seem that myths such as the vampire myth arose around episodes of plagues. The death of one individual followed by the deaths of others commonly has led to the suspicion that the first death was only apparent. That the undead has returned to claim victims. Exhumation often appears to confirm this, as the initial stages of decomposition of a corpse often make it look more unnaturally alive than it was at the point of death. Thereafter all happenings in a vampire-infested community will be grist to the mill.

Something very similar, I will argue, happens in the mental illnesses, especially schizophrenia. All too often in these conditions the appearances of the exhumed corpse are consistent with the bizarre hypothesis of the affected individual. An additional point worth making is that seeing vampires as a myth is not the achievement of heroic or super-rational individuals. It is rather a cultural achievement. In Chapter 7, it will be argued that a similar cultural effort will be required to lay to rest the ghost of mental illness.

DYNAMICS OF DEPRESSION, MANIA AND SCHIZOPHRENIA[6-9]

Take a person who wakes one morning with slightly blurred eyesight. He or she is likely to be alarmed. Calming down, the subject may get up and see if things clear up after getting dressed. He or she may inspect their eyes, possible causes of the problem will probably be reviewed.

Am I on pills? Did I drink too much last night? Have I a fever? A headache? Has this ever happened before? If so how long did it take to clear up then? Do I know anyone else who has had something similar? Didn't Daphne's multiple sclerosis start this way or Bob's brain tumour? Depending on answers to such questions, and whether or not the condition shows signs of clearing up, the subject may decide to visit the GP.

Imagine now if the GP says they can find nothing wrong. This may or may not be reassuring. This will depend on whether the patient is convinced that their eyesight is blurred or not and how concerned he or she is about it. Sooner or later if it remains blurred, our subject is likely to revisit the GP and, if nothing else is suggested, will raise the possibility of referral to an ophthalmic department. Suppose at the clinic our subject is investigated with a number of very large, expensive looking and obviously sophisticated machines and given an appointment for a few days later. Suppose on return he or she is informed that the good news is that there is nothing wrong ... A lot depends from here on our subject's presence of mind and the sensitivity of the clinician.

Our subject may be convinced that their eyesight is still blurred and that something is wrong. He or she may conclude that the doctors also know what is wrong but are trying to spare him/her the difficult news. Another possibility is that he or she may come to doubt their own belief that their eyesight is not what it was. This is particularly likely to be the case if the degree of impairment is relatively minor and can on occasion be ignored. On the other hand, even a minor degree of abnormality may come to be almost blindness depending on how much the subject becomes preoccupied with it. A further option that might be raised by the clinician, or may have already occurred to the patient, is that seeing as there is nothing wrong with the eyes, is there any other strain in the patient's life? Something going wrong at work? With your spouse? Trouble with the children? Would you care to see a psychiatrist? What will the psychiatrist do about it? Well the psychiatrist will start by confronting our subject with the evidence that nothing is obviously wrong. A thorough physical examination proves this conclusively ...

Now suppose that after much time, expense and psychiatric treatment, aimed at working out why you mistakenly think you have a physical problem, it turned out that there had been something physically wrong all along. That there had been a misprint on some test printout. Or that the disorder in question lay outside the experience of the doctors consulted. If this impugning of your sanity, this creation of mental problems, has left you angry, then consider the position of patients with affective disorders or schizophrenia.

Despite all the evidence from clinical features and response to medication that these are physical illnesses, the treatment of affected subjects proceeds as though the physical disorder was imaginary. The spotlight is thrown back on the complaining person, as thorough physical examinations prove that there is nothing wrong. The fact that physical treatments work is convenient, but in practical terms, when it comes to deciding whether the patient has a physical or a mental illness it is an ignored detail. The fact that a patient's complaints are predominantly physical, loss of energy, poor sleep, aches and pains has little impact. These complaints are usually explained away as 'somatization', a supposedly unfortunate recourse of the psychologically unsophisticated who cannot handle their emotions. This is an indication of how the dynamics of the clinical situation evolve, as opposed to the supposed dynamics of the illness.

Depression

It is known that almost all depressed subjects are aware of multiple physical changes. Among these are an increased frequency of aches and pains, pins and needles or other strange sensations throughout their body, gastric discomfort, dry mouth, skin and hair. In addition they have disturbances of their appetite and sleep, as well as a general flu-like malaise including loss of energy and interest. These, we argued in the last chapter, could as well be of physical as of 'psychological' origin.

If the depressed subject is convinced he or she has physical illness and persuades the GP that this is the case, then if the condition does not clear up with some tonic or iron, or without intervention, in the few weeks that may elapse between consultations, it is quite possible that he or she will end up being investigated for every possible physical illness known to modern medicine. Multiple blood tests and X-rays, various different procedures and interviews by several different doctors would have been carried out by the time they come to a psychiatrist. During this time the subject may steadily lose weight, as depression causes anorexia. He or she may become privately convinced that they have a carcinoma and that everyone is conspiring to keep silent about it. (Indeed, given the typical handling of carcinoma cases, they have grounds for such suspicions.)

If not cancer, our subject may associate the symptoms with some other physical illness that can cause chronic physical debility without dramatic outer stigmata. Syphilis has been a favourite hidden fear. AIDS may replace it. Myalgic encephalomyelitis (ME) is currently the most popular refuge of patients who rightly refuse to give up the idea of a physical basis to their condition. In between visits to the hospital, patients will typically read any material they find that seems any way pertinent to their case, whether gathered on purpose or just happened upon by accident.

As sure as not something will come to hand about carcinoma or syphilis that bears out their inner fears. Syphilis, if passed on to children can cause deformity of the teeth; 'I always wondered why Anna's teeth were so poor'. Occult carcinomas can be very difficult to detect and weight loss for no obvious reason may be the best indicator of their presence; 'Why can't my doctor see this?' As well as accidents hinting at possible diagnoses, the vagueness of the clinical picture can feed into deep-seated personal fears. Thus loss of libido may play into a long standing worry about homosexual or lesbian tendencies. Or impairments of concentration and memory may re-awaken fears of dementia kindled initially by having a relative who became demented.

All psychiatrists have had the experience of being confronted with such cases. They are common ways for a depression to present. There would appear to be three possible responses. One is the possibility, that follows if one sees depression as a physical illness, of confirming the presence of a physical illness for the patient. This idea will be developed later when it will also be suggested that this is most likely to persuade the patient that they are understood. A second is to respond to the patient in terms that acknowledge that they have an illness that is not really real but is real for them. This is currently the commonest psychiatric response. The third possibility is to take a patient's often wild personal diagnoses as good evidence of some mental problem. But as regards the irrationality, or dynamics of what is happening, the patients in these cases are simply applying normal rationality to an abnormal experience. Our diagnosis of irrationality on their part stems from a failure to recognize the abnormal experience.

Given a state of affairs that must be explained for the sake of their sanity, the patient has simply set about trying to find answers in the same way as we all set about trying to find answers to countless similar problems. They rely on experts but when experts fail, or fail to convince, they look elsewhere. They draw possible hypotheses from anecdotes exchanged with friends, horror stories heard on television or radio, or read in newspapers by chance, or gathered deliberately. The example of someone who suspects that there is something embarrassingly wrong with them can make very good situation comedy. But the relevant point is that we all, in laughing, recognize how easy it is to twist everything to support quite implausible hypotheses. How easy it was for Othello to bring destruction upon himself.

The medical profession labels these behaviours as neurotic. But even without the help of the medical profession, who are especially skilled at generating neuroses where none existed before, depression is an illness liable to lead to subjects diagnosing themselves as mentally unbalanced. This is because the core experience appears to be of a mild flu-like or jet-lagged type of state, lacking clearcut physical stigmata. So lacking in clearcut stigmata that many subjects, and most therapists, miss the physical illness completely. Especially as the subtle disturbance affects one of our blind spots, our brain.

Even if at first convinced that there was something physically wrong with them, in the absence of supporting evidence many subjects will come round to blaming themselves. This after all is a diagnosis that accounts for a good deal of the data. People who mope around the place and complain all the time without having anything much wrong with them are useless, worthless people (representativeness bias). That is what I am doing therefore I must be useless and worthless. In such instances the immediate evidence, even though it be only of several weeks, will take precedence over the evidence of a lifetime (availability bias).

Seeing oneself as useless and worthless is in turn demoralizing. Blaming oneself rather than one's brain inevitably leads to hopelessness and guilt. Therefore, on top of an initial flu-like lack of energy, slowing of mental functions and feeling 'not right', a secondary demoralization results from judgements that this has all stemmed from the kind of person one is. This leads to negative thoughts and general misery. Indeed these latter features are quite likely to dominate the clinical picture. For example, being demoralized by seeing oneself as worthless is quite likely to lead to a much more dramatic loss of energy than the initial loss caused by the underlying depression. This latter loss of energy is not *caused* but happens for the very good *reason* that having energy seems to be pointless.

In general illness behaviours are likely to amplify the original disturbance. The extreme instance of this in depression is suicide. Brain dysfunction cannot lead to suicide, but coming to the conclusion that one is a worthless wretch can, whether or not one is depressed.

If religiously inclined, it is common to find subjects wondering whether the Lord is not punishing them for some past transgression, whether it be an affair, an abortion, a minor transgression of the law or otherwise. Such a person may become quite convinced that the evidence points to just such a conclusion. They may be well able to quote scriptural references or other indicators to the validity of their belief, while at the same time not having any major crime in their past that would warrant the degree of sorrow and distress they feel. In such cases what appears to happen is that a subject trawls through their past life for evidence that would be consistent with their hypothesis. Naturally they find it, as all of us have at least some minor transgressions or occasions of shame in our past. Alternatively, demoralization may be interpreted as abandonment or spiritual desolation leading to states of mental agony, dark nights of the soul.

If one's own disposition is not the problem, there is always the disposition of others. If it is not something you have done wrong, could it be something they have done wrong or something they are doing to you? Could they be conspiring to harm you? Does everyone know what is happening except you? Such thoughts go through the mind of some depressed people at least episodically. They may issue in particular ideas. For example you are performing poorly or are off colour because drugs are being put in your food or someone hates you and is trying to harm you.

One other disposition, in particular, bears scrutiny: that of one's partner. Rather than blame oneself, an alternative is to blame one's marriage or current relationship. After all books, dramas and innumerable psychology tracts testify to the fact that relationships are more often than not stultifying. What is this inability to articulate what is wrong other than a failure to be honest about the current state of the relationship? Such suspicions may be fuelled if one partner becomes impatient with a state of affairs, where the other is unable to keep up their end of things, despite having nothing obviously wrong with them. These mutual suspicions may fuel an escalating process of recriminations, rising strain and hatred.

Rather than reverse this cycle the attentions of others, even of therapists, may aggravate it. By the time the depressed subject comes to a psychiatric clinic, it may seem obvious to whoever they attend that the relationship is the source of the troubles. Not unnaturally, the partner who is well may refuse to have anything to do with any therapy that implies they are equally (if not entirely) to blame for what is happening. A refusal that confirms the therapist in their hunch and happily absolves them from any failure to right the problem.

Mania

All of the above points made regarding depression are even more likely to apply in the case of mania. Unlike depression, manic illness gives an increase in physical energy and drive. This causes problems on two fronts. One stems from the bias that we normally expect illnesses to cause loss of function and are quite unaccustomed to the idea of them causing excesses of function.[10] Another arises from the fact that, like depression, the basic disturbance in mania is subtle rather than gross (Chapter 6). The kind of increased energy we all occasionally experience during a morning that follows staying up all night or that sometimes can occur after jet travel.

Given, therefore, that someone with mania is even less likely than a depressed subject to make the correct situational attribution regarding their illness, how are they likely to account for increased vitality? Almost the only attribution open to them is in terms of personal qualities. Again as in depression the evidence of a lifetime is liable to be ignored in favour of the facts of several weeks of optimal or super-optimal functioning. The conclusion to be drawn from such functioning will be that the subject is a marvellous person. Seeing oneself as marvellous will in turn generate more energy. And as further projects are conceived and are relatively successfully executed, the evidence that one is marvellous grows. A variant on this belief in one's personal qualities is to believe that one has been chosen for some purpose whether religious or social. The investment of energy into a particular cause is more than likely to yield initial results, thereby further fuelling enthusiasm and the feeling one has indeed found one's vocation.

Such beliefs are likely to lead to a joie de vivre, which will amplify the original increase in energy. A joie de vivre that one has good *reason* for, as life is not as much hard work as it had been before and living has a purpose. It is not caused or forced emotion. In support of this interpretation of the origins of manic elation is the fact that joie de vivre or elation is not a constant feature of mania (and is not found at all in many manic subjects) whereas overactivity is. In many cases the subject is overactive, but irritable and restless rather than elated – something that arguably should not happen if elation was something that stemmed directly from a fevered brain.

Failure to recognize the abnormal experience of an involuntary increase in energy at the heart of mania is not confined to the affected subject. It characteristically also leads to observers labelling the behaviour of a manic patient as disinhibited, grandiose or unrealistic. But in such cases the observers are typically making the same attributional error as the patient and attributing to dispositions what should be interpreted in situational terms. And just as repentant sinners have always been more socially acceptable than prophets, manic subjects are likely to attract a diagnosis of irrationality whereas a comparable mental set in depression does not as readily do so. An accusation of irrationality or insanity would only feed into the current running through the mind of a depressed subject. But those who are elated have usually never felt more rational in their entire lives.

Accordingly, a collision course is set up which frequently ends in the most distressing scenes in psychiatric practice. All too often the outcome is one where subjects are dragged out of their houses to waiting ambulances, protesting their innocence as they go. They leave behind them examining psychiatrists who are all too aware that they were less than convincing in their attempts to persuade the patient that they were irrational and should accept admission voluntarily.

Schizophrenia

In the cases of mania and depression, there are subtle disturbances of basal energy levels that can be plausibly explained in terms of an enhancement or fall off in personal functioning. This is not the case for schizophrenia, where the experience of the subject is at times unusual (to the extent of objects changing size or luminance in front of one's very eyes). There are also feelings of loss of control of thinking and feeling and a sense of not properly inhabiting one's own body. No simple interpretation in terms of moral value or personal functioning will account for all of this.

Accordingly, if the affected subject is normally rational, as the experience involved is often one in which the world seems decidedly abnormal, they are likely to focus on the possibility of malevolent environmental influences. If any ideas of this nature slip out, subjects are liable to be told that the world hasn't changed; that it is as normal as ever. But what is normal? The so-called normal world has always been a dark and dangerous place as various cultural, mythic and folklore materials illustrate. Could it be that these are truer than once thought? Alternatively, genes really are being engineered, viruses are being created in laboratories, minds are being shaped and controlled by the media, poisons are being put in the drinking water and international conspiracies do take place. This way craziness lies.

In all these cases the supposed malevolent environmental influences are liable to be personalized – fundamental attributional error. They are also liable to be coloured by current social concerns – availability bias. Thus, individuals from Western cultures are likely to be worried about manufactured germs and lasers, whereas individuals from less technologically developed societies have until recently focused on witchdoctors or voodoo-type explanations. Representativeness bias will lead to the subject becoming 'mad' as, once diagnosed as mad, the weight of cultural expectations for madmen will bear down on them and affect their behaviour accordingly. As the hallmark of the mad has traditionally been the possession of delusional beliefs, the issue of delusions will be of particular relevance to schizophrenia.

DELUSIONS

The main themes and ambiguities of this and previous chapters converge on the question of delusions. Traditionally, they have been the hallmark of insanity, the prototypical clinical feature of the psychoses. In line with the earliest ambiguous meanings of that term, delusions were seen as affections of the soul or psyche rather than of the brain. However, as we noted in Chapter 2, the psychoses are now seen as brain illnesses rather than disturbances of the soul. As delusions are the characteristic feature of a psychosis, does this mean that they result directly from brain malfunctioning? On this hinges the whole issue of the nature of mental illnesses and the appropriate way to treat sufferers from these disorders. If delusions either reflect a profound defect of judgement or stem uncontrollably from brain disturbances, then notions of psychiatric patients being empirical investigators of their own condition would be seriously compromised.

For the depth psychologies, delusions were extreme instances of a neurosis. A complete rather than partial break with reality. The best known medical psychopathologists before Jaspers, so hostile to analysis on other fronts, in essence agreed on this point. Kraepelin classified delusions among the psychological elements of the clinical picture. In addition, he saw paranoia, a disorder that consists solely of delusions without any other clinical features, as being a functional psychosis but not as being an illness, as it lacked obvious features of cerebral dysfunction. Paranoia for Kraepelin was something that stemmed from instabilities in the personality of the affected subject. Bleuler saw the delusions of schizophrenia as a psychological overlay to the underlying illness. On some occasions he seems to have seen them as extreme reactions to an underlying abnormality, on others as psychological complexes let slip out by an abnormally functioning brain. In neither case were they the direct result of abnormal functioning. Even Schneider saw the majority of delusions as part of the psychological superstructure of schizophrenia, rather than something that stemmed from cerebral dysfunction.

Today, in marked contrast, delusions are typically seen as stemming from abnormal brain function. As being almost as organic as loss of power or increased reflexes. Few psychiatrists would ever stop to consider handling delusions psychologically. The principal factor cited in support of such attitudes is the common response of delusions to neuroleptic medication. But before neuroleptics were introduced into psychiatric treatment, Jaspers had argued for delusions being disorders of form rather than of content.

The issue of whether delusions involve a disorder of content or of form brings us to the heart of darkness in psychopathology. At the start of Chapter 4, it was noted that strange behaviour may reflect a disorder of content or a disorder of form. Thus the sudden jerking upwards of an arm may represent an act with a meaningful content (anger) or it may be a meaningless tic, as can occur with some brain illnesses. But what exactly is the meaning of the term a disorder of psychiatric form? If the reader has difficulty getting this straight in their mind, then do not despair because this is as it should be. The term is used as the symbol x is used in algebraic equations. x is the unknown, which will have a concrete specification once the equation has been worked out. It will never be used again once we know that $x = ab^2$ or whatever. The options for x if delusions are disorders of form rather than of content are that $x =$ a neuropsychological disturbance or $x =$ something else. If delusions are disorders of content, then $x =$ a form of illness behaviour/neurosis or $x =$ some form of inauthenticity.

Jaspers and delusions

Jaspers defined delusions as intensely held beliefs, usually of eccentric quality, not open to rational testing. This is now the commonly cited definition given in psychiatric textbooks. But there are serious problems with this definition. Jaspers recognized these but many others since appear not to have. He conceded that normal people make errors, that logical argument does not necessarily persuade them of their errors and that the incorrigibility of delusional beliefs cannot be shown to differ from the incorrigibility of true insight. Given therefore that Jaspers' definition could apply to many of the cherished beliefs that each of us hold, he was left with the problem of trying to indicate where delusional beliefs differed from other beliefs. What made them the disorders of form rather than content that he held them to be?

One line of thinking he took was that a necessary prior requirement of delusions was a supposed fundamental alteration in the personality of the subject. An alteration, he held, that resisted interpretation. It was this resistance to interpretation that made delusions a disorder of form rather than of content. In addition to this vague criterion, he introduced a criterion of departure from the legitimate pool of cultural beliefs to distinguish delusional from other strongly held beliefs. That is strongly held beliefs not open to rational testing are only delusions if no one else holds them. Similarly, strange beliefs, if held by a number of people, are just bizarre and eccentric beliefs and not evidence of mental illness. This proviso is necessary or else beliefs such as a belief in apartheid or beliefs that are politically deviant could be taken as evidence of mental illness.

Since its formulation Jaspers' definition has been unsatisfactory. This or variants of it have given grounds to many to criticize psychiatric practice in terms of thought police and thought control. Such criticisms follow as the criteria that demarcate delusional from other beliefs are so imprecise that views which differ substantially from the therapist's or views held by people the therapist does not like or feel sympathy for, are open to being labelled delusional. If all that were involved here was simply labelling some patients neurotic, there would be little problem. But as diagnosing the presence of delusions brands the patient as psychotic, and is liable to lead to loss of civil liberties, the issue is more serious. Especially as there is no effective appeal procedure against the diagnosis.

Unlike Jaspers, Schneider clearly stated that most delusions were essentially secondary psychological reactions to underlying abnormalities. However he held that some delusions were primary phenomena. They arose in a non-understandable manner and thus were disorders of form. This distinction between primary and secondary delusions has come under attack, even by some of his colleagues. Matussek has argued that some of the experiences in schizophrenia are so unusual that they cannot easily be expressed other than as delusions. For example, if someone feels controlled by a television newscaster, they are almost certain to express this as a belief that they are being controlled. It would be very difficult to achieve the position of being able to say 'It feels like I am being controlled but I know I am not.' It should be noted, however, that except for primary delusions Schneider saw his first rank symptoms of schizophrenia, such as claims that there are alien thoughts or feelings in one's head, as unusual experiences rather than as delusions.

The modern argument in favour of delusions being disorders of form (organic in origin) is based on their response to neuroleptic medication. Several days or weeks on haloperidol or chlorpromazine in many cases leads to subjects appearing to lose the delusional beliefs that led to their admission to hospital. However, far from proving the point, the response of delusions to neuroleptics can equally be taken to indicate the opposite. The target symptoms of neuroleptics are tension and agitation (Chapter 6). They reduce tension and agitation in subjects who are not deluded as well as in subjects who are. When given to healthy volunteers, they produce a 'who cares' feeling, a feeling of indifference. Therefore, they could be expected to make delusional beliefs less likely, if agitated states of mind rather than agitated brain states are the seedbeds of delusional ideas.

It would be possible to sustain the notion that neuroleptics cure delusions by a direct action on some organic substrate if they had no behavioural effects on volunteers. But as they do have clear effects, this position becomes difficult to maintain. Also awkward is the fact that states dominated by delusions without acute agitation, such as paranoia, show little or no response to neuroleptics. Another problem is that many chronic psychiatric patients remain permanently deluded despite large amounts of neuroleptic medication. However, while these drugs may not reverse their delusions and are later reduced in amount, they can still be used effectively to curb agitation when such patients become agitated.

Depressive, manic and schizophrenic delusions

If delusions are disorders of form, that is as devoid of true content as a tic or an automatism, we should expect them to cut across the comprehensibility of the clinical presentation. If disorders of content, they should show a line of development from the underlying illness.

In the case of depression, the delusions found are generally continuous with the illness behaviours characteristic of this disorder. For example, we have noted that possible hypotheses regarding the origin of the abnormal experience that is depression include ideas of physical illness. Very often a subject goes on to believe that they have cancer or syphilis. One of the features of these beliefs is that it may be extraordinarily difficult to persuade the subject that they are incorrect. It is not uncommon to be faced with a celibate, aged patient who claims to have venereal disease. They will commonly be almost impervious to argument or even to demonstration by blood test.

The other delusions found in depression are equally consistent with the nature of the underlying experience. For instance, there are nihilistic delusions which consist of beliefs that one is already dead or already damned. Or delusions of guilt that something one has done in the past, usually quite minor compared to the degree of distress now being experienced, is responsible for the present state of affairs. An alternative delusion of guilt may be the belief that one is responsible for everything that has gone wrong for one's family, friends or even everything going wrong worldwide. In extreme cases, some people go on to believe themselves to be leprous or pariahs, who should be shunned by others for fear of contaminating them. Paranoid delusions that others are persecuting you or plotting against you, or that one's spouse is being unfaithful, are also found.

As can be seen from the depressive delusions, these are more or less logically derivable from the underlying experience of the subject, shaped perhaps by the other circumstances of their lives. In contrast to depressive delusions, manic subjects get delusions of grandeur or of supernatural assistance. Or they may see clearly what the problems of the world are, whether they be conspiracies or otherwise, and what needs to be done to solve them. Alternatively, they may be quite paranoid and believe that they are being persecuted. This latter set of delusions is not inconsistent with an underlying mania. It appears that mania is best characterized as a state of overactivity or increased energy rather than one of euphoria. In many cases this increase in energy is somewhat uncomfortable. Much as the surge in energy after a sleepless night or in some cases of jet lag may be uncomfortable. Accordingly, it is not surprising that some subjects' interpretation of what is happening to them will lead to a restless irritability rather than to elation. And it is from irritability that delusions of persecution seem to come.

Schizophrenia is somewhat more complex in that many people see the experiences that are central to the first rank symptoms as being delusions. As noted above this is understandable as experiences such as feelings controlled by the environment or not feeling at home in one's own body will almost inevitably be expressed in terms of odd beliefs. Particularly when these experiences become personalized in accordance with the fundamental attributional error. Such delusions, however, will be highly continuous with the underlying experiences.

However, such experiences can also be expected to shatter many basic assumptions about the world. One of the more remarkable things about sufferers from schizophrenia is that so many appear able to rebuild a relatively normal world after such bizarre experiences. A minority do not. They remain deluded indefinitely.

In these cases the delusions take on a life of their own, after the initial provoking experiences have subsided. In due course they will become embroidered and embellished, and continuity with the original core disturbance may be lost. Some subjects will have a single set of delusions, such as tracing all their problems to the anarchists or the South African police. These beliefs will be dramatically elaborated. Others will have multiple, tenuously related or unrelated delusions, many of which will be quite fantastic – such as beliefs that there are little green Martians wandering around, hopping in and out of people's bodies and generally interfering with the workings of things.

A number of things have to be borne in mind when considering the issue of chronic delusions. As we have mentioned the stereotype of the madman is he who is deluded. By virtue of this the capacity to be normally strange or eccentric will be taken away from those who have been labelled psychotic. Any utterance out of the ordinary on their part is likely to lead to others wondering whether they are becoming ill again, or lead to their conversation being increasingly dismissed as inconsequential. Similarly, subjects who feel themselves decompensating and who seek professional assistance will know that the easiest way to obtain this is to appear as deluded. This is particularly the case for longstay inpatients, who almost of necessity must remain deluded in order to stay in hospital. It is not uncommon for such patients to be 'deluded' only when being interviewed by members of staff.

In general, therefore, the delusions found in depression, mania and schizophrenia are consistent with the core disturbances found in each of these disorders and can be seen as exaggerated illness behaviour. So much is this the case that given the delusions a subject has, without any of the other clinical features, a psychiatrist will typically be able to make a diagnosis. In chronic cases, the delusions can also be seen as examples of illness behaviours, even though in these cases the core disturbance has cleared up. In both acute and chronic states, the elaboration of delusional beliefs seems influenced by the heuristic biases outlined earlier. This should not be the case if delusions sprang directly from a cerebral malfunction.

Delusions: psychotic or neurotic?

Arguing that delusions are an exaggerated form of illness behaviour implies that they are essentially psychological reactions. That they stem from fevered psyches rather than from fevered brains or fevered minds. Does this not make them neurotic features of the clinical picture rather than the quintessential features of a psychosis? Arguably it does.

That such beliefs are extreme is unquestionable. But what is commonly neglected in such situations is that depressed, manic or schizophrenic subjects have a real fall off in their level of performance that *must* be explained. The seeming lack of evidence for these extreme beliefs can be taken as supporting an origin in either a fevered psyche or a fevered brain. This claim follows from recent experimental results in dynamic psychology which suggest that some of the most vehemently held beliefs of normal people get erected on the flimsiest of evidence and can be *strengthened* rather than abolished by disconfirmation.[11]

The reader doesn't need to read the latest psychology journals to appreciate what is involved. An analogy with gamblers will suffice. The gambler who has money on the table, must come up with a strategy for winning. It appears to be a classic feature of human behaviour that in such situations we develop hunches often based on minimal evidence. Repeated disconfirmation may not lead us to revise our opinion. However, subjects who behave quite 'insanely' at the roulette table, are usually indistinguishable from the rest of us once they leave it. The apparent clearing up of delusions with physical treatments can, on this basis, be seen as an instance of removing the roulette table rather than providing a treatment which profoundly alters the subject's capacity to be rational.

Furthermore, far from being alien to the reader, some flicker of the thoughts and feelings outlined above for depression, mania and schizophrenia have probably occurred at least briefly to all of us. Usually we lack the necessary stimulus or reason to consider them more seriously. Any hypothesis, no matter how implausible will be entertained by all of us on occasion. Implausible hypotheses get rejected as implausible not because of their inherent irrationality but when the situation begins to follow past experience and we get an inkling of what is wrong and the likely outcome of events. Failing this we would be foolish to reject any hypothesis. In particular, one cannot take it for granted that the world is not dangerous or other people not likely to harm you. Everyday experience confirms the naivety of such assumptions. The experiences of schizophrenia, depression or mania, I am arguing, provide the stimulus to take more seriously possibilities that otherwise would be enter-tained and then discarded.

Despite the example of gamblers and the melting away of apparently unshakeable delusions, once the underlying disorders clear up, delusions are not yet seen as particularly dramatic forms of illness behaviours. The temptation for therapists, whether of psychodynamic or biological orientation, to declare these beliefs as completely irrational and evidence of a break of contact with reality seems irresistible. The patient may also be aware that what they are claiming is eccentric and they may only disclose these hidden fears after a certain amount of trust has built up. They too are quite likely to take their beliefs as evidence of insanity as they often realize the unlikelihood of the thought content but do not recognize its source.

Given the usual definition of a delusion, it may come as some surprise to the reader, that psychiatrists talk about partial delusions. Partial delusions are irrational beliefs that do not have the full measure of conviction found in delusions. As such, given the usual definitions of the word delusions, these partial delusions are impossible entities. How can one have an entity that is both irrational and fixed and yet not fixed? Such states, however, are no problem to the analysis of irration-ality proposed here. Indeed they are required by it. It is quite consistent with this analysis that many subjects attempting to explain an abnormal experience and bringing to the attempt all the illogicality of normal thinking should end up with conclusions that even they find hard to accept. Accordingly, some strange ideas of what is happening are likely to be offered to the questioner, with the qualifying words 'You'll prob-ably think this is crazy but . . .' In the end, however, the necessity to have some explanation that fits a good deal of the facts is likely to push many subjects, dubious of the odd conclusions they have come to, into acceptance of such conclusions.

It may also come as a surprise to learn that clinically it may be impossible to distinguish between a delusion and a phobia.[12] Take the case of a person admitted because they have a complaint about their bowels and wonder if they have a cancer. Repeated negative tests may not set their mind at rest. Have they a delusion or are they cancer-phobic? Similarly, many individuals who present with stories of being persecuted can be readily seen has having a persecution phobia, but they are likely to be diagnosed as being deluded.

Arguably Jaspers' ambiguous definition was forced on him by a failure to appreciate the *inevitable* occurrence of normal irrationality in situations of uncertainty. The discovery of systematic biases in normal rationality make it even less likely that differences from group norms indicate radical personality alterations. No defects of judgement or impairment of the ability to use logic have ever been demonstrated in schizophrenia. Even in subjects who are floridly deluded. Arguably therefore, the fact that the rest of us do not hold the odd beliefs of a schizophrenic can only be explained in terms of the latter's beliefs arising as a result of the biases of normal rationality operating on abnormal experiences. These experiences effectively put the affected subject in a culture of one. Given a similar experience would the rest of us not come to similar conclusions? The answer it would seem from experimental studies, is yes.[13] If so, there need be nothing intrinsically insane or irrational about a deluded person. Nothing more irrational than some communities coming to believe in vampires for instance.

The alternative to delusions being a form of illness behaviour is that they are neuropsychological disturbances or something else. Can they be neuropsychological disturbances? Stimulating the brain by means of electrodes may produce images, affects, memories etc, but it does not produce false beliefs. The fact that I think that there is an international conspiracy to keep quiet about pollutants in the atmosphere, which happen to be causing me ill-health, is a belief. This belief may stem from a vague feeling I have of being physically unwell. But it is neither itself an abnormal experience nor potentially a description of an experience that cannot be expressed in other than delusional terms, such as the even more bizarre statements that alien forces are controlling my will and thoughts might be.

Similarly organic brain disorders may produce isolated perceptual disturbances or memory difficulties but they do not produce delusions in the absence of anything else. Neuropsychologists may be called in to investigate perceptual problems or memory difficulties, in order to determine the area of the brain that is malfunctioning, but they are not called in to deluded subjects, as delusions have never been localized in the way that perception and memory have been. Organic disorders may produce odd beliefs such as simultagnosia that are impervious to reason, but these do not have the quality of delusional beliefs. In addition, they can be clearly shown to be linked to perceptual problems in a way that delusions cannot.

If it is conceded that delusions are not neuropsychological disturbances, but it is nevertheless still maintained that they are disorders of psychiatric form rather than of content, then disorders of psychiatric form cannot be reduced to a set of neuropsychological disturbances. This, it can be suggested was roughly Jaspers' position. A position that straddled the ambiguities we have outlined. He argued that what made delusions a disorder of form was an accompanying change in the personality of the deluded subject. Brain disorders may change personalities. But, in general, it is in the direction of coarsening or disinhibiting them and flattening intellectual range. These features are not typical of deluded subjects.

This issue is important as if disorders of psychiatric form can be something that is neither a neuropsychological disturbance nor an instance of illness behaviour, it would become impossible to pinpoint just what a psychiatric illness is.

Sensitive psychoses

The idea that delusions might be neurotic features of a psychosis is one that is resisted strongly in medical circles. In this regard the fate of the paranoid psychoses is instructive. The term paranoid psychosis is applied to up to one third of the psychoses that present clinically. It is used when the clinical presentation is dominated by delusions and betrays no other clinical features that would indicate whether the illness in question is an affective disorder or schizophrenia. Therefore judgement is suspended until the course of the illness becomes clearer. If it clears up most clinicians will say what has been involved is an atypical affective disorder. If it becomes chronic it will be termed schizophrenia, even though there may never be any first rank symptoms or visible disturbances of thought or affect.

While a good number of these cases almost certainly are affective disorders or schizophrenia, there is an alternative. This alternative has been championed by many investigators at different times under various names; psychogenic psychosis, reactive psychosis, hysterical psychosis, psychoses in a sensitive personality. These terms have slightly different references, but common to all of them is the notion that a psychological shock presented to a vulnerable personality may unhinge them.

For example, a 62-year-old lady came into hospital for an operation on a suspected tumour. She had been an upright hard-working lady all her life and came from a close and respectable middle-class family. She was widowed five years previously and now lived with a sister. She had three children with whom she got on very well. The day after her operation she became very distressed, began talking about being unclean and wishing she were dead. Her agitation grew uncontrollably over the following days. She refused to see her family. Close questioning indicated that she really did believe herself to be unclean and was convinced she was going to be in hell soon. There were no signs to indicate an affective or schizophrenic disorder at the initial interview or at any point during the following weeks before her condition resolved.

Further questioning, however, revealed a hitherto hidden secret. Forty years earlier she lost her first husband during the war.

Two years later an airforce base was located near to where she was living. Many of the women in the area became friendly with the pilots on the base. She went out with several and finally slept once with one. From this encounter she contracted syphilis. When it became clear what she had she was mortified. She had it treated not just once but three times, even though the symptoms had cleared up after the first course of treatment. She told no one of this. Not the man she married after the war. Not her sisters. Not her children. She always dreaded, however, that somehow the secret would get out. Possibly by admission to hospital and revelation through screening tests on her blood. Several days of treatment with neuroleptics and telling her children about the hidden side of their mother, however, cleared up her agitation and delusions and she finally left hospital a happy woman.

Far from this state being an insanity, it in many ways seems to have been very neurotic. This and many other paranoid psychoses can typically be interpreted sensibly. If it is conceded that this lady's condition was neurotic (an illness behaviour) it follows that delusional overlays to affective or schizophrenic disorders could equally be neurotic elements of these latter psychoses. In these cases the underlying cerebral dysfunction experienced by the subject could be seen as the stress that precipitates the neurosis. In support of this position is the general clinical recognition that depression commonly precipitates a neurosis of some sort, whether phobic, obsessional or hysterical or a generalized anxiety disorder.

The neurosis that gets precipitated depends very much on the premorbid personality of the subject. Indeed illnesses may reveal a good deal of the structure of a person's personality. However, personality is not something that medical psychopathology has convincingly come to grips with. This is much more the domain of the depth psychopathologies. But arguably even more the domain of novelists and dramatists. Arthur Miller's recent autobiography *Timebends* contains a particularly rich collection of personality types.[14] What becomes clear from his account is how many people there are who derail. Whose personalities become progressively defined by certain attitudes or values. Who lose the capacity to tolerate ambiguity. It is as though experiences dissolve in personalities. The addition of the wrong experiences or too much of one kind of experience can cause the lot to crystallize out.

Such is paranoia. A state where gradually some dissatisfaction slowly consumes the personality of the subject. Such as the shape of a nose, a hairline, an unjust outcome of a court-case or job interview, a mother's resentment at losing a son to some young girl or an awareness that it is luck rather than lack of ability that has led to one's mediocre life, in contrast to the success thrust upon some of one's contemporaries. These are the stuff that many delusions are made of and that *Timebends* suggests lie just beneath the surface of many lives. In contrast to the abruptly precipitated sensitive psychoses, paranoia takes over an individual insidiously. This often means that their madness may never come to public notice. But like the psychoses of abrupt onset, the roots of this disorder appear to lie deep in the personality affected rather than in any malfunction of their brain.

Suspended revolutions

Why should the idea of a neurotic delusional state be so unpopular? One reason that can be offered is that if it ever were accepted the terms delusion, psychosis and illness would have to be redefined and would part company. Maintaining the link between delusions and psychosis would mean that the link between brain illness and psychosis would be stretched. This was Kraepelin's position. He was happy to have non-illness psychoses. Maintaining the link between psychosis and brain illness means that delusional states that are not clearly linked to an illness, should cause a problem – as they do. As should the idea of a psychosis without delusions. A further almost inevitable development is that delusions, as the hallmarks of brain illnesses, should also be thought to stem from organic disorder.

This confusion has been a legacy of the Jasperian revolution. An understandable one. Often the neuropsychological disturbances at the core of the affective disorders or schizophrenia are so subtle that they cannot easily be detected. Particularly when clinicians are biased against taking the verbal reports of their patients as evidence. In this situation the only 'objective' clinical signs are the illness behaviours that cluster around the underlying disturbance. In the case of the milder illness behaviours, such as the demoralization that goes with depression, it may be very difficult to distinguish these from the range of normal miseries, neuroses or eccentricities. But in the case of delusions, we reach a level of behaviour which is unusual without there being some underlying precipitant.

The difficulty with delusions lies in uncoupling typical association from invariable association. As delusions are typically associated with psychoses and as they have been the defining feature of psychoses from the very start, uncoupling these two terms is not going to be an easy task. It may not even be possible. As noted in Chapter 2, the deliberations of American psychiatry, encoded in DSM III, now define a psychosis solely by the presence of delusions or hallucinations. No mention of neuropsychological disturbances is made at all where the psychoses are concerned.

HALLUCINATIONS

Along with delusions, hallucinations are one of the hallmarks of insanity. What exactly are they? Typically, the definition offered is attributed to Esquirol from 1838. He is quoted as saying that hallucinations are sense perception in the absence of a sensory stimulus. This is then taken to imply that the brain rather than the psyche must be functioning abnormally, when subjects hallucinate. However, this version commonly leaves out an important part of the definition given by Esquirol, which in full states that hallucinations are a *conviction* that sense perception is taking place, despite the absence of a sensory stimulus. If the emphasis is placed on the conviction involved, hallucinations would seem to have more the character of a delusion than anything else. They might therefore occur in subjects with normally functioning brains.

Focusing on the issue of perception, also suggests that hallucinations do not require abnormal brain functioning for their manifestation. As noted in Chapter 1, a lot of perception takes place in the absence of a sensory stimulus. Take dreams, for example. The dreaming subject is not sensing but is perceiving. Perceptions are constructions of the psyche put on sensory data to make sense of them. Perception results in images. The capacity to form images is not limited to the processing of sensory inputs. We all can imagine objects that could never exist or events that could never happen. Furthermore, these images have a life of their own. They can be stored as memories and can reappear in dreams. The distinction between imagination and hallucination essentially depends on the attitude of the subject in according reality to the percepts or not. That is if the subject insists that visions seen in waking dreams are real, they are hallucinating. More commonly, we recognize the unreality and label what is happening as daydreams, fantasizing or overactive imaginations.

It may be argued that imagination operates to yield images inside our heads, while hallucinations refer to perceptions in external space. Surely this is a significant difference? In this regard, we may note that all perception is a gamble. Everyone will be familiar with pictures formed of dots, where the full object is not seen but we fill in the appropriate blank spaces regardless of the absence of a sensory input. This is done on the basis of past experience. We make a guess about what it is that is lying in our field of vision. We may actually see it, even if it is not all there. The completion of several more lines or dots may force us to revise our perception. In such situations the constructive components of perceptions can be clearly seen. These constructions are determined by past experience, current expectations and the wishes of the subject. Thus on a crowded street or across a crowded room one may think one sees the face of a new love, until closer scrutiny disappoints. However, for a brief moment the face was seen. Depending on the intensity of current feeling the face may be seen or the voice heard everywhere.

All this means is that you are not in a calm enough frame of mind to make sensible perceptual bets. Similarly after a bereavement, it is relatively common and accounted normal for a bereaved individual to hear or see, on occasion, a dead spouse or child for some time after their death. Such insanity, however, should not be seen as a fever of the brain but rather as a fever of the psyche; as neurotic rather than organic.

> Or art thou but
> A dagger of the mind, a false creation
> Proceeding from the heat-oppressed brain?
> I see thee yet, in form as palpable
> As this which now I draw

Macbeth, Shakespeare

One strong indication that hallucinations result from fevers of the psyche rather than of the brain is that the perceptions involved are not just any perceptions as one might expect from abnormal brain function. Rather they are very specific perceptions, commonly in line with the expectations of the subject. Thus a depressed subject will hear a voice abusing them, telling them they are worthless or damned, or urging them to kill themselves. The depressed person has a good *reason* to be hearing such voices. Seeing their hallucinations as *caused*, that is as stemming from abnormal brain functioning, makes less sense. Similarly, the hallucinations of mania and schizophrenia also reflect the concerns of affected subjects. In schizophrenia voices discuss the subject in the third person, as though he/she were an object to be manipulated.

In contrast, organic brain disturbances – the fevers of the brain, such as epilepsy, tumours, or drug or alcohol withdrawal – usually give rise to contentless or arbitrary perceptual phenomena, such as noises or flashes of light or colour rather than voices or visions. In some cases, when the subject becomes delirious their visions become more formed. But in these cases unlike depressive or schizophrenic hallucinations, the visions change with great rapidity, merge into one another and, while shaped by the personality of the subject, do not in the same way reflect current concerns. Furthermore in cases of delirium, judgement is affected in that the subject is typically out of touch by virtue of being feverish. When formed organic hallucinations occur without a fever, the attitude of the subject is usually different to that of subjects with affective and schizophrenic hallucinations, in that they typically are aware of the unreality of their visions.

All of these differences give quite a different phenomenological feel to the visions and the voices of the organic psychoses compared to the functional psychoses. So much so that a separate word, hallucinosis, was coined in the last century to distinguish them from the hallucinations of the affective disorders and schizophrenia. (Hallucinations can also occur in the organic psychoses as these also are brain illnesses which are a stress for the affected subject that may lead to bad perceptual bets.) The difference between hallucinations and hallucinosis supports Jaspers' separation of the functional psychoses from the organic psychoses on the basis that the latter showed the hallmarks of crude organic destruction, whereas the former appeared to involve a distraction of the mind.

A further pointer to the psychological nature of depressive or schizophrenic hallucinations comes from the experience of some normal people. It seems that some of us (10 per cent) every so often have strikingly vivid visions on waking from sleep or on falling asleep. These are called hypnogogic hallucinations.[15] The point that these hallucinations illustrate is that it is possible to have hallucinations, when one's brain is functioning normally. Indeed to have detailed and complex hallucinations probably requires one's brain to be functioning normally.

The issue of hallucinations, however, hinges critically on the question of the reality of internal imagery. It is all very well to misinterpret something that is out there anyway. But hearing voices where there are no sounds is something else. Until recently, it was not scientifically respectable to take seriously the idea of internal tape-recorders or video-screens. Given this and in the absence of external stimuli that could be misconstrued, a recourse to cerebral malfunctioning was inevitable. But a number of recent studies, that only make sense if internal representations actually exist, shed light on what goes on when we hallucinate.

It has now been shown that subjects hearing voices typically sub-vocalize. By means of microphones attached to their neck, it has been shown that such subjects are actually quietly speaking the voices they claim to be hearing. When told of this they deny totally that this is what they are doing. This denial, if correct, points to the possibility of a hysterical origin to hallucinations. That is, the subject is dissociated from his or her own psychological processes. They do not recognize their own imaginations or vocalizations.

Far from being mysterious or irrational such states can be induced under hypnosis.[16] Induction by hypnosis suggests that a prerequisite of complex hallucinations is an altered psychological state rather than an altered brain state. Hypnosis does not cause the brain to malfunction. It avails of psychological possibilities that are normally latent. Subvocalization is what one might expect if a subject was actively participating in a conversation or train of thought within their own head. We all do it in daydreams. It is not what one would expect if voices were being forced on one by cerebral malfunctioning. Much the same thing can be shown to happen when subjects are asked to imagine scenes and actions. As they scan the imaginary happenings their eyes can be shown to move as though the activity were happening in external space.[17]

DYNAMIC PSYCHOPATHOLOGY

I have argued that in both the affective disorders and schizophrenia disorders of neuropsychological functioning bring to consciousness experiences that normally operate without the need for conscious aware-ness. In such cases it is unconscious performances that are brought to awareness rather than unconscious motives, reasons or psychological complexes. Becoming aware of these unconscious elements is not an advance in self-knowledge, its significance is more in the area of becoming aware of a knock beneath the bonnet of one's car. Something is happening which shouldn't be. These experiences are hard to ignore yet difficult to articulate as they properly lack content. They persist in awareness as the usual means of removing things from awareness, thinking about them and dealing with them, will not work. Simply trying to attend will not reverse the attentional disturbances of schizophrenia. The exercise of will power will not keep a depressed subject asleep. Indeed thinking about things that cannot be solved by thinking about them, invariably makes them worse.

But as things are not right the inevitable response of all of us will be to ask what has gone wrong and why. The answers we come up with will inevitably be shaped by the biases of normal rationality found in all of us when we are called to make judgements under uncertainty. The answers arrived at and the behaviours consequent on these answers, even when apparently delusional, would appear to be classifiable as a subset of illness behaviours.

As was noted, in the case of clearcut disturbances, such as severe chest pain or broken legs, there is only scope for a limited range of rational hypotheses or responses. But where the disturbance is less specific, hypotheses about what is happening may be much more varied. The neuropsychological disturbances of the affective disorders and schizophrenia might be expected to maximally generate such behaviours, as they almost completely lack physical stigmata. They can be expected, therefore, to function as the psychopathological equivalent of black holes. Sucking in all the surrounding material that comes to hand. Often not directly observable themselves and only detectable by the disturbance that surrounds them.

While surrounding disturbances may indicate the presence of an underlying discontinuity, they will only do so if one suspects what might lie behind the noise. Even then, the surrounding noise may so blur any signal from the epicentre, that a diagnosis and prognosis may not be possible. Pushed into an eccentric orbit by the gravitational tug of neuropsychological disturbances, illness behaviours may amplify the underlying signal or distort it or even obliterate it. Eccentric orbits may also persist long after the original interference is removed.

The idea that most psychotic behaviour is neurotic has been resisted in psychiatric practice. Almost certainly as a reaction against the often exaggerated claims of the depth psychologies. An insistence on the essential uninterpretability of a psychosis, that stems from its being an illness, has helped medical psychopathology successfully defend the illness status of these disorders. But, ironically, over-zealously applied this stance has denied to the affective disorders and schizophrenia one of the hallmarks of other illnesses, a set of illness behaviours.

As a consequence schizophrenia, in particular, has become a caricature of a medical illness. All the behaviour of the schizophrenic subject is put down to their brain not working correctly and none to the interplay between personality and illness that occurs in any other clinical condition. Far from being enlightened, telling a subject that what is happening to them is solely the effect of a brain illness is all too likely to remove hope from the affected individual, as it immediately conveys the idea that there is little they can do to help themselves. This hopelessness is often compounded by confusion, when biologically-oriented therapists then go on to dismiss as neurotic, complaints, such as persistent lack of motivation, clumsiness or the constant presence of anxiety, which are probably often milder versions of first rank experiences. When faced with these symptoms, they are likely to suggest that the illness is now quiescent and that the patient needs to go about life again as best they can.

Incorporating the notion of an illness behaviour overlay would be significant for psychopathology on three points. The first is a symbolic one. The results from studies on the formation of beliefs and the assessment of evidence, on which this concept rests, are formalizable in mathematical terms. The terms involved are probability estimates. As they stem from a recording of outcomes on tasks that can be administered to a large number of subjects, such that other things can be kept equal, they can potentially lead to universal generalizations. The nomothetic character of these findings undermines Jaspers' distinctions between the explanations of the natural sciences and the understanding of the human sciences. Based on these findings the interpretation of what is happening in states of clinical distress can have recourse to concepts as well grounded in probability estimates as those of any natural science. Indeed its concepts most resemble those of quantum mechanics.

The second point is that these experimental concepts are radically unlike the key Freudian concepts of id, ego, superego, libido and Oedipus complex. They do, however, bear a family resemblance to concepts of defence mechanisms (viz. projection, displacement, denial). Their difference from these latter concepts is more one of implication than of the kind of concept involved. The defence mechanisms imply something in the pasts of *some* of us that we need to defend against. Heuristic biases imply that we *all* have uncertain futures that we handle in predictable ways.

At present experimental correlations provisionally support explanatory constructs such as availability, representative and anchoring biases, as well as a fundamental attributional error. These are a current best approximation to explaining why subjects faced with predictive decisions behave in the way that they do. Therefore they might be expected to shed light on clinical presentations, which typically involve subjects facing uncertainty. In the case of these biases their robustness can be determined by determining their frequency across a variety of behavioural situations. Thus, these concepts are provisional and open to revision or abandonment according to the future course of experimental investigation in a way that ids and libidos are not. Therefore, in cases of dispute, an appeal can be made to experimental data and its method of collection rather than to the authority of a master or to the logic of a deduction from first principles.

The third point is that that these biases belong to what is properly called dynamic psychology. Their application to psychopathology will properly result in a dynamic psychopathology. The thrust of this chapter is that if psychiatry seriously wishes to make medical illnesses of the affective disorders and schizophrenia, it will need to embrace the need for a dynamic psychopathology. It will also have to reconcile itself to the idea that the bulk of the 'insanity' associated with these disorders will be best explained in dynamic terms. While the negativism and thought disorder of schizophrenia may be bizarre and beyond the compass of interpretation, there is little that is quite as obviously 'mad' as full-blown hysterical states, as found, for example, in Lear or the Japanese overlord in Kurosawa's film *Ran*.* Similarly 'mad' schizophrenic or depressed subjects would, on the present analysis, be schizophrenic or depressed and reacting hysterically to their situation. Hysteria, however, it should be remembered was the original point of entry for psychoanalysis in its attempt to make sense of the apparently senseless workings of the psyche.

A further important consequence of taking this step is that the affective disorders and schizophrenia should come to be seen as open to 'psycho-

* 'Diagnosing' Lear brings out many of the points made so far. Many would label such clinical presentations as hysterical psychoses. Others would argue that the term hysterical psychosis is a contradiction in terms; hysteria is a neurosis – no one talks of phobic or obsessional psychoses. For some the use of psychosis in this context indicates severity – a more complete break with reality as evidenced by delusions. For others, the presence of delusions means that Lear could not be hysterical, although what state or illness he has is usually not specified in this case.

therapy'. If the larger part of these disorders consists of understandable psychological reactions, then a rational management should be capable of significantly ameliorating these disorders, without the need to resort to drugs. Whether cures are brought about will depend on the natural history of the disease rather than on any quality of the psychological management – a point argued further in Chapter 6.

Another potential change in practice follows from the fact that the heuristic biases, in contrast to psychoanalytic concepts, far from being abstruse terms, only accessible to a psychiatric priesthood, would seem potentially accessible to all affected subjects. There would seem to be no necessary reason why patients cannot themselves work out why they end up in the states they do rather than having to wait for their therapists to interpret for them what has been happening.

Interestingly, the picture of these illnesses that results from proposing that they consist of sets of illness behaviours predicated on an underlying neuropsychological disturbance coincides with the earliest medical intuitions that the functional psychoses might take their shape from an underlying disturbance but not be wholly determined by it (Chapter 2).

six Insights and Oversights

We have been progressing slowly from interpreting all abnormal behaviours in terms of motives, whether psychological or spiritual, to a position of conceding that some behaviours for which individuals were formerly held accountable, actually lie outside their control. In general, the changeover from a straightforward interpretation of such behaviours to an inverse interpretation is taken as an indication of enlightenment. But such enlightenment does not seem to come easily, perhaps because of the general difficulty that inverse insights pose. However, raising the issue in terms of enlightenment suggests another reason why progress is slow. As well as the enlightenment that has come from medical advances, the effort to avoid letting behaviours simply be written off as either spiritual problems or as outright medical problems, has also been a source of enlightenment. When one thinks of enlightenment in psychiatry, one thinks of Pinel's striking off of the chains that had formerly held lunatics and the unlocking of asylum doors and of Freud's struggles to reveal hidden sources of distress neglected alike by pastors and doctors.

Progress, in the case of the affective disorders and schizophrenia, was always liable to be a tortured matter. In these disorders inverse insights need to be achieved and not only achieved in opposition to direct insights but ultimately held in conjunction with direct insights, that can also lay claim to being enlightened. Holding this tension of opposing thrusts toward progress until the issues are satisfactorily resolved can be expected to be one of the most searching tests yet of our ability to be scientific. Progress toward such a goal will inevitably be a dialectical matter.

The problem when dialectics intrude into scientific matters is that the data to be handled become compound. Not only may the views of the various participants in the debate be dialectically opposed, but the facts may be also, as these participants produce those facts. There is no such thing as a pure fact. All 'facts' have theoretical presuppositions built into them. So much so that when one theory succeeds another some facts simply vanish. In the case of depression, mania and schizophrenia, the facts have been produced by researchers committed to seeing them as either medical disorders or psychological problems, but not as compounds of two different sorts of problems. In either case the facts have been produced not only to support one view but also to disconfirm the other. From our perspective therefore the 'facts' should show signs of being compounded of insights and oversights.

THE ORIGINS OF THE AFFECTIVE DISORDERS[1-3]

Popular intuition and early psychiatric opinion regarding the affective disorders and schizophrenia held that one of the ways that they differed from brain disturbances such as tumours or Parkinson's disease was in their being precipitated by behavioural factors. This popular assumption has been resisted in medical circles, where these illnesses have been seen as endogenous psychoses (i.e. arising from within). Medical resistance was most probably fuelled by a wish to make sure that nothing remotely resembling a 'psychodynamic' view of these illnesses was countenanced. But also it had some support from the 'facts'. Psychiatrists exposed to patients who ended up in asylums could rarely find events so remarkable, dramatic or traumatic in the lives of subjects that could account for their ending up confined to an asylum.

Where depression was concerned, it became customary to talk of endogenous depressions, which supposedly arose out of the blue and which were assumed to be a severe medical illness, appropriately handled with pills. In contrast, there were reactive depressions. These were precipitated by life events and were altogether milder. It was argued that they were exaggerations of normal problems rather than illnesses and might be managed psychotherapeutically rather than pharmacologically. However, it has recently been established that both endogenous and reactive depressions are preceded by life events. And also that precipitated depressions cannot be distinguished clinically from unprecipitated depressions by observers blind to whether they were precipitated or not. Both respond to antidepressants. Both also respond to cognitive and interpersonal psychotherapies (Chapter 7). Are both problems or are both illnesses?

As many of the most notable life events preceding depression are events such as bereavement, retirement, children leaving home, change of job or change of house, one of the obvious conclusions is that some psychological problem is involved. An inability to handle loss or change. This perspective carries a further implication. Such events happen to all of us but not all of us seem to end up depressed. Therefore, the events must be awakening in those who do get depressed some earlier unresolved conflict, which then interferes with the proper resolution of the current crisis (see Chapter 2). This line of argument echoes religious debates, in which difficult to account for current failings are blamed on prior original sins. The analogy can be pushed further as the original psychological sin of depression never seems to get specified and has never been proven to occur. Thus, as was noted in Chapter 1, where the mental illnesses are concerned, a whiff of morality still lingers in the psychological air.

But there are serious difficulties in the way of a simple acceptance of the idea that precipitation by life events means that the affective disorders are primarily psychological problems. Many of the precipitating events appear positively beneficial. As mentioned, common events are changing jobs or houses. Far from being demotions at work or change to a lower status house, what is involved is often a promotion or moving to a desired house. The birth of a child is another such event. Post-partum depressions seem to affect mothers who have had children they have wished for no less than mothers coming to the end of an unwanted pregnancy. In awkward cases like this inconvenient facts can be explained away by postulating that the real precipitant for post-partum depressions is hormonal. This escape route, however, is not open as a means of accounting for post-partum affective disorders in fathers, of which there appear to be a substantial number.

Another problem is that recent work indicates that mania is also precipitated by life events. By the very same events that appear to trigger off depressions – birth, death, retirement, changes of house or job. Faced with such facts the common 'psychological' explanation has been to propose that manic subjects are in some way defending themselves against depression by a desperate activity. Or that subjects who become depressed following apparently desirable events have in some way suffered a symbolic loss. Elegant explanations or *post-hoc* equivocations?

Yet another problem is that there usually is a substantial period of time between life events and the onset of depression or mania. Typically a few weeks and often several months. This contrasts with psychological crises which typically follow immediately after their precipitating traumata. For example after a death grief sets in immediately. Commonly, however, grief clears up or at least substantially abates within a few weeks. Depression or mania, in contrast, follow some time after this. Furthermore, in contrast to the immediate precipitation of hysterical amnesia in the face of some anxiety or the often clear moment of sensitization that establishes a phobia, depressions and mania seem to creep up on subjects. Retrospectively, subjects or their relatives can usually identify a lengthy period during which the patient appeared to be slipping into their illness.

Thus depression and mania bear some relation to stress but an ambiguous one. Attempts to handle the matter as a psychological problem are therefore liable to be strained. In the case of depression, for example, subjects functioning at a lower level of performance than usual are liable to be understandably sad. Many depressed subjects see this clearly and say to their examiners 'You also would be unhappy if you felt the way I did.' The common response to this is that they are told that they do not recognize the true origin of their sadness. Denial that the true origin of their sadness lies where their therapist says it does, is taken as evidence of resistance – and proof of the psychological point. The therapist cannot lose taking these approaches, as the protests of the patient or their failure to get well can be, and is, ascribed to their getting something out of being depressed. This immediately sets up the 'psychological' dynamic of not believing the patient.

Awkward patients who do not agree with the interpretations of their therapists become liable to have their personality denigrated – at least in case notes or letters to other therapists. They are especially liable to be held responsible for their own failure to get well. In current psychiatric practice failure to get well is always the patient's 'fault'.

This resort to personality and the propensity to moral castigation of recalcitrant patients is not the result of therapeutic perversity or some unfortunate consequence of our unenlightened times. Rather it stems from exactly the same set of biases that lead patients to construct their psychoses in the way that they do. While one might expect a therapist to be more scientific than their patient, in practice they also start and end by making attributions to dispositions, with the personality of the patient being the obvious first candidate. If this appears not to fit the particular case the dispositions of significant others can be blamed, whether they be stultifying spouses or schizophrenogenic parents. The problem is almost worse if the patient agrees with the therapist. In this case therapeutic interpretations are all too likely to feed directly into the original constructions of patient so that both operate in an unholy rather than a therapeutic alliance.

Just as patients' and therapists' mistakes stem from an oversight so current attempts to pinpoint the psychological origins of the affective disorders are predicated on an oversight. The oversight is that psycho-motor retardation is *inevitably* disheartening. Therefore the sadness of depression need not be continuous with any problem that antedated the illness. If this is the case, it may be a serious mistake to attempt to find the hidden loss in apparently happy life events. Similarly the need to find attitudinal flaws that antedate depressive episodes vanishes, as does the need to taint the patient's personality.

An example may bring out the dangers of the oversight involved. If we take a group of 100 subjects who have jet-lag or shift-work disturb-ances, a third of these will have had childhood traumata, and a goodly number will be categorizable as awkward or 'damaged' individuals. Management of the malaise of jet-lag by investigating the pasts of these subjects or attempting to correct their personalities would be inappropri-ate and would risk creating problems where none existed before. Pre-cisely the same situation applies to depression. But where no one pays much heed to the prior experiences of subjects with jet-lag or shift-work intolerance, in the case of depression, prior traumatic experiences are the focus of attention and, where not clearly present, they are often assumed or manufactured from likely material.

This does not mean that the affective disorders are unprecipitated. Rather it means that the elation or misery that accompanies them does not imply that there was a welcome or a sad event antedating depression or mania. Another possibility is that these events may have triggered a physical disturbance, which in turn is the focus of psychological reac-tions. If this is the case then, there is a psychological crisis in these illnesses but it does not arise from the precipitating event or some re-encounter with buried psychological material. Rather it occurs after an encounter with one's own brain not functioning normally and not recognized as such.

The release of dynamic material in depression, guilt and self-punitive accusations, is often taken to indicate a fault line in the personality stemming from childhood. However, a similar situation could arise by virtue of having had an entirely normal childhood. An analogy can be had with trees. Trees on the west coasts of Scotland and Ireland are typically stunted and lean eastwards, away from the prevailing winds. Unbuffeted by these winds, oaks in the South East of England grow up straight and strong. In most respects they are closer to what trees should be. But in a hurricane, they and not the West coast trees fall. Similarly, and in contrast to many psychological theories on the genesis of mental illness, current research suggests that a certain amount of adversity in childhood increases our abilities to successfully manage stress in later life. The advent of a depressive or schizophrenic disorder, arguably, is stress of a kind that is liable to unhinge even those who have had little cause to doubt themselves beforehand.

Why should a brain disturbance happen after life events? One possibility becomes obvious once the hunt for psychological motives is suspended. All the events that trigger affective disorders produce breaks in routine. Whether good or bad, events such as changes of jobs or houses, or births and deaths, all disrupt routines. Our social routines govern the smooth functioning of a set of internal routines in us called circadian rhythms. Disruption of external routines, therefore, is liable to disrupt internal routines also. There appear to be two possible effects of such disruptions. One is a state which will have been suffered by many readers when their internal and external routines have been desynchronized as a consequence of jet travel or shift-work. The experience is a flu-like one of loss of energy, poor concentration, loss of interest and disrupted sleep and appetite. The other possibility, which is less common and typically goes unrecognized, is a mirror image of the usual jet-lag picture, where instead of a subtle decrease in energy levels there is a subtle increase.

Whether or not this is what happens, a circadian rhythm example may illustrate how the psychological facts may fit into a non-psychological framework. First, this system can be disturbed in two ways, one of which, if amplified by the heuristic biases outlined in Chapter 5, could lead on to mania and the other to depression. Accordingly one could predict that some subjects would be liable to both disorders. Liability would depend not on the psychic structure or personality of the subject so much as on the hardwiring of their brain and the environmental circumstances to which they were exposed. Second, one can predict a delay between precipitating event and onset of illness. This follows because the circadian rhythm system aims at tracking routine. It, therefore, has a certain inertial stability built into it. It follows that such a system will resist disruption during acute crises but may show evidence of disturbance some time after a change in circumstances if old routines cannot be re-established. A third consequence is that the events which precipitate depression or mania need not necessarily be bad. It is the changed routines that such life events bring about that precipitates an affective disorder rather than their aversive quality.

An important further point is that such a disturbance leads to a state that can be experienced by affected subjects but will be difficult to characterize. A noticeable but not disabling state. Just the kind of brain state changes that in the absence of an obvious cause are going to lead to distressed psychological states. Three consequences follow from this. One is that as subjects are reacting to a change in brain state rather than to a psychological problem, their reactions may appear disproportionate to any psychological event that appeared to precede their illness. Accordingly their depression may appear to have arisen for no obvious reason (endogenously). Second, as something physical has been disturbed such subjects are ill. They do not have a primary psychological problem. This will be developed below. Third, as these psychological reactions only evolve after the appearance of the initial brain disturbance, there should be some evidence that many people have changes in brain state, but fewer have state of mind changes. That is, there should be many people who are depressed but not recognized as such.

Labelling

There has recently been a great deal of work done on what is termed 'general practice' depression.[4] Broadly the results support the position outlined here. First it appears that there are a great number of people who meet psychiatric criteria for depression but who do not go to their doctors. Or if they do go, they complain of pain, loss of energy or some non-specific physical malaise. Many of these subjects are not recognized by their general practitioners as being depressed. This is entirely consistent with depression involving a disorder of brain state that is not especially serious. In particular one that is similar to a jet-lag type of state.

Something then happens to make doctors able to recognize that what their patients have is depression. The evidence suggests that it is when they start complaining of hopelessness and worthlessness, rather than, or in addition to, loss of energy and malaise, that general practitioners make a diagnosis of depression. This is consistent with the notion that states of mind lead to an evolution of the disorder. When one starts complaining of worthlessness, in addition to having something that GPs recognize as depression, one will have also begun to feel much worse, as it is one thing to have a flu but it is quite another to have a flu and be demoralized or suicidal. The initial disturbance will have been amplified.

It also seems that older, married and female subjects are more likely than younger, single and male subjects to be labelled as depressed by their doctors even though both sets of subjects meet criteria for the illness. However, males when depressed complain of poor energy, physical malaise or loss of concentration but not of worthlessness, whereas women complain of loss of self-confidence and self-esteem but not prominently of physical complaints. This is not surprising as there is also evidence that women are more likely than men to make dispositional rather than situational attributions. (Perhaps reflecting a greater female interest in or sensitivity to persons?) Therefore higher female rates of depression may actually mean a higher likelihood of being labelled depressed if one is female, but no higher an actual incidence of depression. This explanation stands in marked contrast to current psychological formulations which stress that women are particularly likely to have unfinished psychological 'business'.

A further important point follows from this. If those who end up being labelled as depressed do so as much by virtue of a selective labelling process as by virtue of having this particular illness, one can wonder about the genetic studies done in depression. These typically have been conducted on hospitalized depressives. Repeatedly they have found that depression runs in families. If one member of a family has a major depressive disorder, there is a 15 per cent risk that their first-degree relatives will also at some point suffer from an affective disorder. Does this indicate a genetic risk as is often claimed? Against the likelihood of this being genetic (or all genetic) is the fact that no analysis of the relations of affected subjects to each other has ever convincingly indicated the involvement of a specific gene.

There is an alternative to the genetic explanation of familial aggregation. Living in a home in which one member has been diagnosed as having depression is most likely to increase the likelihood that other family members who pass through a period of loss of energy and physical malaise are going to also be diagnosed as depressed; both by their relatives and by their GPs. Furthermore, recognizing themselves as from flawed stock or brittle families, these subjects are even more likely than others to end up making dispositional misattributions and evolving into 'severe' depressive disorders with suicidal or delusional propensities. Given the indications that labelling plays a part in who ends up 'depressed' and given that so many people meet criteria for being depressed, who never even go to their GPs, one can ask whether we do not all get depressed at some point or other. It seems plausible to suggest that we do, but that this illness clears up quickly for most of us. If this is the case, one can ask whether genetic predisposition has much significance regarding depression, even though it is a physical illness.

The current model of affective disorders suggests that these illnesses are just the kind of illness that are liable to marked selection factors. Social and cultural factors are therefore almost inevitably going to play a part in the final clinical picture. The converse of this is that given such selection factors – operative in both affective disorders and schizophrenia – there will always have been a large amount of good evidence to indicate to concerned investigators that 'mental' illness is created or manufactured by social and familial pressures.[5] Furthermore, there will be a lot of good evidence that exposure to the mental health services opens patients to a substantial risk of having psychological problems created where none existed before.[6]

What is being proposed here is not that depression, mania or schizophrenia are created by social factors but that 'mental illnesses' are. Put another way, if the present proposal is correct depression, mania and schizophrenia will not go away once we become more enlightened but mental illness might.

THE ORIGINS OF SCHIZOPHRENIA[7]

As in the case of the affective disorders, there has been a sustained attempt to find a genetic origin to schizophrenia. It can be suggested that the motive for this has been to establish its credentials as a medical illness in the face of attempts to make it psychological. However, just as with the affective disorders, no clearcut evidence of genetic involvement has been found. There is familial aggregation, but not in a way that supports the idea that a single defective gene might be responsible for this illness.

However, the data from genetic studies are never presented neutrally. Failure to find a single gene responsible for schizophrenia is not taken as an indication that schizophrenia is not genetically determined. Even though it is generally conceded that many factors must summate to precipitate schizophrenia, on reading the literature, the role of the other factors seems one of obscuring the real genetic causation of the illness rather than actually contributing to its cause. This need to believe in a genetic origin to schizophrenia has, it has been claimed by Rose, Kamin and Lewontin, led to many researchers falsifying their evidence or ignoring pointers in their data to the possibility of an environmental precipitant of the illness.[8]

This is an interesting piece of research 'psychopathology', as one has to ask what would be achieved by proving a genetic origin to schizophrenia (or the affective disorders). In the case of single gene illnesses, like Huntington's chorea or cystic fibrosis, in finding the gene responsible one has found if not fully characterized the *cause* of the illness. Arguably many medical researchers would like to see both the affective disorders and schizophrenia as illnesses similar to these, as these are the most unequivocally medical illnesses.

Multifactorial models do not permit this causal claim. Despite this, it is still claimed that establishing the genetic contribution to a multifactorial model would pinpoint the cause of these illnesses. This, however, is not the case. Duodenal ulcers have a multifactorial origin in which genes play some part. But it typically also needs stress to create the ulcer. Coronary heart disease has a similar amount of genetic input as the affective disorders and schizophrenia. But, as most people are now aware, it takes a certain lifestyle combined with this predisposition to bring about a heart attack. Without the lifestyle heart attacks are rare. The situation is like a stone breaking glass. The genetic argument is that the fact that the glass was thin caused it to break. Most people, however, would say that the impact of the stone was the pertinent cause.

One way to tease apart the weight of various causes is to look at the incidence of the illness in children born of schizophrenic parents, who have been adopted. These are presumably at high genetic risk. In a recent study in Finland, a group of these children were found to be more likely than other children to develop schizophrenia.[9] However, their greater likelihood was small. And every child who developed schizophrenia, whether from a high risk group or otherwise, came from a disturbed home. Those also at high risk who were placed in stable homes did not get schizophrenia.

Another way to put the genetic findings in schizophrenia is to say that genetic factors account for a certain amount of the likelihood of getting this illness. In the case of genes and schizophrenia, the amount accounted for is quite small. Where one twin of a monozygotic set contracts the illness, the likelihood of the other developing it is somewhere around 33 per cent. This had led researchers to look for what else it is, that added to genetic factors produces schizophrenia. In the case of twins, of which one gets the illness and the other does not, if one has a large enough group, one can look at whether those who do get the illness were also subject to birth trauma, had head injuries when young, were separated from their mothers or otherwise. The problem is that there seems to be nothing else, that picks out who gets the illness from who does not. We have simply no idea of why only one of two equally predisposed individuals goes on to get the illness. One reason we have no idea may be simply because we have not looked at the right things. But another possibility may be that it is simply a matter of luck.

The same situation applies to genes, life events and depression. Genes and life events combined account for only half the likelihood of getting depressed. A host of factors, such as loss of parents at an early age appear to make one additionally vulnerable. But even so, much remains unexplained. Could it be a matter of luck? An example may indicate what could be happening. Take a subject who moves house. This life event may lead to a subtle fall-off in performance that is noticeable but not disabling. Technically this is depression but it is not likely to be labelled as such. As will be pointed out later, this is a self-limiting condition that will probably clear up in a few weeks. Most individuals will get through such a spell in the doldrums without clearly realizing that there is anything wrong. Suppose, however, something happens at work so that our subject has to operate super-optimally. This is likely to lead to them becoming aware that they are not up to scratch. As there is no obvious physical cause for their doing poorly, they are likely to blame themselves, which will amplify the original disturbance and lead to a full blown depressive illness. But whether demands arise at work at just this time or not is a matter of luck. None of the theories on the origins of schizophrenia or the affective disorders, take luck into account. Arguably because they are too committed to finding prototypical medical illnesses or psychological problems, neither of which involve luck.

A final point can be made about genetic research in schizophrenia. Commonly the pertinent articles are written up in a manner suggestive of older degeneracy theories of mental illness. Until the early years of this century, many believed that there was a primary irremediable failure of the germ plasm in cases of mental illness, a degeneration in the stock (Chapter 1). Such views, just like the recourse to personality found in psychological theories of mental illness, seem to resemble nothing so much as religious views of the original staining of human nature that cannot be overcome by man alone. Where behaviour is concerned 'it is genetic' can often be translated as 'it is written'.[10]

Fate rather than luck seems to be implied, as well as fatalism rather than the hope that one might otherwise expect from the advance of knowledge. Thus it is suggested that the discovery of the genetic basis of schizophrenia would allow for the possibility of therapeutic abortions, if diagnoses *in utero* can be made. In this way schizophrenia might be eliminated. Such views are offered without any apparent consideration of whether factors other than genetic predisposition are important, or whether the illness if contracted is so unmanageable as to make life worthless. They are also offered despite the example of illnesses such as phenylketonuria, where the discovery of a genetic cause led to the development of an environmental cure – not eating foods containing phenylalanine for the first three years of life.

Before asking how stress could cause schizophrenia, one further group of patients at risk from the illness needs to be mentioned. It seems that all subjects with brain disorders or decreased brain reserves seem to be at a higher risk than others. Following severe head injuries, tumours, infections or metabolic disorders of the brain, the risk of schizophrenia is increased. Likewise it is increased in any of the conditions that cause mental handicap or epilepsy. A group of such subjects that has recently attracted research attention has been those who have had obstetric complications perinatally. (These can be expected to cause minimal brain damage.)

Why or how in cases of diminished brain reserve or in cases loaded genetically should stress convert a disposition to an illness into an overt illness? Several possibilities can be noted. First, adolescence seems to be the time of earliest onset of schizophrenia. There are good reasons why this should be the case. The symptoms experienced by affected subjects and the disorders of attention they show are all consistent with those of a frontal lobe disorder. This has been recognized since Kraepelin, but not proven conclusively. A good deal of recent research has established, however, that schizophrenic subjects have particular difficulties with tasks that involve frontal lobe abilities. They also show brain scan indications of impaired frontal lobe functioning. The relevance of this to adolescence is that the frontal lobes are an area of the brain that keeps maturing until adolescence. One can presume that this is because new skills required at adolescence need the type of operations that the frontal lobes specialize in.

In general, it seems that there are periods built into all animals, including humans, at which certain skills are optimally acquired. Extensive brain remodelling occurs during such periods. For example night-time urinary continence is best acquired around the age of three. Later on it becomes harder not easier to acquire this skill. If acquired later, the skill seems to be more vulnerable to breakdown under subsequent stress. Fluent speech is achieved around the age of four or five and stress at this age may lead to subsequent non-fluent speech such as stammering. Similarly it can be proposed that stress during adolescence is liable to disrupt the acquisition of those skills whose substrates lie in frontal lobe functioning. If these skills are not acquired during the appropriate sensitive period, it is likely that not only will a skill deficit result, but also that brain function may not subsequently be entirely normal. This is because the normal maturing of brain functioning depends as much on the development occurring, as development depends on brain maturation. Any subsequent acquisition of the skills in question is likely to be by compensatory means rather than an acquisition of the real thing. However, as the examples of stammering and eneuresis suggest, it is not a foregone conclusion that the problem cannot be overcome. And indeed overcome by psychological means.

Second, no one, at present, knows how widespread are schizophreniform experiences in adolescence. Typically subjects who end up being diagnosed as schizophrenic have had the illness for a year prior to diagnosis. If they can escape diagnosis so long it would suggest that many others may escape diagnosis entirely. Further pointers in this direction are findings that outcome in schizophrenia depends on how well developed the personality of the subject was before the onset of the illness, as well as the stability of their lifestyle and the supportiveness of their home environment. In general, the more supportive the background the greater the likelihood of a remission of the illness. This would increase the probability that a substantial number of subjects from supportive backgrounds are never diagnosed.

Being diagnosed schizophrenic, therefore, like being diagnosed depressed is partly accidental, a matter of luck. As mentioned earlier a certain amount of adversity in childhood is increasingly being recognized as fostering an ability to handle stress later in life. Chronic unremitting stress on the other hand is likely to diminish coping skills. Individuals, therefore, from chronically stressed homes who contract schizophrenia should cope with it less well – interpret what is happening in ways that far from alleviating the problem are themselves a source of further distress. Whether one comes from such a background or not, however, is to a great extent a matter of luck.

PSYCHOSOMATIC DISEASES[11]

It seems possible that both the affective disorders and schizophrenia are illnesses that are precipitated by behavioural stress. Does this make them psychosomatic illnesses? If so what are the implications of this? In Chapter 4, it was noted that for the early dynamic psychologists ulcers were something to be interpreted. The hole in a gut was an alternative expression of a conflict or symbolic in some way of something happening in the subject's life. Extensive research aimed at providing support for this viewpoint has come up with nothing. Currently few people see ulcers as a direct expression of conflict or stress. However, this is exactly how the affective disorders and schizophrenia are still being seen, as elements in some ongoing psychic drama.

One currently fashionable way of putting the matter is to invoke an ethological perspective. Ethologically speaking, the behaviours that constitute mania, depression and schizophrenia would be seen as the adopting of certain primitive preprogrammed communicative postures or adaptive strategies by affected subjects. Seen this way depression can be conceived of as a strategy to get others to look after one. Or alternatively as some wisdom of the organism, which leads to a hibernation-type reaction or other adaptation, when pressures get too much and behavioural coping fails. In the case of schizophrenia, Laing proposed that what was involved was a posture taken up when the spiritual illnesses of society are such that the subject has no other recourse in order to stay sane. It was also proposed that schizophrenia represented a transitional stage toward some higher spiritual plane.

Common to such approaches is the notion that mental illnesses provide a time of possible growth. That certain non-verbal communicative, emotional or behavioural imperatives have come to the surface and if heeded will lead to a fuller life. This perspective is also caught by everyday references to one being sadder but wiser after a breakdown. Such notions follow from insight into the psychological facts of these illnesses but an oversight of the pointers to biological disruption.

One way to fudge this difficulty has been to distinguish between illnesses and diseases in the following manner. Illnesses are what I have when I complain of something. Diseases involve biological disorder. Thus I may be diseased without being ill – if I am unaware of anything wrong. As subjects with psychiatric problems have complaints, it can be conceded that they are ill, while at the same time the idea that they are diseased may be resisted. Being ill but not diseased opens the way to a medicalization of misery. It leads also to patients being told that their 'symptoms don't seem to have a physical basis. The lack of a physical basis doesn't mean that the symptoms are not real'.

This elegant way out of the knotty issues raised by mental illnesses looks better in theory than in practice. In practice subjects whom one might wish to legally specify as having a mental illness – those who have mania or who are deluded – are liable to strenuously deny being ill. Unless one postulates a disease as the basis for detention, one has to side-step denials of illness as indicative of loss of insight. But forcing treatment on this basis means that there is, in practice, no recourse against ECT being administered to anyone on the same basis. This raises the spectre of civil liberties which dogs psychiatric practice. But it is not just a matter of civil liberties. Treatment may also be compromised.

For example, schizophrenic or depressed subjects are commonly committed to hospital because of a stated intention to kill themselves. As things stand, they (and sometimes their therapists) believe that it is wishes such as the wish to kill oneself that constitute a psychiatric illness. The implication of this is that the having of certain thoughts is something which society is not prepared to tolerate. However, nowhere are there spelt out any criteria of which thoughts are acceptable and which are not. Or how to stop having unacceptable thoughts. Nor is it clear that the so-called sane among us never have such thoughts. Furthermore having such thoughts may even be held to indicate growth by the very people who urge detention of subjects for having them. Given that being 'ill without being diseased' results in such ambiguities, perhaps it can be seen that detentions on this basis are as likely to interfere as much with therapy as with civil liberties. Neither is it surprising that such contradictions have led critics to suggest that mental illness as thus conceived is a myth (Szasz), or a mechanism for social coercion (Foucalt).

Mind over matter

Biting the bullet of biological, rather than psychological, breakdown has important further consequences. While very few researchers now see ulcers as hidden messages in some intrapsychic or interpersonal drama, there is still a general suspicion that they mean something compared to broken legs, for example. This suspicion probably stems from the fact that minds really do exert control over matter. While obviously our minds move our legs and arms in various activities, we also seem capable of influencing processes not normally thought of as being under direct control. We can increase our heart rates at will with a little practice, as well as decrease urinary output or either increase or decrease gastric acid secretion. This has been known for some time. But the extent of mental influence on physiological processes has been further demonstrated by experiments which show that emotional events can shape the responses of systems such as the immune system. Through such mechanisms our emotions probably do influence our liability to develop carcinomas, infections and other illnesses.

Anxiety is one emotion that seems to affect all these internal processes. The physiological reactions that accompany anxiety are appropriately seen as part of the anxiety. Heart rates increase, acid output increases, hands start to shake, butterflies take over the stomach and the urges to micturate or defecate may become insistent. However, no matter how unpleasant these reactions may be, they indicate that the physiology in question is working normally, preparing its owner to fight or flee or otherwise handle some fear. We learn to be afraid of things and therefore such physiological reactions can be seen as being learnt too. They may even survive the disappearance of the initial threat in the form of habitual anxiety.

They can also be unlearnt. When facing the interview panel one can learn to control one's breathing, slow one's heart rate, take the quaver out of one's voice. Such learning requires presence of *mind*. It can be described as pulling oneself together. No pills can do the job for you. Indeed reliance on pills to help out in this kind of situation may ultimately make it harder to exert personal control over one's own physiology. The morality of a treatment that would advocate pills as a substitute for helping individuals get to grips with these kind of problems (with themselves) can be questioned.

Extreme or chronic anxiety may, by pushing up gastric acid output, lead to a hole in the gut. But while mental influence may produce ulcers, it cannot reliably cure them. Once a hole has been produced a pathological process is established. Psychological factors may influence it but cannot wholly determine it. Biology has been disrupted rather than simply extended. A psychosomatic illness or disease rather than just a psychosomatic reaction is involved. In this case learning to decrease gastric acid output may assist healing, but if the subject eats green peppers or smokes, the ulcer will be liable to remain open even in the face of reduced acid output. Or if the ulcer is on the posterior wall of the gut, the same voluntary control of acid output is less likely to lead to a cure, or will lead to a slower cure than if the ulcer were on the anterior wall. The rate of healing is determined by the rate at which cells migrate into the exposed ulcerous areas rather than by the rate at which one can learn to reduce gastric acid secretion. In many cases, despite the most relaxed approach possible and avoiding all possible irritants such as green peppers or smoking, the ulcer will not heal, necessitating pharmacological or even surgical intervention.

If mania, depression and schizophrenia involve neuropsychological disruption, then they differ from anxiety in the same way that heartburn differs from an ulcer. Under the stress of an interview increased acid output may lead to the symptom of heartburn, but once the interview is over the heartburn goes.

However, if the increase in output leads further to a hole being burnt in the gut lining, successful completion of an interview will not lead to the symptoms going. Instead they may intensify. What happens in the case of an ulcer, as opposed to heartburn, is that a physiological function breaks down. Once breakdown occurs, the resulting experiences of the subject or the objective manifestations of breakdown on X-rays are not properly seen as physiological correlates of a state of mind, whereas the heartburn is. States of mind may come and go but the ulcer will remain. At least for as long as the time it takes cells to cover over the area that has been exposed. Mental influence on physiological functions cannot increase that speed beyond what is biologically possible.

The situation is analogous to a wound on the hand. Healing does not depend on mental effort. It happens at a predetermined biological rate. Mental factors can, however, retard the successful closure of the wound, as when subjects pick at the scabs of their wounds. In such states of biological disruption, the best role for the mind appears to be one of keeping out of what is going on and letting nature take its course. Even if this approach is adopted other factors such as infection of the wound may lead to seriously delayed healing. All of this seems fairly uncontroversial, when put in terms of a wound on the hand, but it is not as readily conceded when the issue is a wound in the gut. Perhaps because we cannot see what is going on, there is more scope for us to imagine mysterious mental forces affecting what is happening – unconscious resistances. This is all the more likely to be the case for wounds in the brain which cannot yet be seen at all.

In practice this leads to the physical concomitants of depression, mania and schizophrenia being seen in terms of the equivalents of a psychic heartburn rather than a psychic ulcer. That is, manifestations of altered physical state such as loss of energy, loss of appetite or inability to attend are treated as though they are further equivalents of a state of mind. To be altered by altering that state of mind, by pulling oneself together. That this is the case is seen in the frequent dismissal of physical complaints as neurotic. And also in the popular view that cures brought about by antidepressants or ECT without changes in lifestyle, or the discovery of skeletons in the mental cupboard are somehow incomplete or even morally wrong. This attitude is also found in the widespread use of group therapies in psychiatric units, which at least implicitly suggest that all these physical discomforts a patient is suffering are in reality the consequences of or the embodiments of a frustrated communication act.

As they involve neuropsychological *disruption*, the affective disorders and schizophrenia cannot be psychosomatic reactions. Yet they are frequently precipitated by behavioural factors. This makes them psychosomatic diseases, with the brain being the target organ. An important consequence of this concern for the right words is that if this analysis is correct, depression, mania and schizophrenia are no more 'mental' than ulcers or Parkinson's disease. Granted they are 'ulcers' that are uniquely disturbing. But the kind of disturbance they provoke happens to some extent in all illnesses.

Natural history

Psychological problems in general involve behaviour being determined by factors which lie beyond the boundaries of a subject's awareness. As such they will tend to persist and often to worsen, unless the subject seeks help. However, when contrasted with mental *illnesses*, psychological problems are usually seen as being remediable. The mental illnesses involving biological disruption supposedly have a much gloomier prognosis. As mentioned the hidden agenda of genetic or biological arguments is often one which implies that the affective disorders and schizophrenia are illnesses that must inevitably arise and irremediably persist.[12] This being so, undertaking to handle them by psychotherapy would seem to be a noble gesture, but no more likely to succeed than Canute's attempt to stem the flowing tide.

Paradoxically, however, one benefit of an illness perspective, if looked at dispassionately, should be to raise hopes of a cure. Illnesses unlike problems have natural histories. They run courses. Each has a typical course. The psychosomatic diseases, in the main, are self-resolving illnesses. Ulcers, for example, almost inevitably heal with time, although they may be aggravated or maintained by further stress. Indeed, ironically, our ability to modify many psychological problems, such as personality disorders or severe obsessional or hysterical reactions, is much less than our ability to heal ulcers *without medication*.

Accordingly, the natural history of the affective disorders and schizophrenia is of central importance to their management. Until very recently, however, there has been little objective evidence on these questions. There have been impressions that schizophrenia is an invariably chronic illness. And there has been the impression that depression and mania would be liable to persist for months if not years, if we did not have the benefits of antidepressants.

However, contrary to these assumptions the evidence suggests strongly that both depression and mania are self-limiting illnesses. Many people on community surveys meet criteria for depression yet never attend their GPs for treatment. Of those who do attend 50 per cent get well without ever being diagnosed as depressed. These facts suggest a self-limiting disturbance, as does the high rate of placebo response and the documented natural histories from the pre-drug era, even of the most severely ill subjects. Current estimates are that depressions on average last for fourteen weeks, treated or untreated.[13]

Similarly, mania is increasingly being recognized in forms which apparently resolve without the need for hospital admission. There are the low-grade manias, which involve hyperactivity and exuberance, but may only be diagnosed as such in retrospect. Manias which lead to hospitalization are typically self-limiting. In a matter of weeks, whether treated or not, they resolve or swing into depression. Only a very small proportion of cases last longer.

The situation for schizophrenia is a good deal less clear cut. A further consideration of possible interactions between illnesses and illness behaviours may illustrate why this should be the case.

We have argued that the neuropsychological disturbances in the affective disorders and schizophrenia should lead to interpretations of what is happening that are likely to lead to greater distress and more dramatic action than the provoking disturbance. For example, in depression the core disturbances unelaborated or unamplified are most probably noticeable but not disabling. They consist of a subtle fall off in energy and a physical malaise. It does not produce suicidal ideation or illogicality. But the interpretation by an affected subject of their experience in terms of worthlessness is liable to bring someone who may be only minimally slowed down to a full-stop by adding the ennervation of demoralization to depression. Demoralization is also liable to lead to thoughts of suicide and guilt regardless of the presence or absence of a provoking neuropsychological disturbance.

It is typically the agitated psychological states that result from misinterpretations of the core disturbances of schizophrenia and the affective disorders that bring these disorders to professional attention. However, while a penumbra of illness behaviours may make the underlying neuropsychological disturbance visible, it can also be expected to cloud many issues. For example, depressed subjects lose an involuntary, rhythmic component to their energy – much as jet-lagged subjects do. Yet stimulated by desperation they may still summon up energy and charge around frantically – just as jet-lagged subjects, who have something important to do can set about it, even though they are not brimful of energy. Conversely, many subjects with mania find the extra energy thrust on them uncomfortable and as a consequence get irritable rather than euphoric. These desperate depressed and irritable manic subjects may be difficult to tell apart. Both may be difficult to distinguish from agitated schizophrenic subjects. Similarly, schizophrenic subjects as well as depressed subjects can be expected to be hopeless, guilty and demoralized on occasion. And subjects who are depressed, manic, schizophrenic or have a sensitive psychosis may well share common delusions. Thus the illness behaviour of each of these states is only approximately specific to each illness. It takes its shape from the illness, but that shape may overlap with that of other illnesses and that of neurotic states.

A further problem is that illness behaviours may outlast the illness that gave rise to them. For example, depression we have argued gives rise to demoralization. In most cases self-confidence and morale are restored within weeks of the underlying depression clearing up. But in many cases demoralization persists. This is not really surprising as sudden and radical re-evaluations of oneself are not necessarily going to simply be forgotten once one's sleep returns to normal and one's appetite is restored. It is common to find people who say that they have never been the same since their 'nervous breakdown'.

It is also common to find that many people affected this way rediscover themselves or a zest for life when their spouse falls ill. Having to cope with added responsibilities, they often find they can manage better than they expected. Another way out can be if they meet someone new and fall in love. In both these cases it can be argued that what is changing is morale rather than mood. But as loss of morale is often the most prominent part of a depression, it follows that if demoralization persists, neither the affected subject nor their therapist may be able to see that the illness has actually cleared up, even though the patient may not feel well.

All of these factors can be expected to apply to schizophrenia. Many of us need little to convince us that the world is a hostile and dangerous place. A set of disturbing and bizarre experiences will almost inevitably tip the balance toward paranoia for many. Once paranoid, it may be difficult to recover the ability to tolerate ambiguity when the bizarre experiences resolve. It may be much more difficult than before to face the mess that is our world and say that this mess has arisen largely by accident rather than by design. Accordingly, many schizophrenic subjects can be expected to remain 'deluded' or hallucinating, even though the underlying psychosis has cleared up. That is, many cases of chronic schizophrenia may well represent instances of chronic neuroses rather than ongoing illnesses. There has been no attempt to date to explore this issue as it is assumed that ongoing delusions must necessarily indicate an ongoing illness.

Two other factors confound the issue. One is that given a label of schizophrenia, there is a medical tendency to write off everything to the illness and in particular to write off 'bad behaviour'. For example, I know a thirty-two-year-old spirited woman who has been diagnosed as having schizophrenia. One day on my way through a ward, she came the opposite way through a door, slamming it behind her. So hard that the glass panels in the door shattered. I innocently asked whether the voices had been getting at her or told her to do this. Grinning, she said no: that when you are labelled as having schizophrenia, you can get away with anything. Getting away with anything is likely, however, to lead to a diagnosis of ongoing illness. These are just the behaviours, however, that a streetwise social worker sees often, leading them to have serious reservations about medicalization.

In general, the fact that we tend to base our diagnoses on the characteristics of the illness behaviours of schizophrenia and the affective disorders creates a gap. A gap that to some extent is inevitable given the difficulties in distinguishing, for example, between the wilfulness that is malingering, from the seeming wilfulness that may be hysteria and both from the apparent wilfulness that can occur in schizophrenia and other frontal lobe disorders, where the patient is unable to prevent themselves doing the opposite to what they have been requested to do. (A comparable gap applies also to the affective disorders, where it may, for example, be difficult to distinguish between the sadness of demoralization arising within a depression and the sadnesses that may accrue from a re-awakened sorrowful life event, or the sadness that may stem from contemplating the human condition or recent human affairs.) Through these gaps march manipulative patients, who are enabled thereby to get away with much that they should not get away with. Through these gaps also march charismatic healers and speculative theoreticians, who equally get away with much as a result.

Conversely, in the absence of outright delusions, few GPs or psychiatrists would be happy to diagnose schizophrenia, as such a diagnosis is felt to be a death sentence. This, however, is self-fulfilling as it means that one has to be severely ill in the first place to be diagnosed as having schizophrenia and hence less likely to have a good outcome. However, many people in their late adolescence and twenties present to GPs with 'neurotic' complaints of anxiety or bodily dysfunction, which later clear up. The issue of whether any of these have a subclinical schizophrenia has not been looked at. It is an important one as, if they do, pessimistic attitudes to this illness would be challenged.

For these reasons it is difficult to be precise about the natural history of schizophrenia. What seems increasingly clear, however, is that the natural history of mania and depression suggests an illness that is much milder and more self-limiting than was thought before. Previous judgements seem to have been over-influenced by the availability of an unrepresentative asylum sample of dramatically malignant cases. In the case of schizophrenia it is not possible to even offer vague pointers. All that can be said is that the same impressionistic rather than scientific factors which led to a mistaken estimate of the severity of the affective disorders are likely to have also influenced the perception of schizophrenia. In a very provocative study of this issue, Richard Warner has recently argued that pessimistic impressions regarding the outcome of schizophrenia have not only been shaped by the above factors, but also by potent social and political influences.[14]

If it is the case that the greater part of the distress in the affective disorders and schizophrenia stems from misinterpretations, then given these indications that the natural history of these illnesses does not preclude spontaneous recovery, we can suggest that rational management (a psychotherapy) should greatly alleviate them and may even promote recovery.

PHARMACOTHERAPY

The combined effects of insights and oversights can in many respects be seen most clearly when it comes to treating these disorders by physical means. While drug companies seem intent on ensuring that a modern physician confronted by a Macbeth wanting a remedy for the troubles plaguing his wife would not be reduced to hand-wringing impotence, many of us still feel that for troubles of the mind the patient must minister to themselves. That physical treatments are positively immoral. The fact that they appear to work is dismissed as superficial. Something that many affected subjects may agree with, conceding that they know themselves no better after antidepressant treatment than before. This can appear also to be supported by the fact that many fall ill again and so, it is argued, talk of cures is misplaced.

In contrast, the development of antidepressant and neuroleptic agents more than anything else reinforced some of the crudest medical attitudes and the prejudice that the functional psychoses are really organic psychoses only to be called functional until their organic origins are determined. In the case of an organic psychosis one would not expect disturbances of behaviour that result from the growth of a tumour or elevated brain calcium levels to get well spontaneously or with psychological management.

These issues have been a problem since Descartes. Before him, the Greeks were happy with the idea of influencing the mind through the body. *Mens sane in corpore sano* (a healthy mind in a healthy body). But there was not the radical discontinuity between Greek minds and bodies that arose with Descartes. After Descartes, the question of how action on a mechanical body might bring about effects on a spiritual mind became a knotty one. It was addressed most notably by Jerome Gaub in 1747.[15] He proposed that interactions might come about in the following way. Imagine two pendulums swinging side by side. Neither touches. But altering the swing of one pendulum will bring about a gradual change in the arc of the other. This happens because oscillating systems harmonize. As Gaub saw it, something similar might happen between brain and mind.

However, whether this was how effects were brought about or not, Gaub felt he had a trump card up his sleeve. He agreed that 'at first sight it may appear, not without reason, that a physician who undertakes to deal with this subject is wielding his scythe in a stranger's field, rashly claiming as his own that which belongs to the philosopher'. However, mentally distressed people came to physicians rather than to philosophers because what physicians did often worked. If the philosophers objected, he said, he would be quite happy to let them take over his clinic. As we argued in Chapter 3, it is effective doing rather than logic or sublime insights that distinguishes scientists from philosophers.

Antidepressants

Modern psychotropic medication allows much more effective doing than Gaub was capable of. In the case of depression, antidepressants or ECT effectively clear up 70 per cent of patients treated with them. In mania, lithium and ECT do likewise. This clearing up amounts to a cure. The fact that the disorder recurs is neither here nor there. Anti-ulcer agents cure ulcers but they may recur. Influenza clears up but may recur. Neuroleptics do not cure schizophrenia but they are immensely helpful when used properly. But what is it that is done?

The case of the antidepressants is most instructive. When first introduced it was widely supposed that these agents must be stimulants of some sort. Most of the early antidepressants however had sedative side-effects. Nevertheless, clinicians described their effects in terms of an 'alert drowsiness'. In fact antidepressants do not stimulate and do not tranquillize. They most closely resemble antihistamines in their effects. The average reader taking them for several weeks would be aware of little more than a dry mouth, a liability to feel faint if they leap off a chair or minor difficulties passing water. If anything the combined weight of side-effects would yield an experience that was somewhat depressing in the sense of impairing efficiency, rather than stimulating. But for subjects who are depressed, two or three weeks of treatment brings about a change. Sleep improves, appetite increases, energy creeps back and interest reawakens. All of these things happen subtly rather than dramatically, rather like jet-lag or a flu clearing up.

This is important as, if antidepressants were euphoriants, it could be argued that two or three weeks in a stimulated state might be expected to blow away psychological problems. There could be legitimate moral concerns about this kind of treatment, despite its cost-effectiveness in clearing psychiatric wards. But other agents which are euphoriants, such as cocaine, do not cure depression. In the short term, however, unlike antidepressants, cocaine or alcohol may temporarily ameliorate a depression. Such agents, however, can also be expected to at least temporarily alleviate most distressed states of mind. This combination of pharmacological effects points to the dual nature of depression – brain disorder and psychological distress. The latter may be modified by stimulants but the former needs antidepressants or time.

In support of this analysis is the fact that antidepressants are not anti-guilt or anti-hopelessness agents. When given to guilty or hopeless subjects who do not meet criteria for depression, they have no effect on guilty ruminations or suicidal ideation. Yet depressed subjects are activated by these drugs and their thoughts of hopelessness and guilt melt away. This is rather like the effects of anti-ulcer treatment for anxiety. Ulcers cause anxiety. Healing an ulcer commonly relieves that anxiety. Anti-ulcer agents are therefore indirectly anxiolytic for subjects with ulcers. They have, however, no effect on anxiety where this occurs in the absence of ulcers. There is good evidence that both antidepressant and antimanic treatments act to correct circadian rhythm disturbances. Whether this is how they produce cures or not, a therapeutic action of this kind would be consistent with what happens when these drugs are used clinically. That is they correct a general malaise like jet-lag. Removing the stimulus to misinterpretation leads to a consequent alleviation of distressed states of mind.

This point is brought out further in cases of treatment resistance. If depression were some simple enzyme deficiency disorder, treatment with antidepressants could be expected to invariably produce a cure. But a notable aspect of antidepressant treatment is that 30 per cent of those treated do not get well. This has led to intense competition among drug companies to come up with an antidepressant that would cure more than 66 per cent of subjects or that would cure the 33 per cent that conventional antidepressants do not seem to help. Thirty years of research and billions of dollars have not produced an answer. Rather it has become increasingly apparent that all antidepressants cure roughly the same kinds of patients.

Some of the 33 per cent who do not recover readily have been shown to have biological factors militating against a response to antidepressants – such as co-incidental, neuroendocrine abnormalities. Others respond to much higher than the usual doses of antidepressants or to combinations of antidepressants, strongly suggesting a biological resistance to recovery. But in most cases neither of these factors seems to account for non-response.

In terms of the model being outlined here, there are several possible ways that such failures to respond might arise. One is that illness behaviours clustering around an initial disturbance may prevent its resolution, in much the same way that anxiety may perpetuate an ulcer or abnormal postures a lumbago. In such cases management will involve a managing of states of mind as much if not more than brain states. Far from such treatment resistance being the result of a flawed personality, in my experience, the most seriously resistant depressed patients are those who have high standards for themselves. Standards which have led them to achieve more than the average when well and which are accordingly a valuable feature of their make-up. But which when they are depressed make them less prepared to tolerate any fall-off in their level of perform-ance and makes them impatient with a slow pace of recovery. This intolerance and impatience inevitably leads to setbacks and demoralization.

Alternatively, as illness behaviours are often the most salient aspect of the clinical picture, their persistence, despite the resolution of the underlying disturbance, may give a misleading impression that nothing has changed. This seems particularly likely if the illness has lasted a long time untreated. Where the natural tendency may be for a restoration of self-esteem and morale some time after the provoking disturbances have cleared up, too lengthy a demoralization, or in the case of schizophrenia too lengthy an exposure to a 'crazy' world, may overstretch the capacity to bounce back. Among those depressed subjects seemingly resistant to treatment, most sleep and eat normally. Similarly, subjects who appear to have a resistant schizophrenia, in that they are still deluded or hearing voices, rarely continue to experience first rank symptoms and do not stay as agitated as when they first presented.

These resistant states are predictable if, in the affective disorders and schizophrenia, distressed psychological states have an existence that is predicated on but independent of the underlying brain disturbances. Once a psychological state becomes fixed, no amount of pharmacological treatment will bring about an improvement. We have no antidemoraliz-ation agents. No agents that can stitch up a mind that has been rent apart. Yet the drug industry searches for the antidepressant that will cure resistant depressions or the neuroleptic that will bring about changes in chronic schizophrenia. This in itself is not harmful, as a likely spin off of this enterprise will be a greater understanding of the biological bases of these disorders. But another by-product that has been engendered is a belief that resistance to treatment is a matter of a resistant biological illness rather than a scrambled state of mind for which patient unscram-bling is the only possible treatment.

Neuroleptics

In contrast to the rather mysterious actions of antidepressants, neuroleptics are more like tea, coffee, alcohol or cocaine, in that their effects are felt within half an hour and they affect everyone who has them, both volunteer and schizophrenic. They work on incentive motivational systems in the brain, where they block D_2 receptors. This produces a 'who cares' feeling; a certain indifference to what is going on. When first introduced they were clearly described as agents which reduced agitation without unduly sedating patients. Increasingly, however, they are seen as being antischizophrenic and thought to have much the same effects in schizophrenia that antidepressants have in depression. The principal reason for this is that it takes several weeks of their administration before improvement is seen. In the case of schizophrenia, improvement commonly means a resolution of delusions and hallucinations rather than a restoration to normal functioning.

Of central importance is the fact that quite unlike antidepressants, neuroleptics have an acute behavioural effect. An effect that would be likely to lead to a resolution of states of mind born out of agitated distress, provided the subject is themselves intrinsically rational and capable of re-appraising their situation, once offered respite from the stress they have been under. Several weeks in congenial hospital surroundings without neuroleptics also leads to delusions and hallucinations melting away. And as will be mentioned in Chapter 7, there are psychological techniques for the management of delusions and hallucinations.

These latter psychological recourses are rarely taken up, however. Instead, neuroleptics are used in vast amounts in psychiatric clinics and wards. Patients are commonly put on them before they have had a chance to settle on the ward or before ward staff have got to know them. This would be understandable if what was involved was the giving of a specific cure for schizophrenia. In this case delay in medicating the patient means a delay in their recovery. This, however, is not the case. It is convenient to overlook this for cost-effective considerations. Neuroleptics in high doses immobilize patients. On wards where the staffing levels are scandalously low, such benefits cannot be neglected. Sedatives such as the minor tranquillizers and barbiturates could achieve the same effect, but moral questions would be raised in that the control of patients by putting them to sleep is only marginally more 'morally' acceptable than strait-jacketing them. Neuroleptics have the advantage of immobilizing patients while leaving them awake. An illusion can therefore be maintained that they are being 'worked with' as well as medicated.

There are further ambiguities in the way neuroleptics are administered. They are drugs that physicians are happy to give to agitated patients. In contrast if agitated themselves, they would be much more likely to prescribe a sedative for fear of exposing themselves to some of the dramatic and uncomfortable side-effects that neuroleptics can have. Thus, where the prescription of neuroleptics is concerned there is evidence of double standards. This moral issue, however, is quite a different one to those that are typically offered as reasons against taking psychotropic medication.

All psychoactive agents are tainted with the suspicion that they cannot be good as they bring about by artificial means what patients should do for themselves. They must therefore generate an inappropriate dependence. However, neither the neuroleptics or the antidepressants interfere with individual abilities to be authentic. Indeed quite the reverse. Overlengthy exposure to the subtle disturbances of depression or the bewildering ones of schizophrenia, without some assistance, is quite liable to seriously compromise one's ability to be authentic. Even after the underlying illnesses have cleared up. Neither class of drugs produce the physical dependence that leads to serious withdrawal problems, as is found with alcohol, the opiates, barbiturates and benzodiazepines. Nor do either the neuroleptics or antidepressants generate cravings for more, as the opiates, cocaine and amphetamine do. Both these forms of physical dependence are accidents of drug designs and brain wiring. The former results when drugs have particular effects on an area of the brain called the locus coeruleus, the latter if drugs have particular effects on the ventral tegmental area of the brain.

Nevertheless the way in which neuroleptics and antidepressants are used can produce dependency. For example, most depressed subjects lose self-confidence. Antidepressants usually lead to a great improvement if not a complete restoration of self-confidence. Because of current clinical practice, the very use of antidepressants may inhibit a full restoration of self-confidence, as typically the perception of the patient and of many of those treating them is that the drugs have directly restored confidence. Halting them then becomes a problem. And even when halted self-reliance is necessarily affected. This comes about because no one makes clear to the patient what the drugs do and do not do. All of this also applies to neuroleptics and schizophrenia. Far from attempting to build on a patient's strengths, it is much more common to find clinicians writing off their patient's lack of compliance with neuroleptics as evidence of almost 'moral' weakness. Arguably, however, the moral ambiguities in these cases are to be found in the prescribers rather than in what is prescribed or to whom.

It seems rather obvious to say that antidepressants and neuroleptics work on the brain. But in line with the distinctions drawn in Chapter 1, we can give a more precise meaning to that statement. The term working on the brain does not mean working on the mind, in that neither class of agent has any effect on our desires for or ability to strive for authenticity. Neither does working on the brain mean working on the psyche, in that antidepressants and neuroleptics do not affect the constructive activities that we suggested are what is distinctively psychological. In the case of the antidepressants, working on the brain means working on the basic vegetative functions that are prewired into areas of the old brain. In the case of neuroleptics, it means lowering levels of arousal. This being the case, far from physical and psychological treatments being mutually exclusive options, there would seem to be no good reason why these brain treatments could not be combined to a patient's advantage with psychological treatments.

The fear of antidepressants and ECT, as well as the abuse of neuroleptics and the belief that depression, mania and schizophrenia should not respond to psychological management, arguably all stem from a common set of insights and oversights. As a result these illnesses are seen as some nether category of disorders, partly a mythic kind of illness and partly some atypical moral failing. In steering a path between a medical Scylla and a psychological Charybdis, there are few fixed points to guide us. In such a situation of uncertainty, of reaching for the unknown, as Gaub pointed out, reliably demonstrated effects are worth far more than imposing intellectual edifices. Recently a new effect has been demonstrated – the response of endogenous depression to particular forms of psychotherapy. What does this mean for the psychopathology of the psychoses?

SEVEN

The Science of Psychotherapy

In the late 1960s a new form of psychotherapy, cognitive therapy, was outlined by Aaron Beck.[1] Although a psychoanalyst by training he found himself increasingly handling depressed subjects in a common sense, behaviour therapy-oriented fashion. In some respects what happens in cognitive therapy is not far removed from what many of us would do instinctively if confronted by a depressed friend. Where they might point out how useless they are, we would respond by challenging them to square their stated beliefs about themselves with the evidence of past achievements and the estimation of present friends.

As might be expected this form of therapy was initially geared to people who appeared to be neurotically demoralized rather than to people who were waking up early in the morning and losing weight. These latter, Beck felt, were better treated with antidepressants. Cognitive therapy has been surprising on two scores. One has been the fact that a systematic application of such rational strategies brings about a quick therapeutic response in many depressions. The second has been that it is the kind of depression normally expected to respond to pharmacotherapy which responds the quickest.

Shortly afterwards, interpersonal psychotherapy was introduced by Gerald Klerman, Myrnna Weissman and colleagues at Yale and Harvard.[2] Their programme involved focusing on and sorting out some interpersonal difficulty the subject is having. It also brought about a response in a matter of weeks, in subjects who had that kind of depression that would until then have had psychiatrists reaching for their prescription pads. A time period much closer to that brought about by antidepressants than by the depth psychotherapies.

These 'effects' seem to be reliably reproducible. They pose a serious challenge to orthodox medical psychopathology for two reasons. One is that for many on the medical side of the psychopathological divide psychotherapy has been something that has not been considered seriously. The idea of a scientific psychotherapy is taken by many as a contradiction in terms. Its subject matter is seen as intangible, its methods unsystematic in contrast to the natural sciences and it has not been clearly shown to work. The second reason is that even were psychotherapy demonstrably effective and scientific, depression, mania and schizophrenia are thought *in principle* not to be open to treatment by psychotherapy. At the most 'supportive' psychotherapy is seen as appropriate. This is a fancy term for *ad hoc* common sense advice. It has never been systematized as no one appears to have believed that it could amount to much more than a few soothing words.

Accordingly, there has been no development of a theory of psychotherapy in medical psychopathology since Jaspers. He, it was noted in Chapter 3, advocated a psychotherapy based on hermeneutic principles aimed at reconstructing what had actually been happening in an individual's life; the concrete, specific and accidental details. While such a therapy is not linked to technical concepts of the analytic type that would account for how it brings about change, his contention was that such a therapy could be potent. General medical practice strongly supports this possibility.[3] But, he argued, it should not work for depression, mania or schizophrenia.

The definition of psychotherapy

In order to determine if psychotherapy can be scientific, it is necessary to define what it is. Saying that it is the management of psychological problems does not get us very far, as the next question inevitably is, what is a psychological problem? In Chapters 1 and 2, some indications were offered as to what psychological problems are and are not. Broadly speaking, it was suggested that specifically psychological problems arise when current coping strategies, or self-symbolizations, make the solution of present problems more difficult or practically impossible. Thus parents used to looking after children and anticipating every danger for them, may not easily be able to allow those children more independence, when the time for independence comes. There is necessarily a historical dimension to such problems as current coping, and self-conceptions are heavily influenced by past coping and self-conceiving.

In general, current coping strategies and symbolizing tend to focus attention on a certain range of options and away from other possibilities. Ordinarily this focusing allows efficient functioning. But in certain cases it may inhibit it. For example, it allows someone who has mastered driving to attend to other things while they drive, relegating awareness of the road to the margins of attention. But someone who has had a crash or been sensitized to the possibility of a crash, may end up focusing so much of their attention on the road that they end up more liable to crash than others. In the latter case, it can be hypothesized that what is inhibiting the subject is something like images of themselves, involved in a car crash, lying on the margin of their awareness. These distract them from the task in hand, so that attention feels like it is slipping dangerously away from the road. This provokes further anxiety and the feeling that not enough attention is being paid to the road. In contrast, normal driving indicates that there is nothing pathological about things lying outside the margin of conscious awareness. Attending to everything would paralyse ongoing activity.

Putting this in terms of what is traditionally thought of as psychological problems suggests that the issue is not one of a patient's unwillingness to accept what lies 'in their subconscious', so much as their inability to switch attention flexibly. As a result of this, certain possibilities are closed off. They become partially desymbolized. Treatment is not a matter of coming to the truth but of restoring flexibility. Becoming aware of other possibilities does not necessarily mean endorsing them. The best option may be an inhibition; much as my blocking out of my mind the images of some recent quarrel while driving my car on a busy motorway would be.

What a psychological problem is may be further clarified by indicating what it is not. It is not a matter of authenticity or inauthenticity. There is no question that my actions may be influenced by motives of which I am not aware, that I may be blind to many consequences of what I am doing, that a chance encounter or an analysis offered by another may confront me with myself. Still, being authentic is not a matter of being capable of flexible attention. Nor is it a matter of being capable of more extensive attention than the average. It is a matter of choosing and doing, often where it may not be clear what the correct choices and actions are.

While both psychological operations, such as perception, and mental operations, such as being authentic, construct a world, there are profound differences between psychological and mental operations. Perception happens largely automatically. It constructs in order to test reality. Misperception may be fatal. In contrast, being authentic often involves going against the automatic and spontaneous. Failures of authenticity may leave one morally dead, but they are not liable to be lethal. Being authentic or inauthentic is a matter of creating realities.

There are a number of reasons why a confusion of psychological problems with issues of authenticity is almost inevitable. The first is that being authentic is not some faculty of the mind that has nothing to do with the psyche. Rather being authentic involves an organization of psychological capacities aimed at self-definition. Second, while both perceiving and being authentic involve making sense of ambiguity, the perceptual world is largely a given one, whereas the authentic world remains to be created. The struggle to create that world involves juggling ambiguities, the outcome of which may lead to liberation or to compromises that lead on to oppression. Compromises which seep through the psyche to restrict imaginative possibilities, warp personalities and lead to emotional over-investment in doomed solutions. Given the charging of the psychological with the call to authenticity, failures of authenticity will have their psychological correlates. Conversely, the dissecting out of psychological problems will commonly involve picking over issues of meaning in order to pinpoint failures of awareness.

These points may be clarified further through a consideration of the role that symbols may play on both mental and psychological levels. As was noted in Chapter 1, humans respond to symbols in a way that animals do not. Symbols may be used in a linear manner in mathematics, logic, science or as letters in alphabets. It is with these symbols that we construct much of our world. But as opposed to logic or logical argument, which lead linearly to inevitable conclusions, symbols may also be multivocal and admit of internal discourse. They can be constructed from a conjunction of opposites or a juxtaposition of elements not normally associated with each other. They can awaken affects and drives as well as communicate information. Thereby they can link the brain, psyche and mind. Courses of action and values thereby become emotive. Thus the planting of flags on mountain tops or the slaying of dragons are immensely significant acts. In turn emotions reveal values. As Keats put it 'beauty is truth and truth beauty'. Similarly our innate drives are transformed into symbol laden passions and thereby are accommodated in the drama of human living.

Such multivocal symbols can be interpreted. Their interpretation is a matter of moving from elemental meaning to univocal linguistic meaning using language as an arsenal of clues. Freud discovered that blocks in affective development could be pinpointed through an advertence to the symbolic aspects of discourse or behaviour. Some of us dream of fiery dragons, but they usually shrink in the cold light of day. If not or if the tops of mountains keep on receding before us in our dreams, one possibility is that there is an affective block. These symbols may be interpreted in terms of a frustrated sexuality or a thwarted will to power or otherwise. The block can be worked on using differing leads and the success or otherwise of treatment can be followed through any transmutation of pertinent symbols. But, in general, interpretation is likely to be best rewarded, when it follows from close attention to the details of a subject's actual life rather than when it stems from some ideological conviction.

In these cases what is being aimed at is using the way symbols are being used by subjects to pinpoint blocks in awareness rather than using them to analyse a subject's level of authenticity. At the end of the day an ability to flexibly attend to the road while driving does not involve authenticity. Conversely, no amount of liberated attention can guarantee that one will be authentic – that one will do the good thing. Psychotherapy attempts to find an order in the disorder of the past. Living authentically involves creating the order of the future from the disorder of the present.

Neuroses

Put like this it immediately becomes apparent that psychotherapy cannot be an answer to all human problems. Indeed arguably it can only properly be the answer to a very limited number of psychological problems (neuroses). These, however, should have a different character to the other problems of human living, although superficially this may not be apparent. By a neurosis, therefore, we mean a paralysis of attention by anxiety. Traditionally the anxiety neuroses have been broken down into depressive, phobic, obsessive-compulsive, hysterical and hypochondriacal neuroses. These need to be clearly distinguished from psychiatric illnesses, which involve biological disordering.

They also need to be distinguished from the mental terrors that lie in wait for all of us. Thus the demoralization of a depressive neurosis should not be confounded with the despair that may grip us when faced with the intractability of many of the problems of living. And anxiety itself needs to be kept apart from the legitimate angst that should arise at the contemplation of the fact that human beings in a very real sense do make and break each other. In the case of demoralization and anxiety, there has been a deskilling of the subject, a limiting of attention to a very restricted round, whereas this is not the case in states of angst and despair.

The neurotic limitation of attention to a restricted round of feelings also needs to be distinguished from the resentment (ressentiment) consequent on individual or social injustices or accidents of fate. Many thinkers from Nietsche onwards have argued that much of our feelings of being ill at ease stem from poorly understood resentments.[4,5] Although reflection in the company of another may help to focus such feelings, psychotherapy will not provide the answers for this inner discontent. Changing these feelings will be a matter of changing our world rather than changing ourselves.

REVOLUTION IN PSYCHOTHERAPY

In chapters 1, 2 and 3, it was argued that Freud established a psychotherapeutic paradigm. That he was the first to define the psychological and to establish that interpretation is a valid approach to issues of psychological distress. However analysis all too quickly involved itself in questions of what it is to be authentically human. Far from settling for the satisfactory resolution of psychological problems. Freud took on the challenge of determining the significance of human behaviour. A challenge doomed to failure as without knowing where we come from or where we are going, the true significance of human behaviour remains obscure. Everyone responds to the mystery of the human as they see fit. In venturing into these 'religious' waters, *psycho*therapy lost itself.

Freud saw the discovery of the dynamic psyche as something comparable with the discovery of the Americas. He often compared himself to Columbus. However history contains what I believe is an appropriate irony here. Columbus rediscovered America. As Freud's discovery was a discovery rather than a rediscovery, it was something more like the discovery of America by Leif Ericsson rather than its rediscovery by Columbus. Like Ericsson's discovery, Freud's new found continent was also lost sight of, even by himself. It has had to be rediscovered in recent years. Rediscovery has involved revolution, but a revolution that unlike Freud's did not involve an open and dramatic assault on the citadel of orthodoxy. A revolution that like some other long revolutions began as a barely discernible popular movement in the hinterlands. Such a long revolution, I suggest, has been in the making ever since the introduction of behaviour therapy for the various neuroses in the late 1950s and early 1960s.

Unlike the depth psychotherapies, behaviour therapy has a proven effectiveness. Its cure rates for phobic and obsessional neuroses surpass those of many supposedly effective medications in other branches of medicine. However, this success has not led to any large scale change in medical attitudes regarding psychotherapy. Arguably because behaviour therapy was not seen as a psychotherapy. Not even though increasingly behaviour therapists have worked on the images in people's minds or the thoughts that come into their minds in anxious situations. This is because to many what seemed involved in behaviour therapy was no more than applied common sense, a world away from the arcane mysteries of the depth psychotherapies. It often seems to involve little more than procedures that are at only one remove from telling someone who has just fallen off a horse to make sure to ride again sooner rather than later.

There is no a priori reason why a *psycho*therapy should be more complex than this. Mundane though such manoeuvres might appear the strength of behaviour therapy as it has evolved has been that it has stuck closely with what clearly works rather than adhered to dogma. So much so that many behaviour therapists openly concede that the effectiveness of current behavioural techniques cannot be explained by an appeal to the learning theories, which were the ideological launching pads for this form of therapy.

Another reason why behaviour therapy has been so acceptable in medical circles has almost certainly been that behaviour therapists, for their own ideological reasons, have from the start disassociated themselves from the 'interpretative' psychotherapies. However, while behaviour therapists may baulk at the idea that they engage in interpretations, in practice behaviour therapy first involves a detailed reconstruction of what has been happening to an individual in order to determine the precise shape of their particular problem and the factors influencing it. Such reconstructions are implicitly hermeneutic.

However, unlike interpretations that aim at timeless truths, behavioural reconstructions aim at the concrete, specific and accidental. 'Interpretations' are rarely formally communicated. But they do become explicit in the course of the behavioural programme drawn up on the basis of the historical reconstruction. If the treatment decided on involves a graded programme of re-exposure to the feared stimulus, the implicit interpretation of the problem behaviour is that it is a matter of habitual anxiety that can be uprooted much as one would other habits. In other cases the subject's attention may be drawn to the fact that when they become anxious, they become vigilant and in so doing they attend selectively, which leads to certain things being overlooked. One of the overlooked things commonly is an anxiety about being anxious. Not recognizing this as a source of anxiety, they become increasingly aroused, increasingly less likely to recognize the true source of their distress and increasingly inflexible.

The concrete, accidental and specific[6,7]

Whatever about the mundane quality of behavioural interventions, they deal with what are clearly psychological problems uncontaminated by issues of authenticity. They also deal with concrete, specific and accidental situations. This, it may be remembered from Chapter 3, was the issue that determined the future shape of psychoanalysis. Freud was anxious to find the necessary laws of the psyche behind the chaos of fleeting psychic appearances given to us on introspection. This led him to his topographical theory of the psyche, with its ids, egos and superegos. It also led him away from the appearances of things and away from 'opinions'.

Apart from a hermeneutic reconstruction of specific psychological problems, which behaviour therapy took over from psychoanalysis when the latter moved on to weightier issues, another psychotherapy emerged to address the chaos of fleeting psychic appearances, when Freud retreated from this battleground. This was gestalt therapy. From Chapter 4, it may be remembered that gestalt psychology emerged from phenomenology, when the latter veered off into philosophy. It returned to the earliest concerns of phenomenology, which were with the appearances of mental life. The fleeting impressions we have of things, which Brentano argued are the data that must be collected if any science of the psyche was to have empirical validity, and which philosophy had ignored until then.

Among the discoveries of gestalt psychology were findings that our perceptions are constructions rather than sensations. For example, when confronted by ambiguous stimuli, we see patterns in them. But to appreciate this aspect of perception required the experimental manipulation of appearances, to see which appearances suggest which constructions. This kind of research has heavily influenced advertising techniques, which ironically many are more likely to think of as stemming from psychoanalysis.

When faced with the chaos of internal appearances, gestalt psychology paid heed to them as much as it had done to external appearances. This approach was taken over by Fritz Perls in 1950 and applied to psychotherapy. He used Freud's method of free association but adapted it. In the first place free association was not seen as a prelude to interpretation. In the second place, gestalt psychotherapy turned away from associations focused on an individual's past and turned toward encouraging subjects to grasp current impressions and appearances, especially interpersonal ones.

This led to the methodological dictum of therapy being a matter of approaching the *here and now* – the concrete, specific and accidental. Anyone who has taken part in properly conducted gestalt or encounter groups will know that the effects of following this approach can be extraordinarily powerful. And furthermore that marked changes in self-awareness may be brought about by these techniques in a matter of hours or days, in contrast to the months or years commonly associated with classic analysis. What is happening to bring about such changes? Well nothing so 'deep' as a restructuring of the personality or the uncovering of buried conflicts. Rather arguably what is happening is a very pure form of 'reality testing'. A fantasizing in the company of others, so that one's most intimate hypotheses get measured against reality.

Why should this lead to anyone changing their hypotheses? After all reality for me is what is real for me and there can be no arguing with this as no one can see into my mind and tell me I am cheating. While this is true, something else happens in the company of others, where one is unable to totally fashion reality as one might wish. Something that is close to the experience we all have when, having rehearsed some talk or argument privately, on coming to give it we find that what we were sure we had wanted to say is not what we wanted after all. Or again when writing an article or book that will be reviewed by others, it may be only when the reviewers' comments come back that one may realize that what one has actually written is not what one had in mind. That is, while the construction that one had intended was implicit in the appearances of one's speech or article, this is not the only possible construction that these appearances will sustain. When one is made aware of other possibilities, one can set about trying to tie the appearances down to a specific construction. But frequently this is the point where creative change in the original construction may come about, as one becomes aware of neglected possibilities.

Considering only the psychological aspects of what is happening in such cases, the process involved appears to be a pushing back of the margin of awareness. This leads to subjects appropriating, making their own, aspects of their experience that they are commonly cut off from.

They are cut off by their own conceptions of what they spontaneously are; conceptions that restrict attention to certain possibilities only.

This formulation of what happens in psychotherapy seems supported by a good deal of research work that has looked at what ingredients are both effective and common to the various schools of therapy.[8] Abstractions such as empathy or the ability of the therapist to sensitively and accurately understand the client, or unconditional warmth, appeared to be common to all approaches. But these are such multidimensional factors that they are not particularly useful in identifying what specifically can be done to improve practice on the ground. In contrast to these semi-mystical processes often assumed to be at play in psychotherapy, all to a large extent beyond the consistent control of therapist or patient, another common variable is concreteness. Concreteness is something that can be achieved even if all the other elements are lacking. It can be achieved reliably.[9] Furthermore, if given a clear idea of what is needed, patients can make an active contribution toward its achievement rather than having to take the passive role usually thrust on them.

THE PSYCHOTHERAPY OF THE PSYCHOSES

Cognitive and interpersonal psychotherapies appear to cure one of the psychoses, depression. How? What is going on and can it be generalized to the other psychoses, mania and schizophrenia?

In attempting to account for responses to these therapies, there seem to be two possibilities. Response might be brought about directly because the interpretative intervention has hit on some home truths; i.e. that the patient is being illogical or that they have interpersonal difficulties. This would conform to an older notion of what psychotherapy should be all about. But apart from running against the grain of history, the response of what appear to be the same group of depressions to both interpersonal and cognitive approaches, which have different sets of aetiological home truths, would appear at odds with this explanation of what is happening.

Another possible explanation can be drawn from what both treatments actually do as opposed to what they think they aim at doing. While both differ in theory from each other and from the depth psychotherapies before them, they have a common feature that they do not share with the depth psychologies. This is an explicit pursuit of pragmatic courses. For the sake of this both are prepared to prescind at least somewhat from their theoretical presuppositions. Cognitive therapists see their task as one of helping a subject to handle their actual experience empirically rather than experiences in general. To stand back from preconceptions and see what constructions the evidence on specific incidents reasonably supports. To help them to distinguish abstract from concrete specifications of problems and push them toward the concrete. To do this the therapist will often ask the patient to keep a diary of what actually happens to them between sessions and how they felt at the time various things were happening. Similarly, interpersonal therapy picks a current interpersonal difficulty and aims at tackling that rather than the issue of relationships in general and their significance. Perhaps then it is the systematic challenge to specific salient concerns, whether interpersonal or otherwise, that brings about cures.

This is possible in the case of a depressive neurosis. But not in the case of a major depressive disorder. The only way that such an approach could work in the latter case is if such challenges remove an aggravating or maintaining factor, allowing an illness to resolve that has a natural history of resolution – as the evidence suggests both depression and mania have. An analogous resolution of an organic disturbance that can be brought about by rational management without pharmacotherapy can be found in the treatment of ulcers. Identifying for a person what the cause of their distress is, insisting that they relax for a few weeks and ensuring that they eat regular bland meals and abstain from things such as alcohol and smoking will frequently bring about a cure.

Indeed our abilities to treat ulcers successfully without pills still far exceeds our ability to change personalities. This being the case one can argue that many clearly 'biological' depressions *should* respond more cleanly to cognitive and interpersonal psychotherapies than do definitely neurotic depressions. This seems to be the case. Neurotic 'depressions' are more likely to take months or up to a year to show much response to these new therapies.

Of pertinence to the argument is the issue of what happens to the cognitive style of subjects who have recovered from depression after treatment with antidepressants. In fact it is indistinguishable from that of recovered subjects who have been treated with cognitive therapy. It hardly seems possible that antidepressants in some way make one more logical. The alternative – that the errors in logic that lead to the typical beliefs of a seriously depressed person have been simply those of normal irrationality operating on an abnormal experience – seems more reasonable. Such biases are liable to distort the interpretation of significant interpersonal relationships as well as everything else. But again subjects treated with antidepressants commonly find that their interpersonal relationships have a way of straightening themselves out on recovery even without any expert counselling on these matters.

Despite their current theoretical commitments, therefore, both cognitive and interpersonal psychotherapies leave themselves open to reformulation in terms of being psychotherapies aimed at the concrete, specific and accidental. Both focus explicitly on well-defined discrete problems or instances of poor handling of situations rather than on global interpretations of what is happening or why. While not heavily emphasized in either approach, this is a novel development. Although a biological illness is being treated in the case of depression, the practice of cognitive and interpersonal therapies regarding depression are psychotherapeutic in the sense of dealing with psychological rather than mental issues. They are concerned with adaptive and maladaptive attention or with perception and misperception, rather than with authenticity or inauthenticity. They take issue with the constructions of the depressed subject and challenge them to a reality test – to approach the concrete.

Psychotherapy of a disease

While the demonstration of reliable effects in the psychotherapy of depression is new, the ideas which underlie cognitive and interpersonal therapies are not wholly novel. In 1958, Samuel Kraines advocated a rational management of manic-depressive disorders recognizing the role that states of mind play in the clinical evolution of the disorder and the degree of distress occasioned to affected subjects.[10] His views came close to the current practice of cognitive and interpersonal psychotherapy. In 1963, James Chapman and Andrew McGhie offered similar strategies for handling schizophrenia – that is recognizing that the subject being treated is ill, attempting to pinpoint what the experiences consequent on the illness are and trying to disentangle the illness from reactions to it.[11] These ideas fell on deaf ears it seems. In large part this can probably be attributed to the introduction of antidepressant and neuroleptic drugs around the same time. These have monopolized research and therapeutic attention.

What is offered now differs little from what was advocated by Kraines in 1958. What has changed since then is not our ability to tackle such problems rationally, but the willingness to tackle the problems of depression systematically. Current willingness has arisen from demonstrations that such approaches can yield results and also a growing appreciation that what needs explaining is why some cases of depression do not get well rather than why some do. It seems likely that those who are slowest to respond have suffered the greatest loss in morale. Kraines facing a manic depressive believed that the disease process took a natural course, typically lasting over a year until resolution. Accordingly, while suggesting that psychological reactions should be handled rationally in order to minimize the long-term damage a subject inflicted on themselves, he could offer little to boost morale in the short term. Interpersonal and cognitive therapies in contrast can offer more. And it is possibly simply the hope that they offer that tilts the balance toward recovery.

Like Kraines, and Chapman and McGhie, both cognitive and interpersonal treatments also have in common an explicit recognition of disease elements in the clinical picture. Conceding that disease processes should be recognized and not interpreted constitutes a radical break with older ideas of what a psychotherapy is. However, while cognitive and interpersonal therapies concede this point, neither approach exploits it as of yet. Exploiting the point rather than simply conceding it would seem to be required, however, as success in many cases of depression is all too likely to have stemmed from the strong tendency to natural resolution for this disorder than from any optimum application of rational strategies to the problem. However, resistant cases of depression, as well as mania and the more complicated case of schizophrenia, challenge us to make thoroughly scientific our psychotherapeutic strategies.

Explicitly building around the natural history of the disorders in question would make it clear that the psychotherapy involved is a matter of harnessing spontaneous tendencies to recovery rather than one of pulling therapeutic rabbits out of black recesses of the mind or achieved because of any heroic qualities of the therapist. Mania might be a good testing ground for this approach as it, even more than depression, tends to run a clearly circumscribed course. It would be a worthy endeavour as the current physical treatment of mania relies heavily on neuroleptics – not to reduce agitation so much as to immobilize the patient in a chemical straitjacket.[12]

Schizophrenia will arguably provide a more testing challenge. In this case it is not clear what the natural history is. Accordingly, it is not possible to say whether psychotherapy can facilitate a cure. However, it can be noted that there have been a number of neglected reports of chronic delusional states responding to cognitive-type approaches.[13,14] There are also reports of hallucinations responding to the quite simple behavioural strategies of getting subjects to talk about something else. Bearing in mind the subvocalization that accompanies hallucinations, noted in Chapter 5, this should and does have the effect of interfering with auditory hallucinations. These strategies, however, are not being put into practice anywhere, despite the many complications that result from over-reliance on neuroleptic drugs.

Psychotherapy and inverse insights

Having developed the notion of inverse insights, we are in a position to propose something more than simply grafting cognitive and behavioural strategies onto spontaneous healing processes in the affective disorders or onto a disease of undetermined course in the case of schizophrenia. The thrust of Chapter 4 was that these disease processes provide an ongoing set of stimuli that will inevitably be interpreted and can only be correctly interpreted counter-intuitively. This focuses attention on a cardinal point of hermeneutic method which is to avoid misunderstanding by giving the to-be-interpreted subject the benefit of the doubt as a rational subject, particularly when the behaviour under investigation appears to fall short of rationality. Suspending interpretation, however, does not come easily to either affected subjects or, it seems, to their therapists.

It is with the constructions that subjects have put on what is happening that cognitive and interpersonal therapies explicitly take issue, by pointing to the evidence that is not accounted for by the subject's construction. Such a method, in the case of schizophrenia and the affective disorders, approaches the concrete indirectly. A more direct approach would attempt to seek out what may be briefly uncovered by the stripping away of misconstructions. But neither therapy explicitly acknowledges that there are core experiences that may be approached independently of the attempt to strip away misconstructions. The addition of inverse insights to the therapeutic process would lead to a revealing of the actual experiences liable to misconstruction – a time-honoured psychotherapeutic goal.

Indeed one can argue that unless cognitive and interpersonal therapies do more to take on board the basic experiences of their subjects, they are going to remain less than wholly empirical. Furthermore, simply taking issue with the constructions of a patient, apart from being potentially wrong, risks descending into a benevolent supportiveness rather than being an ascent to the concrete. The addition of inverse insights to uncover experiences that have intruded into awareness but which resist adaptive symbolization would provide a therapy that more clearly aims at the concrete, specific and accidental and at what are clearly psychological issues.

For example, it was noted in Chapter 4 that there are differences in the concentration disturbances of depressed subjects from those found in preoccupied subjects. These seem distinguishable simply on the basis of what people say, if their experiences are sufficiently probed. The loss of interest or energy found in depression is also likely to be differentiable on phenomenological grounds from losses of interest or energy encountered normally. If, for example, circadian rhythms are disturbed in depression, something like the following differentiations should be possible. Normally we have a stream of images flowing through consciousness. This happens to a large extent automatically and involuntarily and is probably dependent on automatic turnover in the neurophysiological milieu. Disruption of this turnover might plausibly be experienced in terms of loss of texture to thinking, an emptying of the mind or a loss of creativity. In contrast to boredom or states of existential despair this should be describable in specific, if subtle, terms – such as a drying up of image flow. In the case of energy, rhythmic and involuntary surges of energy occur normally as a part of the basic rest–activity cycle. We all take advantage of these during the day but rarely recognize them as being involuntary and automatic. A disturbance of rhythms would lead to a specific failure to 'get going' rather than an absolute loss of energy.

These examples, whether actually correct or not, indicate the kind of specific phenomenological differentiations that a thoroughly scientific application of hermeneutic method demands. Failure to recognize the need for an inverse insight, in such instances, is likely to lead to both the clinical picture and the therapeutic process being dominated by the consequences of this oversight. However, while inverse insights restrict the subject matter to be interpreted, they also highlight what *is* to be interpreted.

For most of the past ninety years, delusions and hallucinations have been seen as psychological rather than neuropsychological phenomena. Yet the psychotherapies to date have studiously steered clear of attempting to resolve these psychological issues. They have concentrated instead on the easy meat of apparently neurotic phenomena, such as feelings of alienation or awkwardness in the case of schizophrenia or the loss of energy or concentration in depression.

Working out how to interpret what is to be interpreted remains as big a challenge to psychotherapy as coming up with a methodology for avoiding inappropriate interpretation. While behavioural techniques have led to substantial advances in the psychological management of phobic or obsessive neuroses, there have not been any comparable developments in the management of hysterical reactions or in the understanding of what happens in hypnosis. The issues of paranoia, sensitive reactions and the issue of personality development also need attention, as manic depression and schizophrenia are illnesses that will seek out the vulnerable points in a personality. In order to properly disentangle abnormal experiences from abnormal constructions, the full range of possible abnormal constructions needs to be known as well as the range of abnormal experiences. This will permit distinctions between normal constructions of abnormal experiences, abnormal constructions of normal experiences and abnormal constructions of abnormal experiences.

Negligent therapy

What is not needed is any focus on authenticity or programme to advance self-knowledge. Any raising of the spectre of authenticity is probably a good indication that other factors are being dragged into the therapeutic situation inappropriately. Many, if not all, subjects being treated will be to some extent inauthentic, to some extent drifting through life rather than self-actualizing, will be involved in at least some ambiguous relationships and will have some skeletons boarded up in some recess of their minds. But as a rule they are unlikely to be any more inauthentic than their therapists. Depression, mania and schizophrenia function as black holes in regard to issues of authenticity such as these, sucking in all possible failings the subject has in the attempt to account for what is going wrong. Far from promoting authenticity, the therapist's task should be one of disentangling the subject from these issues. Failure to do this is liable to be spiritually oppressive. Indeed is even more liable to have serious long-term side-effects than any drug treatment. Side-effects that arguably should as readily sustain a charge of clinical malpractice as the induction of side-effects by drugs may do.

It is equally important to stress that no improvement in a patient's capacity to communicate is being proposed. At present the therapeutic urge to improve the communication skills of those with an affective disorder or schizophrenia seems to be equivalent to general medicine's desire to get everyone fit. But while being fit may be desirable, in the case of heart attacks no one comes to the bedside of the sick person and suggests that they get out of bed and start push-ups or other exercises. Effectively, however, this is what we do to subjects with psychiatric illnesses. As soon as they are admitted to hospital they are inducted into therapy groups. The idea that a subject might wish to shut themselves away from that kind of thing is strongly disapproved of.[15]

However, just as with the issue of authenticity, if the present view is correct, the possession of communications skills will do little to protect one from these illnesses. There should be a wide range of abilities to communicate emotional material, but these should bear little or no correlation with the likelihood of becoming depressed, manic or schizophrenic. In contrast, many therapists are likely to have entered the field of mental illness in an effort to sort out their own communication problems, rather than because of any proven ability to help others communicate. There is a further irony, if the present view is correct, in that a good part of the problem of mental illness would stem from a failure of therapists to listen rather than of patients to communicate.

A further point that needs to be stressed in view of the successes of cognitive therapy is that it is not envisaged that subjects will become any the less biased as a consequence of the procedures outlined. In some of the cognitive therapy literature, making subjects take an empirical stance on particular problems seems to be equated with making them more empirical generally.

In contrast, Mark Williams has re-interpreted the cognitive programme in terms quite different to those originally put forward.[16] He has argued that far from assisting patients to function normally, what cognitive therapy requires of them is something quite artificial and quite specialized. As artificial as the speech techniques that a stammerer will use to produce the illusion of normality. As artificial as science which so often turns common sense upside down and does so by suspending the normal biases of human knowing. However, these biases cannot be eradicated. At most they can be suspended with great difficulty in limited areas of functioning, such as is achieved by scientists in a single area of expertise. Being 'scientific' does not generalize even though many scientists act as though their opinions on a vast variety of things should be taken to have scientific weight. The reason why not is that these heuristic biases form the basis of common sense.

THE EMPIRICAL PATIENT – AN AGENDA

The management and, potentially, the resolution of schizophrenia and the affective disorders by a psychotherapy would fulfil the original agenda for psychotherapy. It would also see the confirmation of an even older intuition, noted in Chapter 2, that the functional psychoses were disorders open to non-physical management. Furthermore, the effectiveness of cognitive and interpersonal therapy as they stand and the potential that might result from adapting them in the manner outlined above, would highlight the revolution in psychotherapy that has been occurring over the past thirty years. A revolution that has been progressively restoring the psyche to psychotherapy.

As a matter of strategy the kind of operation that the new psychotherapy involves has been painted in prosaic terms, with behavioural managements of phobias and obsessions as its exemplars. This has been deliberate in order to illustrate the departure from psychoanalytic involvements in philosophical and other existential affairs. But it is not being suggested that in order to make psychotherapy look scientific that all manifestations of creative imagination should be suppressed. Rather it will take a full flowering of artistic imagination to encompass the tension of opposites and co-existing contradictions that can be found in even the most average of psychiatric problems.

Something else is required in the case of the potential psychotherapy of the psychoses. To achieve the concrete will require not the heroic detachment of an empirical therapist, but an interplay between two individuals or a group of individuals. The myths of science hitherto have portrayed scientists as somehow innately more empirical than the rest of us, or empiricism as being some mysteriously acquired virtue tucked away in the minds of scientists. In contrast, the myths about the mentally ill have portrayed them as the least empirical of people, with those who are psychotic being by definition inaccessibly unempirical. This view of how science ascends to the concrete has been rejected in Chapter 3, as has the complementary view of subjects afflicted with a psychosis in Chapters 4 and 5.

It was suggested that science involves an approach to the concrete by agreement among investigators competent to decide on the claims of formulations put forward to grapple with concrete and specific issues. The empirical nature of the enterprise does not stem from the qualities of any one individual but from the fact that the enterprise is a collaborative one. Left to their own devices, without a peer group to winnow the wheat from the chaff, even the most eminent of scientists lose touch with reality. On this basis, psychotherapy could be the model scientific enterprise as it, more clearly than any other field of endeavour, involves an ascent to the concrete by collaboration.

Far from being some mysteriously private exercise, that involves the application of established rules, it can be expected that such a psycho-therapy would be a collaborative exercise that like any other science can be expected to yield cumulative results. It would not be simply the curing of individuals through the laying on of therapeutic hands, but would require a recording and cataloguing of the experiences of depression, mania and schizophrenia. These would build up cumulatively through the efforts of affected subjects and their therapists. They could then be made available to everyone.

There is a very important sense in which such an enterprise is scientific and indeed capable of being free of many of the controversies that surround other scientific endeavours. When we think of science we normally think of theories and experiments, with theories being tested by experiments and experimental results suggesting new theories. So it is assumed we advance. Many of the scientific disputes and disputes about science centre on whether theory or experiment should be given primacy (Chapter 3). But as Einstein noted, neither theory nor experiment are particularly reliable. Theories are what no one really believes, except their inventor. And experiments are what everyone believes, except the experimenter.[17] However, there is another type of scientific exercise that everyone seems happy to accept, and this involves descrip-tion. Vast amounts of science involve neither theory nor experiment but are based on cataloguing and establishing a bedrock of descriptions – botany, zoology, much of geology and geography. The endeavours made to produce these data were of the essence of science – moving ever closer to the totality of the concrete, in an enterprise that is collaborative, methodical and yields cumulative results.

So also, it can be argued, should science approach the core experiences of the psychoses and especially schizophrenia. Many individuals have written their accounts of schizophrenia from the inside.[18,19] A number of researchers have wondered why no heed has been paid to such accounts.[20,21] One good reason perhaps has been that accounts to date have not been systematically collected. They have been individual. All too often what has been written are individual constructions rather than raw experiences.

It is only likely to be when the effort to describe is made in collabor-ation with others that what is happening can be *deconstructed*. Only then will the common core experiences of the psychoses emerge in a way that will command general consent and provide data that can be built on. Until then individual accounts remain harbingers of what might be achieved rather than useful data. Given the myths surrounding science and the psychoses outlined throughout this book, the appropriate break with the past and symbol of what might be achieved would be for some individuals affected with schizophrenia to be awarded scientific recognition for their work on schizophrenia from the inside.

In recent years there have been hints of a growing awareness on the part of some researchers that many people with schizophrenia have been handling their illness quite successfully for years, without the aid of the caring professions. Surveys have been done on the management of hallucinations, delusions and basic disturbances by a number of groups,[22-24] with findings that suggest that many patients have worked out strategies for the management of these difficulties. But evidence from patients as to what works is accorded a very low priority.

It should be possible to work towards a management package consisting of accurate descriptions of what experiences the core brain disturbances of the affective disorders and schizophrenia entail, as well as practical manoeuvres to contain their disrupting effects. This could be expected to lead to a cure in many cases of affective disorder. While not necessarily leading to cure in the case of schizophrenia, such a therapeutic approach would lead to a handing back of the control of these illnesses to those who are affected.

This is not intended as a subversive statement but to echo what Isaac Marks, one of the most eminent behaviour therapists, believes is possible regarding the behaviour therapy of the neuroses. He has argued that a motivated individual armed with the right books and a supportive general practitioner or friend should be able to do nearly as much for themselves as a psychiatrist or psychologist could do for them.[25] It may well be that individuals and groups will have to take the initiative on this score rather than wait to be enfolded in the therapeutic embrace of the caring professions: an embrace that until now has been more of a bear hug.

The example of Gilles de la Tourette syndrome may provide a paradigm of what is needed. This disorder is very visible, consisting as it does of marked involuntary tics and automatic movements, sometimes accompanied by grunts, swearing or obscene language. Yet both the medical and psychological communities managed for seventy years after its first descriptions to deny its existence. It is only now being investigated intensively thanks to the efforts of sufferers and their relatives acting through associations.[26] Their success suggests that the motive of healing is not confined to members of the therapeutic professions, but is an aspiration of all people. An aspiration that also suggests that our vital engagement in scientific progress is for those reasons of the heart, which reason does not know of – to cite Pascal, who in discovering probability perhaps did more than anyone to impel us towards the concrete and its mysteries.

FROM MYTH TO MYSTERY

The arguments of this book are pitched at a general level rather than at the specific level of so-called matters of fact. As there are no matters of fact that are not constructed, the general level would seem to be as important as the specific level. Viewed from the general perspective, it would seem that when dealing with the psychoses, whether we are medically or psychologically oriented, we are still all too often grappling with 'spiritual' issues. There is a ghostly halo around our facts, despite successive scientific revolutions. This perhaps is not surprising as the original meaning of both the terms revolution and conversion implies an ebbing and flowing over the same piece of ground.

Viewed generally, science can be characterized as a process of moving from myth to mystery. Where once we accounted for the origins of the universe and mankind, and for the nature of human diversity and good and evil, by means of myths, scientific advance toward the concrete reality of our existence has replaced these myths with mysteries. The very essence of being scientific lies in the ability to face the mysterious unknown, without resorting to myth. This is not an easy achievement and sometimes science serves to perpetuate myths by cloaking them in scientific legitimacy.

William Arens has written about a notable instance of this.[27] It seems that there is no reliable evidence that cannibalism has ever been practised routinely by any group of people anywhere. Yet the entire structure of anthropology rests on the belief that people differ and that their differences are an appropriate matter for scientific investigation. In this context, anthropology it would appear has perpetuated the man-eating myth, as the acknowledgement of cannibalism and scientific interest in it is a potent symbol of what anthropology is all about – the detached recording of human differences. When faced with a choice between this myth and the facts, anthropology has chosen the myth.

Although most clearly developed by Arens, this ambiguous relationship between anthropologists and anthropophagists was first noted by Claude Levi-Strauss. He also proposed that a similar relationship exists between 'mental patients' and those who study and treat them, with the science of mental illness commonly being one that legitimizes the alienation of the mental patient rather than seeking their re-integration. To a great extent both he and Arens argue that that the meta-anthropology of anthropologists and mental health theorists is shaped by the culture from which these scientists come. In both cases 'we – the civilized and sane' appear to need boundaries beyond which lie the primitive and the mad. Our scientists cannot avoid coming to data, or creating data, without bringing these biases to bear.

Just as Arens and others have found that the supposedly cast iron evidence of cannibalism vanishes when one goes in search of it critically, so it has increasingly seemed to me that the patients I have had to treat or seen treated are no more out of touch with reality than the rest of us. There are certainly patients with depression, mania and schizophrenia who are difficult, immature or objectionable, but so too are many patients in other branches of medicine, many of the therapists who treat them and many people in other walks of life. But the idea that 'mental' patients are in some additional way out of touch with reality is a notion for which I can find no good proof. Rather in searching for the evidence it has seemed to me that this is a notion that anteceded modern psychiatric practice and that modern practice does precious little to dispel.

Change will not be simply a matter of producing new facts as inconvenient facts can simply be ignored. This is particularly the case in the human sciences. In the physical sciences, where the macrocosmos is the object of investigation, the universe gives unequivocal answers to our questions. Yes, man can fly: no, you cannot build a perpetual motion machine. In many cases, these answers confound the expectations of our senses and go against the grain of common sense. For example, when concrete ships float or string vests are shown to retain more heat than vests without 'holes' in them. However, being the creatures we are, we adjust to these novelties and the control over the universe they afford, particularly if there is money to be made out of what has been discovered.

This process does not apply as smoothly in those sciences through which we investigate ourselves, the microcosmos. Adjustment in these cases often involves adjusting our ideas of who we are or more disturbingly what we are to make of ourselves. Failure to grasp this nettle often leads to the control that scientific advance should confer becoming in the human sciences, all too often a control that oppresses rather than a control that leads to liberation. The latest revolution all too often has seemed to end up as the newest oppression.

Liberation will involve changing ourselves and removing the biases embedded in our culture. This is most clearly so in the case of schizophrenia. So long as the expectations of all of us contain the belief that those who have this and other psychoses are tainted with otherness, the ability of each of us who have these illnesses to grapple with them will be lessened thereby. As a consequence we will all be less likely to learn what there is to be learnt about ourselves from these illnesses and from the history of attitudes to them. Less likely to move from myth to mystery. Can we effect this change in ourselves? This is the point at which mental issues intrude into psychological problems. This is the point at which it is pertinent to talk of authenticity. This is the point at which we must create reality.

> Sara, little seed,
> Little violent diligent seed. Come let us look at the world
> Glittering: this seed will speak,
> Max, words! There will be no other words in the world
> But those our children speak. What will she make of a world
> Do you suppose, Max, of which she is made.

'Sara in her Father's Arms', *Collected Poems*, George Oppen[28]
© George Oppen, 1962. Reprinted by permission
of New Directions Publishing Corporation.

References

ONE Mind, Psyche and Brain

1   Snell, B., *The Discovery of the Mind*, Harper Torchbook, New York, 1960.
2   Voegelin, E., Reason: the classic experience, *Southern Review*, 10, 237–264, 1974.
3   Prigogine, I., and Stengers, I., *Order Out of Chaos*, Fontana Books, 1985.
4   Ibid.
5   Rosenberg, A., *The Structure of Biological Science*, Cambridge University Press, Cambridge, 1985.
6   Ibid.
7   Oakley, D., *Brain and Mind*, Methuen, London, 1985.
8   Kosslyn, S. M., *Ghosts in the Mind's Machine*, W. W. Norton and Co., London, 1983.
9   Sacks, O., *The Man who Mistook his Wife for a Hat*, Picador, 1985.
10 Luria, A. R., *The Mind of a Mnemonist*, Harvard University Press, 1965.
11 Neisser, U., *Cognition and Reality*, W. H. Freeman and Co., San Francisco, 1976.
12 Gould, S. J., *The Mismeasure of Man*, Penguin Books, 1981.
13 O'Donnell, J. M., *The Origins of Behaviourism*, New York University Press, New York, 1985.
14 Ibid.
15 Gardner, H., *The Mind's New Science*, Basic Books, New York, 1985.
16 Neisser, U., *Cognition and Reality*.
17 Popper, K. R. and Eccles, J. C., *The Self and its Brain*, Routledge and Kegan Paul, 1983.
18 Searle, J. R., *Intentionality*, Cambridge University Press, Cambridge, 1984.
19 Voegelin, E., *Plato*, Louisiana State University Press, Baton Rouge, 1966.
20 MacMurray, J., *The Self as Agent*, Faber and Faber, 1957.
21 Searle, J. R., *Intentionality*.
22 O'Neill, Y. V., *Speech and Speech Disorders in Western Thought Before 1600*, Greenwood Press, London, 1980.
23 Voegelin, E., *Reason: the classic experience*.
24 Jackson, S. W., *Melancholia and Depression from Hippocratic Times to Modern Times*, Yale University Press, New Haven, 1986.
25 Dowbiggin, I., Degeneration and heredetarianism in French mental medicine

1840–1890. In *The Anatomy of Madness*, (Bynum, W. F. *et al.*, eds), vol. 1, 188–232, Cambridge University Press, Cambridge, 1985.

TWO   The Suspended Revolution

1   Kuhn, T. S., *The Structure of Scientific Revolutions*, Chicago University Press, Chicago, 1962/1970.
2   Cohen, I., *Revolution in Science*, Harvard Belknapp Press, 1985.
3   Ibid.
4   Lopez-Pinero, J. M., *Historical Origins of the Concept of Neurosis*, Cambridge University Press, Cambridge, 1983.
5   Pichot, P. A., *Century of Psychiatry*, Edition Roger da Costa, Paris, 1983.
6   Berrios, G. E., Historical aspects of the psychoses: 19th century issues. *British Medical Bulletin*, 43, 484–98, 1987.
7   Kendler, K. S., Kraepelin and the diagnostic concept of paranoia. *Comprehensive Psychiatry*, 29, 4–11, 1988.
8   Berrios, G. E., Historical background to abnormal psychology. In Miller, E. and Cooper, P. *Textbook of Abnormal Psychology*, Churchill, London, 1988.
9   Berrios, G. E., Depressive pseudodementia or melancholic dementia: a 19th century view. *Journal of Neurology, Neurosurgery and Psychiatry*, 48, 393–400, 1985.
10 Beck, A. T., *Cognitive Therapy and the Emotional Disorders*, International University Press, New York, 1976.
11 Klerman, G. L., Weissman, M. M., Rounsaville, B. J., Chevron, E. S., *Interpersonal Psychotherapy of Depression*, Basic Books, New York, 1984.
12 Maier, S. F. and Seligman, M. E. P., Learned helplessness: theory and evidence. *Journal of Experimental Psychology*, 105, 3–46, 1976.
13 Jaspers, K., *General Psychopathology*, Manchester University Press, Manchester, 1965.
14 Schneider, K., *Clinical Psychopathology*, Grune and Stratton, New York, 1959.
15 Healy, D., The structure of psychopharmacological revolutions. *Psychiatric Developments*, 5, 349–76, 1987.
16 *Diagnostic and Statistical Manual of Mental Disorders*, 3rd edition, American Psychiatric Association, 1980.
17 Healy, D., Schizophrenia: basic, release, reactive and defect processes. *Human Psychopharmacology*, 5, 105–21, 1990.
18 Dowbiggin, I., Degeneration and heredetarianism in French mental medicine 1840–1890. In *The Anatomy of Madness* (Bynum W. F. *et al.* eds) vol. 1 188–232, Cambridge University Press, Cambridge, 1985.
19 Oyama, S., *The Ontogeny of Information*, Cambridge University Press, Cambridge, 1985.
20 Dowbiggin, I., Degeneration and heredeterianism in French mental medicine, 1840–1890.

THREE   The Successors of Paracelsus

1   Butterfield, H., *The Origins of the Scientific Revolution*, Bell and Hyman, London, 1949/1958.
2   Popper, K. R. and Eccles, S. J., *The Self and its Brain*, Routledge and Kegan Paul, 1983.
3   Lonergan, B. J. F., Lectures on religious studies and theology. *A Third Collection* (papers edited by Crowe, F. E.), G. Chapman, London, 1985.
4   Popper, K. R. and Eccles, S. J., *The Self and its Brain*.
5   Lonergan, B. J. F., *Lectures on Religious Studies and Theology*.
6   Hacking, I., *The Emergence of Probability*, Cambridge University Press, Cambridge, 1975.
7   Lonergan, B. J. F., *Insight*, Darton Longman and Todd, 1958.
8   Fleck, L., *The Genesis of a Scientific Fact*, University of Chicago Press, Chicago, 1979.
9   Mendelssohn, K., *The Quest for Absolute Zero*, World University Library, Weidenfeld and Nicolson, London, 1966.
10 Melzack, R. and Wall, P., *The Challenge of Pain*, Penguin Books, Harmondsworth, Middlesex, 1982.
11 Fish, F., *Clinical Psychopathology*, John Wright and Sons, Bristol, 1974.
12 Kline, M., *Mathematics: The Loss of Certainty*, Oxford University Press, 1980.
13 Lonergan, B. J. F., *Method in Theology*, Darton, Longman and Todd, 1980.
14 Collingwood, R. G., *The Idea of History*, Clarendon Press, Oxford, 1945.
15 Marrou, H. I., *The Meaning of History*, Helicon Press, Dublin, 1966.
16 Gadamer, H. G., *Truth and Method*, Sheed and Ward, London, 1979.
17 Brown, R., *The Community of the Beloved Disciple*, Geoffrey Chapman, London, 1979.
18 Gadamer, H. G., *Truth and Method*.
19 Gauld, A. and Shotter, J., *Human Action and its Psychological Investigation*, Routledge and Kegan Paul, London, 1977.
20 Arens, W., *The Man Eating Myth*, Oxford University Press, 1980.
21 Darnton, R., *The Great Cat Massacre*, Peregrine Books, Harmondsworth, Middlesex, 1985.
22 Gadamer, H. G., *Truth and Method*.
23 Allport, G., *Becoming*, Yale University Press, 1955.
24 Gould, S. J., *Time's Arrow, Time's Cycle*, Penguin Books, Harmondsworth, Middlesex, 1988.
25 Ibid.
26 Gould, S. J., *Ontogeny and Phylogeny*, Belknapp Press, Cambridge, Massachusetts, 1985.
27 Masson, J. M., *The Assault on Truth*, Penguin Books, Harmondsworth, Middlesex, 1983.
28 Darnton, R., *The Great Cat Massacre*.
29 Shorter, E., *Bedside Manners*, Viking Press, 1986.
30 Smail, D., *Illusion and Reality*, J. M. Dent and Son, 1984.

FOUR The Romantic Science

1   Sacks, O., *The Man who Mistook his Wife for a Hat*, Picador, 1985.
2   Luria, A. R., *The Working Brain*, Penguin, 1973.
3   Le Doux, J. In Oakley, D., *Brain and Mind*, Methuen, London, 1985.
4   Oakley, D., *Brain and Mind*, Methuen, London, 1985.
5   L'Hermitte, F., Pillon, B. and Serdau, M., Human autonomy and the frontal lobes. *Annals of Neurology*, 19, 326–43, 1986.
6   Luria, A. R., *The Mind of a Mnemonist*, Harvard University Press, 1968/1987.
7   Ibid.
8   Luria, A. R., *The Man with a Shattered World*, Penguin Books, Harmondsworth, Middlesex, 1975.
9   Sacks, O., *Awakenings*, Picador, London, 1982.
10 Sacks, O., *The Man who Mistook his Wife for a Hat*.
11 Vaughan, I. *Ivan*, Papermac, London, 1986.
12 O'Donnell, J. M., *The Origins of Behaviourism*, New York University Press, New York, 1985.
13 Laing, R., *The Divided Self*, Penguin Books, Harmondsworth, Middlesex, 1965.
14 Berrios, G. E., *Phenomenology, Psychopathology and Jaspers*, in press.
15 Healy, D. and Williams, J. M. G. Dysrhythmia, dysphoria and depression. *Psychological Bulletin*, 103, 163–178, 1988.
16 Healy, D., Rhythm and blues. *Psychopharmacology*, 93, 271–85, 1987.
17 Healy, D., Schizophrenia: basic, release, reactive and defect processes. *Human Psychopharmacology*, 5, 105–21, 1990.
18 Chapman, J., The early symptoms of schizophrenia. *British Journal of Psychiatry*, 112, 225–51, 1966.
19 Koehler, K. and Sauer, H., Huber's basic symptoms; another approach to negative psychopathology in schizophrenia. *Comprehensive Psychiatry*, 25, 174–82, 1984.
20 Watts, F. N., Sharock, R., Description and measurement of concentration problems in depressed patients. *Psychological Medicine*, 15, 317–26. 1985.
21 Koehler, K., First rank symptoms of schizophrenia: questions concerning clinical boundaries. *British Journal of Psychiatry*, 134, 226–48, 1979.
22 Arieti, S., (ed.), *American Handbook of Psychiatry*, 816–39, 964–84, 1974.
23 Jonas, G., *Stammering: the disorder of many theories*. Routledge and Kegan Paul, 1979.
24 Healy, D., *Rhythm and Blues*.
25 May, P. R., Van Putten, T., Yale, C., Potepan, P., Jerder, D. J., Fairchild, M. D., Goldstein, M. J., Dixon, W. J., Predicting individual responses to drug treatment in schizophrenia. *Journal of Nervous and Mental Diseases*, 162, 177–83, 1976.
26 Baldessarini, R. J., Cohen, B. M., Teicher, M. H., Significance of neuroleptic doses and plasma level in the pharmacological treatment of psychoses. *Archives of General Psychiatry*, 45, 79–91, 1988.

27 Stigler, S. M., *The History of Statistics*. Belnapp Press, Harvard, Massachusetts, 1986.

FIVE   The Dynamics of a Psychosis

1   Kahneman, D., Slovic, P. and Tversky, A., *Judgement under Uncertainty*, Cambridge University Press, Cambridge, 1982.
2   Ross, L., Anderson, C. A., Shortcomings in the attribution process. In *Judgement under Uncertainty*, 129–52, Cambridge University Press, Cambridge, 1982.
3   Mechanic, D., Social psychologic factors affecting the presentation of bodily complaints. *New England Journal of Medicine*, 286, 1132–9, 1972.
4   Sacks, O., *A Leg to Stand On*, Picador, London, 1984.
5   Barber, P., *Vampires, Burial and Death*. Yale University Press, New Haven, 1988.
6   Healy, D. and Williams, J. M. G., Dysrhythmia, dysphoria and depression. *Psychological Bulletin*, 103, 163–78, 1988.
7   Healy, D., Rhythm and blues. *Psychopharmacology*, 93, 271–85, 1987.
8   Healy, D., Schizophrenia: basic, release, reactive and defect processes. *Human Psychopharmacology*, submitted.
9   Healy, D. and Williams, J. M. G., Moods, misattributions and mania. *Psychiatric Developments*, 7, 49–70, 1989.
10 Sacks, O. *The Man who Mistook his Wife for a Hat*, Picador, 1985.
11 Ross, L., Anderson, C. A., Shortcomings in the attribution process.
12 Berner, P. and Kufferle, B., British phenomenological and psychopathological concepts: a critical review. *British Journal of Psychiatry*, 140, 558–65, 1982.
13 Kahneman, D., Slovic, P. and Tversky, A., Judgement under uncertainty: heuristics and biases.
14 Miller, A., *Timebends: a Life*, Methuen, London, 1987.
15 Mavromatis, A., *Hynogogia: the Unique State of Consciousness between Wakefulness and Sleep*, Routledge and Kegan Paul, London, 1987.
16 Oakley, D., *Brain and Mind*, Methuen, London, 1985.
17 Kosslyn, S. M., *Ghosts in the Mind's Machine*, W. W. Norton and Co., London, 1983.

SIX   Insights and Oversights

1   Healy, D. and Williams, J. M. G., Dysrhythmia, dysphoria and depression. *Psychological Bulletin*, 103, 163–78, 1988.
2   Healy, D., Rhythm and blues. *Psychopharmacology*, 93, 271–85, 1987.
3   Healy, D. and Williams, J. M. G., Moods, misattributions and mania. *Psychiatric Developments*, 7, 49–70, 1989.
4   Blacker, R. and Clare A., Depressive disorder in primary care. *British Journal of Psychiatry*, 150, 737–751, 1987.
5   Cochrane, R., *The Social Creation of Mental Illness*, Longman, London, 1985.

6 Ibid.

7 Healy, D., Schizophrenia: basic, release, reactive and defect processes. *Human Psychopharmacology*, 5, 105–21, 1990.

8 Rose, S., Kamin, L. and Lewontin, R., *Not in our Genes*, Penguin Books, Harmondsworth, Middlesex, 1985.

9 Tienari, P., Sori, A., Lahti, I., Naarala, M., Wahlberg, K. E., Morvig, J., Pohjola, J., Winne, L. C., Genetic and psychosocial factors in schizophrenia. *Schizophrenia Bulletin*, 13, 477–84, 1987.

10 Oyama, S., *The Ontogeny of Information*. Cambridge University Press, Cambridge, 1985.

11 Healy, D., The comparative psychopathology of animal and human affective disorders. *Journal of Psychopharmacology*, 1, 193–210, 1987.

12 Oyama, S., *The Ontogeny of Information*.

13 Blacker, R., Clare, A., Depressive Disorder in Primary Care.

14 Warner, R., *Recovery from Schizophrenia*, Routledge and Kegan Paul, London, 1985.

15 Rather, L. J., *Mind and Body in Eighteenth Century Medicine*, Wellcome Historical Medical Library, London, 1965.

SEVEN The Science of Psychotherapy

1 Beck, A. T., *Cognitive Therapy and the Emotional Disorders*, International University Press, New York, 1976.

2 Klerman, G. L., Weissman, M. M., Rounsaville, B. J. and Chevron, E. S., *Interpersonal Psychotherapy of Depression*, Basic Books, New York, 1984.

3 Shorter, E., *Bedside Manners*, Viking Press, Harmondsworth, Middlesex, 1986.

4 Smail, D., *Taking Care: an Alternative to Therapy*. J. M. Dent and Sons, London, 1987.

5 Deeken, A., *Process and Permanence in Ethics: Max Sceler's Moral Philosophy*, (especially Chapter 5: Resentment and the historicity of ethics: resentment as a source of value-deception), Paulist Press, New York, 1974.

6 Perls, F., Hefferline, R. and Goodman, P., *Gestalt Therapy*, Pelican Books, Harmondsworth, Middlesex, 1951.

7 Rogers, C., *Encounter Groups*, Pelican Books, Harmondsworth, Middlesex, 1973.

8 Truax, C. B. and Carkhuff, R. R., *Concreteness: a Neglected Variable in Research in Psychotherapy*. Unpublished Manuscript, Psychotherapy Research Programme, Universities of Kentucky and Wisconsin.

9 Ibid.

10 Kraines, S. H., *Mental Depressions and Their Treatment*, Macmillan, New York, 1957.

11 Chapman, J. and McGhie, A., An approach to the psychotherapy of cognitive dysfunction in schizophrenia. *British Journal of Medical Psychology*, 36, 253–60, 1963.

12 Healy, D. and Williams, J. M. G., Moods, misattributions and mania. *Psychiatric Developments*, 7, 49–70, 1989.

13 Watts, F. N., Paun, G. E. and Austin S. V., The modification of abnormal beliefs. *British Journal of Medical Psychology*, 46, 359–63, 1973.

14 Healy, D., Schizophrenia: basic, reactive, release and defect processes. *Human Psychopharmacology*, 5, 105–21, 1990.

15 Gray, E. G., Severe depression: a patient's thoughts. *British Journal of Psychiatry*, 143, 319–22, 1983.

16 Williams, J. M. G., *The Psychological Treatment of Depression: a Guide to the Therapy and Practice of Cognitive-Behaviour Therapy*, Croom Helm, Beckenham, 1984.

17 Holton, G., *The Advancement of Science and its Burdens*, Cambridge University Press, Cambridge, 1986.

18 Freedman, B. J., The subjective experience of perceptual and cognitive disturbances in schizophrenia. *Archives of General Psychiatry*, 30, 337–46, 1974.

19 Garmezy, N., Psychology and psychopathology of attention. *Schizophrenia Bulletin*, 3, 360–9, 1977.

20 Freedman, B. J., The subjective experience of perceptual and cognitive disturbances in schizophrenia.

21 McGhie, A., *Pathology of Attention*, Penguin Books, Harmondsworth, Middlesex, 1979.

22 Falloon, I. R. and Talbot, R. E., Persistent auditory hallucinations: coping mechanisms and implications for management. *Psychological Medicine*, 11, 329–39, 1981.

23 Boker, W., Brenner, H. D., Gerstner, G., Keller, F., Muller, J. and Spichtig, L., Self-healing strategies among schizophrenics: attempts at compensation for basic disturbances. *Acta Psychiatrica Scandinavia*, 69, 373–8, 1984.

24 Birchwood, M., Hallett, S. and Preston, M., *Schizophrenia: an Integrated Approach to Research and Treatment*, Longman, London, 1988.

25 Marks, I., Behavioural psychotherapy in general psychiatry: helping patients to help themselves. *British Journal of Psychiatry*, 150, 593–7, 1987.

26 Sacks, O., *The Man who Mistook his Wife for a Hat*, Picador, 1985.

27 Arens, W., *The Man Eating Myth*, Oxford University Press, 1980.

28 Oppen, G., *Collected Poems*, New Directions Publishing Corporation, New York, 1975.

Index

anthropology
  hermeneutics, 90–2
  mental illness, 34–8, 142, 219–21
antidepressants, 65, 193–5
anxiety, 19, 49, 185, 200–4
appearances, 74–83
  concrete, accidental and specific,
    206–8
  historical, 94–5
  phenomenology, 111–13
Arens, W. 91, 219–21
Aristotle, 2–4, 28–9
authenticity
  hallmark of the mental, 28–33
  mental illness, 34–8
  psychotherapy, 200–4, 214–15
autism, 123

Bayle, A. 44–5
Beck, A. 52–3, 199–200
behaviourism
  mental imagery, 24–6, 51–2
  phenomenology, 112–13
  therapy, 204–6
bias
  availability, 137–8, 144–50. 168
  fundamental attributional error,
    140–2, 144–50
  representativeness, 136–7, 144–50,
    168
  therapeutic mystique, 141
blindsight, 12–13
brain
  blood filter, 2–3
  evolution, 11–12
  illnesses, 1
  neuropsychology, 103–8
  organic psychoses, 44–5
  pharmacotherapy, 192–8

  relation to mind, 29–32
  relation to psyche, 20–2
Brentano, F. 111

catecholamine hypothesis, 65–7
Charcot, J. 48–50
Chapman, J. and McGhie, A., 210–12
cognitive therapy, 52–3, 199–200,
  208–14
computers
  model of mind, 4–5, 26, 30
concrete
  inverse insights, 130–2
  psychotherapy, 83, 206–8, 215–19
  science as ascent to concrete, 82–3
content and form, 85–6, 102–3
Cullen, W., 41–2

degeneration, 36, 67, 180
de La Mettrie, J. O., 4–5
delusions
  150–62
  manic-depressive, 153–5
  neurotic, 156–9
  schizophrenic, 153–5
  sensitive, 159–61
Descartes, R.
  dualism, 1–5
  imagery, 112
  loss of psyche, 24
  universal doubt, 90
dialectics, 170–1
dopamine hypothesis, 67
Droysen, G., 88–93
DSM III, 64, 162
dualism
  Descartes, 1–5
  loss of mind, 26
  loss of psyche, 24

mental illness, 35–8
dynamic psychology
  discovery of dynamic unconscious,
    49–50
  dynamic psychopathology, 165–9
  modern dynamic psychology, 134–6

emergence
  chemistry, 8
  life, 8
  mind, 22–9
  psyche, 11–13
emotion, 16–17
empirical
  concrete detail, 82–3
  hermeneutics, 92–3
  inverse insights, 130–2
  method, 82–3
  patients, 119–21, 215–19
  testability, 82–3
epilepsy
  neurosis, 42
  psychosis, 61
  split brain, 105–6
evolution, 5–33
  biological, 8–10
  chemical, 5–8
  mental, 22–3
  psychological, 11–22

Feuchtersleben, E. von, 43
Freud, S.
  Hegelian turn, 96–7
  hermeneutics, 94–100
  irrefutability, 84
  Newtonian, 74
  paradigm, 48–50
  psychotherapeutic revolution, 204
  scientific, 95–101
  suspicion, 97, 131–2
frontal lobes
  autonomy, 107–8
  schizophrenia, 118n, 181–2

Gadamer, H. 92
Gaub, J. 192
genetics
  depression, 177–8
  fate/luck, 180–2
  hereditary degeneration, 36, 67–8
  schizophrenic, 178–82
Gestalt psychology, 112–14

therapy, 206–8
Gould, S. 94–5

hallucinations, 162–5
  hypnogogic, 164
  hypnotic, 165
  psychotherapy, 211
Hegel, G. 94
  influence on Freud, 96
hermeneutics
  crisis of historicity, 94–5
  Droysen, 89–93
  epistemological revolution, 93
  Freudian hermeneutics, 95–8
  inverse insight methodology, 126–30
  Kant, 91
  Little Red Riding Hood, 97–8
  revolution, 88–95
  second enlightenment, 90–2
  sympathy, 91, 124
  universal doubt, 90
Husserl, E. 111

illness behaviour, 139–40
  delusions, 156–9
imagination, 13–16
insight, 62–3, 123
  inverse, 124–32
  oversight, 170–1
interpersonal psychotherapy, 53,
  199–200, 208–14
inverse insights, 124–32
  dialectics, 170–1
  empirical method, 130–2
  functional psychoses, 126–30

Jaspers, K. 47, 56–7
  antipathy to Freud, 57, 132
  delusions, 151–3
  failed revolution, 68–71
  functional psychoses, 60–1
  hermeneutics, 86, 94
  Jasperian paradigm, 56–63
  neuroses and psychoses, 59
  phenomenology, 86, 114–17
  psychotherapy, 100, 200

Kandinsky, W., 114
Kant, I., 91
Klerman, G., 53, 199–200
Kraepelin, E. 43, 46–7
  paranoia, 161

Kraines, S., 210–12
Kuhn, T., 39
  history of science, 73
  tradition, 92

labelling, 176–8
Laing, R.
  ethology, 183
  phenomenology, 115
learned helplessness, 53–5
L'Hermitte, F., 107–8
life events, 54, 55, 171–6
Little Red Riding Hood, 97–8
Luria, A. R., 105–10

manic-depression
  circadian rhythms, 118n.
  delusions, 153–5
  demoralization, 189
  dynamics, 144–9
  endogenous and reactive, 171–2
  general practice, 176–8
  genetics, 177–8
  Jaspers, 57
  Kraepelin, 46–7
  labelling, 176–8
  origins, 171–8
  psychotherapy, 208–15
mechanism, 1–5
mental illness
  anthropology, 142, 219–21
  delusions as hallmark of, 150–62
  disease, 183–4
  fate/luck, 180–2
  impossibility of, 37
  Jaspers, 70–1
  spiritual problems, 35
  psychological problem as illness, 36
  wild beast test, 35
Miller, A., 160–1
mind:
  Aristotle, 3
  authenticity as hallmark, 29
  autonomy, 30
  definition, 27–9
  discovery, 2–5
  emergence, 22–9
  ghost in psyche, 27
  ghosts in the machine, 1–5, 15
  mind–body dualism, 1–5
  psychic correspondence, 29–33
  psychic exploitation, 22–3, 29–33

psychology and the mind, 26–9
morality
  mental illness, 1–5, 34–8

neuroleptics, 65, 129–30, 196–8
  delusions, 153
neuropsychology, 103–10
  phenomenology, 111–14
  psychopathology, 116–17
neurosis
  Cullen, 42
  definition, 203
  Jaspers, 59
  in schizophrenia, 121, 190
  mental illness, 61–3
  psychoneurosis, 49

Oakley, D., 12–13
opinio, 74–83
  empirical, 82–3
  historical, 88–90
  medical, 77–80
  philosophy, 80–2

pain, 126–9
Paracelsus, 76
paranoia, 46–7, 161
pharmacotherapy, 192–8
  morality, 192–8
  psychotherapy, 198
phenomenology, 86, 111–16
  Gestalt psychology, 112
  Jaspers and Schneider, 111–16
  psychopathology, 114
Popper, K., 66, 75
probability, 74–80
  diagnosis and prognosis, 77
  discovery of, 76
  diseases, 79
  statistical correlations, 81
  statistics and inverse insights, 132
psyche
  autonomy of, 20–1
  basis of mind, 22–30
  biological exploitation, 22
  definition of, 20
  effect of Descartes on, 23–6
  emergence, 11–20
  emotion, 16
  individuality and selective attention, 18–20
  memory, 17–18

perception and imagination, 13–16
psychoanalysis
  concepts, 98–101
  paradigm, 50–1
  testability, 66
psychological problem, 18–20, 200–4
psychopathology
  dynamic, 165–9
  flowering, 46–7
  neuropsychology, 118–23
  suspended revolution, 68–71, 161–2
psychosis
  delusions as hallmark of, 150–62
  functional, 44–7
  Jaspers, 60–3
  non-interpretability, 58–62, 86–8,
    102–3
  organic, 44–7
  sensitive, 159–61
  von Feuchtersleben, 43
psychosomatic
  ethology, 183
  mind over matter, 184–7
  natural history, 187–91
  psychosomatic disease, 183–91
psychotherapy
  behaviour therapy, 51, 204–6
  cognitive, 52, 199
  definition, 200–4
  delusions, 211
  empirical, 94
  Freudian, 48–9
  Gestalt, 206–8
  hallucinations, 211
  interpersonal, 53, 199
  inverse insights, 212–14
  Jaspers, 100, 200
  manic-depression, 208–15
  negligent therapy, 214–15
  psychoanalysis, 50–1
  revolution in, 204–8
  schizophrenia, 208–15
  scientific, 83

reasons and causes, 58–60, 121–3
  attributional error, 140–2
revolution
  epistemological, 93
  first psychiatric revolution, 41–3
  Freudian, 48–9
  hermeneutic, 88–95
  Jasperian, 57–61

suspended revolution in
    psychopathology, 68–71, 161–2
  psychotherapeutic, 204–6
  scientific, 39–41
Ryle, G., 112

Sachs, O., 104, 110
Schildkraut, J., 65
schizophrenia
  Bleuler and schizophrenia, 43–4
  chronic neurotic, 190
  delusions, 153–5
  dynamics, 149–50
  frontal lobe, 108, 118n.
  genetics, 178–80
  Jaspers, 57
  Kraepelin, 46–7
  origins, 178–82
  psychotherapy, 208–15
Schneider, K., 47, 56–7
  delusions, 151–3
  first rank symptoms, 115
  phenomenology, 115
science
  ascent to concrete, 82
  describing and science, 216–17
  empirical, 82–3
  Freud's scientia, 86–7, 95–105
  high and low, 74–7
  Jaspers' scientia, 86–7
  medical science, 77–80
  probability and, 76–80
Searle, J., 30
sensitive periods, 181–2
sensitive psychoses, 159–61
signs
  appearances, 75
  content, 85–8
  form, 85–8
  historical, 88–90
  opinions on, 76–80
  psychological signs, 83
  significance, 75
Socrates, 2–4, 28–9
somatagnosia, 121
Sperry, R., 105–6
split brain, 105–6
stammering, 122–3

Tourette syndrome, 110, 218

unconscious, 19, 165–9

understanding and explaining, 86–8,
  92–4

Vaughan, I., 110

Wegener, A., 40–1
Wittgenstein, L., 112
Wundt, W., 24–6, 112